CLOCK MAKING
IN NEW ENGLAND,
1725-1825

An Interpretation of the
Old Sturbridge Village Collection

BY PHILIP ZEA AND ROBERT C. CHENEY

CAROLINE F. SLOAT, EDITOR

PHOTOGRAPHY BY THOMAS NEILL

OLD STURBRIDGE VILLAGE
STURBRIDGE, MASSACHUSETTS
1992

Acknowledgments

Old Sturbridge Village
gratefully acknowledges the support of
Mr. and Mrs. Harry E. Figgie, Jr.,
and Figgie International Inc.,
for making this publication possible.

© Old Sturbridge Inc. 1992
1 Old Sturbridge Village Road, Sturbridge, MA 01566

Zea, Philip
Clockmaking in New England, 1725-1825: an interpretation of
the Old Sturbridge Village collection by Philip Zea and Robert C.
Cheney; Caroline F. Sloat, editor; photography by Thomas Neill.
  p.   cm.
  Includes bibliographical references.
  ISBN 0-913387-03-7 (pbk): $34.95
  1. Old Sturbridge Village. 2. Clock and watch making—New
England—History.   I. Cheney, Robert C. II. Sloat, Caroline F.
III. Title.
TS543.U6Z45   1992
681.1'13'097409033—dc20   92-27611
                        CIP

*Front Cover: Painted iron dial illustrating the four seasons,
Osborne Manufactory, Birmingham, Eng., part of tall clock, Simon
Willard, Roxbury, Mass., ca.1800, OSV catalog no. 57.1.131;
Back Cover: Tall clock, Simon Willard, ca.1800, 57.1.131;
Title Page: Painted iron dial, dwarf clock, Peter Hawkes Cushing,
Braintree, Mass., ca.1825, OSV catalog no. 57.1.25
OSV Photographs: Thomas Neill (front cover);
Henry E. Peach (back cover and title page)*

Contents

FOREWORD

KEEPING TRACK OF TIME'S ever-rolling stream is done with ingenuity, elegance, beauty, and surprising accuracy by the clocks displayed in the J. Cheney Wells Clock Gallery at Old Sturbridge Village. Our forebears had a special understanding of the place of time in their lives for it was by creative and productive use of those precious hours left after the bare needs for subsistence and shelter had been met that the torches of learning and culture were kept ablaze. The antique clocks and their makers presented in this catalog reflect a dedication to quality as well as mechanical competence and design skill. It is our hope that this publication will provide an important new perspective on some of New England's foremost craftsmen and entrepreneurs and the products of their labors which now serve yet another generation of an admiring public.

Crawford Lincoln
President, Old Sturbridge Village
July, 1992

INTRODUCTION
The Clock Maker's Skills

THE OLD STURBRIDGE VILLAGE collection of New England clocks was the gift of J. Cheney Wells (1874-1960) of the American Optical Company in Southbridge, Massachusetts. During the 1930s, he and his brother, Albert B. Wells (1872-1953), were avid collectors of Americana. A.B. Wells was fascinated by the the tools and technology of everyday life in the past, while Cheney was attracted to clocks for their unique combination of beauty with historical technology. When the concept of displaying these collections in a museum village that would illustrate life in early New England emerged at a board meeting of the nascent museum in 1936, Cheney Wells was inspired to contribute his clocks to complement his brother's generosity. The clocks, then being displayed in Wells's family homes and the offices of the American Optical Corporation, were installed as a formal collection at Old Sturbridge Village.

We can appreciate Cheney Wells's collecting passion by viewing the elegant clocks, which are kept in running condition, and hearing them strike on the hour. His copy of the minutes of the Boston Clock Club from 1934 to 1939, now in the collections of the Research Library, reveals Wells as a collector informing himself about the subject. A small pamphlet illustrating some 40 clocks with an introduction by Amos G. Avery was published by the museum in 1955. Since that time, the collection has been refined to focus on New England clocks before 1840 following the museum's general collecting guidelines. Additions have been made and the entire collection was moved to the J. Cheney Wells Clock Gallery, opened to the public in 1982.

The collection provides museum visitors with a broad overview of clocks made in New England between 1725 and 1825. This volume interprets the clocks in their historical context and shows how they are part of the fabric of New England life. This study follows the contours of the collection and is not, therefore, a review of the science of clock making, nor is a checklist of New England clock makers included. Descriptions of each clock in the

Fig. Intro.-1. Lantern Clock, Peter Closon, London, ca. 1635. This weight-powered clock measures the passing time with a balance wheel mounted under the bell, sounds the hours, and has an alarm mechanism. The single hand indicates the time to the nearest quarter hour. This early domestic clock requires winding every twelve hours and is an unreliable timekeeper. There are no known American examples. Private Collection.

collection appear in Appendix I and additional information in Chapter Six and the brief glossary.

CLOCKS WERE AMONG THE first machines to capture the fancy of mankind and provide a measurement of time. Daniel Boorstin describes the timekeeper as the mother of machines because it measures distance or effort through the regulation of passing time.[1] But clocks measure more than time and distance.

Their makers were the first craftsmen to combine science and machinery. Ingenious blacksmiths in 16th-century Europe made the first domestic clocks with Gothic ornament. Weight-powered, they evolved into brass house clocks now called "lantern" clocks in the next century. These showy timekeepers were suspended on a heavy frame supported by four brass posts and finished with shining brass plates and engraved fretwork. (Fig. Intro.-1) They were not housed in wooden cases. The clocks themselves were precisely crafted, single-production items that required individual fitting. Labor-intensive work and costly materials meant that these clocks were expensive symbols of status and order.[2] Early weight-powered clocks with balance wheels are ponderously inaccurate by contemporary standards of micro measurement.

In 1657, a Dutch astronomer Christiaan Huygens (1629-1695) devised a 9 3/4-inch pendulum that beat half-seconds. The advantage lay in the free, frictionless travel of the pendulum through most of its swing. Pendulum clocks lost roughly 15 seconds per day, an enormous improvement in accuracy over those which had lost roughly fifteen minutes per day.[3] A second improvement followed about 1671 when the anchor recoil escapement replaced the crown wheel and verge escapement (see glossary).[4] This device reduced the interference transferred from the movement to the pendulum, which the clock maker lengthened. Resistance from friction was decreased by lessening the arc of the swing and doubling the time of each swing to one second.[5]

Clocks with these improvements required added protection from the likes of dust, cats, and children and cases were constructed for them. The prevailing architectural style in England in the last third of the 17th century was adapted to the clock. A glass insert in the waist of a clock was a sign that its fashion-conscious owner could afford a fine movement with a long pendulum. After 1675, most stylish English clocks were equipped with a seconds hand, a statement of style rather than technical complexity.

Further experimentation resulted in a third improvement about 1715, when George Graham (1673-1751) perfected the dead-beat escapement. It worked like the anchor recoil escapement, but the shape of the anchor and the pallets at each end were made more angular to arrest the swing of the pendulum at its extremes without recoiling the escape wheel. Graham's plan decreased friction by reducing the wasted motion of the pendulum and its swing from an arc of eight degrees to one of about two degrees.[6] The dead-beat escapement remained the most accurate found in domestic clocks during the period represented by the Old Sturbridge Village collection.

IN NEW ENGLAND successful urban clock makers were businessmen who orchestrated the assembly of the clock. The wide range of sources for a clock's parts reveals the web of commercial relationships and the hierarchy of skills among craftsmen who made luxury products.

Many metalworking skills were invested in the movement by the clock maker himself or by other specialists. A brass and lead founder cast parts of the movement, pendulum, and the weights; a bell founder cast a resonant tone into the metal; a brazier made the sheet metal in the dial; a die maker cut the screws; the maker of the springs allowed the levers in the movement to perform; an ironmonger stockpiled material of appropriate grade; and a blacksmith made iron fasteners like nails and pins.

Similarly, the parts of the case passed through many hands. The sawyer with his knowledge of lumber cut the planks and boards that were properly dried and would not warp. The cabinetmaker applied templates and a system of proportions patterned after a column to build the case. The turner's long-handled chisels and gouges applied to whirling billets of wood on his lathe made the finials and columns on the hood and the quarter columns on the waist that were then fluted and cut to size. A carver applied his freehand skill on the finials, the termini of the broken scroll pediment, and especially on the shell in the waist door. If the clock case were ornamented with beautifully figured veneers, a veneer maker with his fine-toothed saws, glue, and steady hand was required. If the clock case were "japanned" with raised gesso figures in imitation of oriental lacquer work, the case would have been consigned to the japanner for his application of gesso, pigments, and varnishes and the products of the specialized craftsmen on whom he relied for materials.

The trade and its complexity is well illustrated by a clock made by Caleb Wheaton (1757-1827) of Providence, Rhode Island. About 1790, he crafted a mechanism that bears his name and housed it in a beautiful and elaborate case. (Fig. Intro.-2) Over eight feet in height, the clock is a bold statement about Wheaton as a master clock maker, the craftsmanship of the unknown cabinetmaker, and the taste and wealth of its first owner. (Pl. 2) Wheaton was probably the founder who cast most of the brass parts; the neo-chemist who applied the silver wash to the dial; the cutler who cut, filed, and blued the hands; and the machinist who applied mathematical calculations to the gear ratios, cut the teeth in the wheels with his engine, and assembled the movement. Throughout the clock the materials used are consistently of high quality. The clock is a document of Wheaton's horological knowledge and skill, although it is not known where or with whom Wheaton learned to make clocks. When he died in 1827, the appraisers of his estate found "1 vol. Elements of Clock and Watch Work" in his large library. This was likely *The Elements of Clock and Watch-Work, Adapted to Practice* by Alexander

Fig. Intro.-2. Tall Clock movement, Caleb Wheaton, Providence, R.I, ca. 1790. Eight-day, brass movement with rack and snail strike system and additional gearing to trip the moon's-age dial and day of the month hand. The strike train is mounted on the left of the movement and the time train on the right. The front plate of the movement (unseen behind the dial) was left as an unfinished casting. See Pl.2. 57.1.107

Cumming published in London in 1766.[7]

Wheaton also drew on the specialized products of such other tradesmen as the glassmaker, the gilder, and even the catgut maker whose cord allowed the weights to descend. The clock's multi-part face combines several specialties, if dial making was not among Wheaton's skills: the ornamental painter who decorated the lunar dial with its darkened sky and stars and benevolent moon; and the engraver whose burin inscribed the numbers so that the dial would tell time and whose flourish recorded Wheaton's name.

The unknown maker of this clock case is an important link to understanding late 18th-century Rhode Island furniture. The traditional attribution to John Goddard of Newport is based on another Wheaton clock that survives with a receipt rendered by the clock maker to Townsend Goddard, John's executor, for two clock cases in 1786. However, the strongly vertical proportions, slight variation from the carving styles documented to the Goddards and Townsends, and the use of a flat roof behind the scrolled pediment supporting the flanking finials of the hood suggest the possibility of a Providence cabinetmaker, someone who might have been trained by the Goddards.[8]

Finally after considering all the people who would have played a part in the production of a clock, one might wonder what entitled the 18th-century clock maker to sign his own name to the dial? A clock by John Rogers (1724-1815) of Newton, Massachusetts, underscores the dilemma.[9] Although the Rogers clock lacks the moon's-age and center calendar dials, the movement is identical in virtually every other respect to the Wheaton clock. Were these complex movements made by one clock maker for the other or possibly by a third party?

Each clock, with its combination of complex, divergent, and expensive materials, is an individual time capsule of an economy and a way of life. Human fascination with the synthetic heartbeat of a costly clock tells a tale of economic growth fueled by consumerism. The expanding ownership of clocks in New England with cheaper materials and improved manufacture is a litmus of regional development. Ever cheaper production made precision more available and difficult to ignore. Inexpensive clocks allowed the transfer of organized work from the farm where natural cycles are guides, to the workshop and factory, where artificial time measurement is required to systematize labor. Clocks assumed social implications by disciplining the work force in town and country. This story is usually told as a broad interpretation of the emergence of modern society.[10] Timekeeping has rarely been examined as a yardstick of regional economic history and cultural growth.[11]

This study exhibits the stages of commissioned clock making, standardized parts, eventual interchangeability, batch and mass production, expanded marketing, and distribution far beyond the factory site. If the use of clocks measures the growing sophistication of society, improvements in their manufacture plot the industrialization of New England where so many clocks were made.

LIKE THE CLOCKS OF EARLY NEW ENGLAND, more individuals have contributed to this book than the names inscribed on the cover would suggest. We must acknowledge the assistance and encouragement of several people in writing this book. Caroline Sloat is our editor and project director whose own interest in 19th-century New England is reflected in the research and text of Chapter Five on Connecticut clock making. We benefited greatly from the help of Jack Larkin, Director of Research, Collections, and Library at Old Sturbridge Village and his departmental colleagues, Theresa Rini Percy, Joan Allen, Donna Baron, John O. Curtis, Frank White, and Meg Haley. Museum Photographer Thomas Neill's superb photographs are evident throughout the book. Many photographs were taken by his predecessor, Henry E. Peach. We were aided by several interns, especially Pieter Roos, whose research on the Willards' neighborhood in Roxbury and Boston is reflected here, and Leslie Dotson. Edward T. Anderson, Chris H. Bailey, Melissa Bowhers, Herschel B. Burt, Joyce E. Cheney, Bruce B. Cheney, Douglas R. Currie, Paul J. Dumanoski, Donald R. Friary, Robert P. Hendrikson, Clarence M. Mollett, Howard V. Neff, Jr., Jane C. Nylander, Elizabeth Pols of North Pols Design, David R. Proper, Kimberly King Zea, and many others provided greatly appreciated research, observations, and support.

In closing, we offer words of appreciation for special friends of the Old Sturbridge Village clock collection. Trustee and former Chairman of the Board, Howard Sloane, himself a knowledgeable collector, has taken a personal interest in the collection over the many years of his association with the museum. The descendants of J. Cheney Wells: his daughter Gertrude Wells Brennan, son, the late John Morse Wells, grandchildren, and other members of the Wells family have provided generous support for the collection and the gallery which houses it, a fitting memorial to their father and forebear. Finally thanks go to Mr. and Mrs. Harry E. Figgie, Jr., and Figgie International Inc., whose generous gift funded this work.

NOTES

[1] Daniel J. Boorstin, *The Discoverers* (New York: Random House, 1983), 64-72.

[2] Ernest L. Edwardes, *Weight-Driven Chamber Clocks of the Middle Ages and Renaissance* (Altringham, England: John Sherratt and Son, 1965), passim; *The Clockwork Universe: German Clocks and Automata, 1550-1650*, eds. Klaus Maurice and Otto Mayr (New York: Neale Watson Academic Publications, 1980), 162-164, 167, 176-201; George White, *English Lantern Clocks* (Suffolk, U.K.: Antiques Collectors Club, Ltd., 1989), passim; W.F.J. Hana, *English Lantern Clocks* (Poole, Dorset, England: Blandford Press, 1979), passim. Prof. Linn Hobbs of MIT pointed out that the later use of the word "lantern" may be a corruption of the word "latten" for sheet brass rather than a reference to the shape of lanterns; conversation with the authors.

[3] Frederick James Britten, *Old Clocks and Watches and Their Makers: Being an Historical and Descriptive Account of the Different Styles of Clocks and Watches of the Past, in England and Abroad, to which is Added a List of Eleven Thousand Makers* (London: B.T. Batsford, 1911; since edited by Clutton, Baillie, and Ilbert) 71-76, 321-322; Christiaan Huygens' *The Pendulum Clock or Geometrical Demonstrations Concerning the Motion of Pendula as Applied to Clocks*, tr. Richard J. Blackwell (1673, 1724; Ames, Iowa: Iowa State University Press, 1986), passim.

[4] Britten, 77, 111, 118; Tom Robinson, *The Longcase Clock* (Suffolk, UK: Antiques Collectors' Club, 1981), 44-45. Three men could lay claim to the invention of the anchor-recoil escapement: William Clement, Robert Hooke, and Joseph Knibb.

[5] Britten, 76-78.

[6] Robinson, 158; Britten, 125-127. Deadbeat escapements were tested by Thomas Tompion at the Greenwich Observatory on two-year duration clocks between 1675 and 1678.

[7] James W. Gibbs, "Horologic Rhode Island Visited," *Bulletin of the National Association of Watch and Clock Collectors* (cited hereafter as *NAWCC Bulletin*) 149 (December 1970): 801-811; Probate Records, Providence, Rhode Island, Will Book 2, 530-531.

[8] There are at least thirteen Rhode Island clocks with stepped pediments. Michael Moses, *Master Craftsmen of Newport, The Townsends and Goddards* (Tenafly, N.J.: MMI Americana Press, 1984), 31, 93-98, 103, 137-138, 143-145, 175-176, 332-334, 337-339; J. Michael Flanigan, *American Furniture from the Kaufman Collection* (Washington, D.C.: National Gallery of Art, 1986), 76-79; Wendy A. Cooper, "The Purchase of Furniture and Furnishings by

John Brown, Providence Merchant, Part I, 1760-1788," *Antiques* 103 (February 1973): 328-339; Cooper, "Part II...1788-1803," Antiques 103 (April 1973): 734-743; Margaretta M. Lovell, " 'Such Furniture as Will Be Most Profitable': The Business of Cabinetmaking in Eighteenth-Century Newport," *Winterthur Portfolio* 26 (Spring 1991): 27-62; Jeanne Vibert Sloane, "John Cahoone and the Newport Furniture Industry," *New England Furniture: Essays in Memory of Benno M. Forman* (Boston: Society for the Preservation of New England Antiquities, 1987), 88-122. A virtually identical clock by Caleb Wheaton is owned by the Museum of Art, Rhode Island School of Design. See Christopher P. Monkhouse and Thomas S. Michie, *American Furniture in the Pendleton House* (Providence, R. I.: Museum of Art, Rhode Island School of Design, 1986), 89-90.

[9] The clock by Rogers is in a private collection and was examined by Robert C. Cheney in September 1991.

[10] Studies of the history of timekeeping, the measurement of space through the passage of time, and the perception of time: Carlo Cipolla, *Clocks and Culture, 1300-1700* (New York: Walker, 1967); David S. Landes, *Revolution in Time: Clocks and the Making of the Modern World* (Cambridge and London: The Belknap Press of Harvard University Press, 1983); and Daniel J. Boorstin, *The Discoverers.* Other authors, like Frederick James Britten, cited above, have cataloged technological changes, the physical description of timekeepers, and the biographies of clock makers with little interpretation of the impact of timekeeping on society. Also Samuel Guye and Henri Michel, *Time & Space: Measuring Instruments from the 15th to the 19th Century* (New York and London: Praeger 1971). The most current survey of American clock making is Chris H. Bailey, *Two Hundred Years of American Clocks & Watches* (Englewood Cliffs, N.J.: A Rutledge Book, Prentice-Hall, Inc., 1975). There are numerous regional studies and, since 1944, useful articles have appeared in the *Bulletin of the National Association of Watch and Clock Collectors*, Columbia, Penn.

[11] Few works address the significance of clock making as a vehicle for interpreting the social and economic history of a region or community in America. One excellent exception is Charles F. Hummel, *With Hammer in Hand: The Dominy Craftsmen of East Hampton, L.I.* (New York. Charlottesville: University Press of Virginia, 1968). Another insightful book is Penrose R. Hoopes, *Shop Records of Daniel Burnap, Clockmaker* (Hartford: Connecti-cut Historical Society, 1958). The best references for brief biographies of New England clock makers are Bailey; Lilian Baker Carlisle, *Vermont Clock and Watchmakers, Silversmiths, and Jewelers, 1778-1878* (Burlington: Privately printed, 1970); James W. Gibbs, "Horologic Rhode Island Visited,"; Penrose R. Hoopes, *Connecticut Clockmakers of the Eighteenth Century.* (New York: Dodd, Mead and Co., 1930); Joseph R. Katra, Jr., *Clockmakers & Clockmaking in Southern Maine, 1770-1870.* NAWCC Bulletin Supplement 17 (Summer 1989); Charles S. Parsons, *New Hampshire Clock and Clockmaking* (Exeter, NH: Adams Brown Company, 1976).

CLOCKS WERE APPARENTLY FAMILIAR enough to the passengers of the *Arabella* in 1630 for John Winthrop to use them as a metaphor in his description of divine mercy.

> As when wee bid one make the clocke strike, he doth not lay hand on the hammer, which is the immediate instrument of the sound, but setts on worke the first mover or maine wheele; knoweing that will certainly produce the sound which he intends.[1]

Despite Winthrop's assumption that his readers would understand the principles on which clocks operated, it is not likely that many had clocks to bring to the New World. Only a few of New England's earliest probate inventories list them. When Henry Packs (or Parks) died in 1640 at Hartford, Connecticut, his will "bestow[ed] upon the Church the Clocke that Brother Thornton had bought."[2] The estate inventory of the Reverend Thomas Hooker, founder of the Connecticut Colony, taken in 1649, lists "a clocke" among the furnishings of the "new or best parlor."[3] For most people, however, timekeeping continued to follow ancient and natural forms, like the daily path of the sun, the monthly passage of the moon, changing seasons, menstrual cycles, and shifting tides. While few residents of the new colonies used the precision of a clock to guard against idle hours and minutes, time was a valuable commodity. The General Court of Massachusetts proclaimed in 1633 that "No person, householder, or other shall spend his time idly or unprofitably."[4] As the population of the New England colonies increased in the years of the Great Migration, house clocks, tower clocks, and watches came in larger numbers from England, and were soon followed by the individuals who could repair and make them.

Immigrants who brought clocks and others who brought mechanical skills set the stage for the transfer of advances in clock technology to the New World. The first public clock was mounted in Boston in 1668, and the selectmen contracted with a blacksmith for its maintenance. When William Davis arrived a generation later in 1683, the New World

CLOCK MAKING IN COLONIAL NEW ENGLAND

Fig.1-1. Tall Clock, Gawen Brown, Boston, Mass., ca.1760-1770. See Pl.3. 57.1.132

had a resident who considered himself a clock maker.[5] Between 1683 and 1735 the names of almost a dozen clock and watch makers appear in the records of colonial Boston,[6] a bustling town of about 4000 inhabitants. Their work as makers and repairers of clocks and watches made Puritan commentary about the efficient use of time less abstract.[7] "I preached a sermon," wrote the Reverend Cotton Mather (1663-1728)

> which I then printed with a purpose to lodge it where I came in pastoral visits....An Essay upon, Time spent as it should be; with PROPOSALS to prevent that great Mischief, The Loss of time; and employ the Talent of Time so watchfully and Fruitfully that a good Account may at least be given of it.[8]

Only imported clocks could be purchased by men of wealth, but they could be kept in repair locally; only a few clocks were made in the colonies at this time. Ones by Benjamin Bagnall Sr. (ca. 1689-1773) are the earliest Boston-made clocks to survive. He also trained his sons Benjamin Jr., (b. 1715) and Samuel (b. 1718). Their competitors who were active in the mid-18th century immigrated from England or Ireland.[9] Clock makers John Doane (1734-ca. 1801), Joseph Hiller (adv. 1768-1800), Joseph Pope (1748-1826), and John Roulstone (adv. 1768) stressed that they were trained in Britain. Another group, trained as watch makers, also settled in Boston, advertised repair work, and made and sold jewelry and instruments to make a living. The two earliest clocks in the Old Sturbridge Village (OSV) collection are by two contemporaries, Gawen Brown (1719-1801) and William Claggett (1696-1749). Like their peers these craftsmen enjoyed the competitive edge of urban training and English connections.[10]

Gawen Brown, who arrived in Boston in 1749, remained active throughout the century. Through his three marriages he allied himself with the elite of Boston, whose patronage advanced his career.[11] His work can be documented through surviving clocks, his newspaper advertisements, the registration of his journeymen with the town clerk in compliance with the colony's laws of settlement, and in 1753 and 1754, the notes he kept in his "Calibre Book."

Together, clock and case record technique, purchasing power, and perceptions of taste.(Fig. 1-1) Initially Brown established himself in the workshop of Boston's leading ornamental painter and japanner,

Thomas Johnston (1708-1767), a location shrewdly selected to assure his patrons 'one-stop' shopping!

This is to give Notice...that Gawen Brown, Clock and Watchmaker lately from London, keeps his shop at Mr. Johnston's Japanner, in Brattle-Street, Boston, near Mr. Cooper's Meeting House, where he makes and sells all sorts of plain, repeating [for convenience at night, the mechanism will strike the last hour upon command] and astronomical Clocks, with Cases, plain, [imported] black Walnut, mahogany, or Japann'd or without; likewise does all Sorts of Watch Work in the best Manner and sells all sorts of Clock Strings, London Lacker, and white Varnish for Clocks, a great variety of Files for Clock Work, Glasses or Crystalls, Keys, Strings, Pendants for Watches, &c.[12]

To serve his wealthy patrons, Brown needed to employ journeymen in his shop: in 1766, Lawrence Ash from Philadelphia and Thomas Jackson from Canada worked for him.[13] Three years later "John Harris, harpsichord, spinnet, watch-case maker, turner, &c from London," was living "at Gawen Brown's in King Street."[14]

Domestic tall clocks were Brown's specialty. "All sorts of clocks, cheaper than you could buy from London," he advertised in 1752.[15] (Fig.1-2). Gawen Brown's system of serialized parts to avoid confusion while several movements were under construction is illustrated in a clock made by him. Each of the dozen components of its dial, (Pl. 3) overseen by Father Time, is marked on the back with the letter "D" . The rear of the dial is further coded with two punch marks. The "D" also appears on the back of the pendulum bob with two punch marks. Matching punch marks appear at the bottom of the front plate of the movement. Each component of the dial and pendulum is inscribed with a "D," while the punch marks relate the completed movement, pendulum, and dial of this clock to one another.

The case was made by an anonymous Boston cabinetmaker collaborating with Brown. Cherry was an unusual choice as a primary wood, suggesting that it was once darkly stained to simulate walnut or mahogany or "japanned" in imitation of Oriental lacquerwork by Johnston or another of Boston's score of japanners.[16]

Notes in his "Calibre Book" indicate that repair work constituted a significant part of Brown's in-

Fig.1-2. Tall Clock movement, Gawen Brown, Boston, Mass. Rack and snail strike systems are commonly found on New England, eight-day tall clock movements. See Pl.3. 57.1.132

come. As clocks by other makers came into his shop, he kept notes on their workmanship and technical refinements, making annotated drawings and wheel counts. To measure the accuracy of his machines against solar time, Brown recorded "A Table of Equation, Shewing how much a Clock, or Watch, ought to be Faster, or Slower, than a Sun Dial, any day of the Year" except on April 16, June 18, and December 24, when there should be "no Equation of Time: a Good Dial and Clock must be exactly at the same minute." [17]

He also recorded the results of his experiments with materials, possibly hoping that they might benefit him in his work.

A piece of Lead Wire when Warm lenthens very much. Ivory lenthens by heating very little and Silv r [sic] very little. Iron lenthens a Great deal, and so does Brass. Gold swels longer w th ye heat of Fire also considerably. Pine Wood lenthens nothing at all when it is very hot. Cedar ye Same as Pine, lenthens none.[18]

The "Calibre Book" shows his awareness of the importance of observing clocks by others and reveals the depth of his interest in science and horology.

William Claggett of Wales, arrived in Boston with

Fig.1-3. Tall Clock movement, William Claggett, Newport, R.I., ca. 1740. Early movements feature heavy brass plates separated by five pillars, deeply cut teeth on the wheel work, and a fine finish to the brass and steel parts. See Fig.6-13. 57.1.99

Fig.1-4. Tall Clock dial, William Claggett, ca.1740. Composite dials have a silvered brass chapter ring, second's bit, and name boss. Applied spandrels provide decoration in the corners and flank the name boss in the arch. Note the quarter-hour markings on the inside of the chapter ring, the half hour marks between the numerals, and the "half quarter" diamonds on the Arabic ring. See Fig.6-13. 57.1.99

his family at the age of 12 in 1708, and learned how to make clocks of great sophistication from an unidentified master, possibly Benjamin Bagnall.[19] Advertising in 1715 as a "Clock-maker near the Town House," he offered "a new Fashion'd Monthely Clock & Case lately arrived from London, also a new Fashion'd Camblet Bed Lin'd with Saten."[20] Whether for business or personal reasons,[21] he found little success in this venue and perhaps attracted by the potential of the prospering seaport of Newport, Rhode Island, Claggett moved there and proved that the colonial market for sophisticated clocks in the British manner was not exclusively in Boston.

In Newport, Claggett not only established himself as a successful artisan, who made a substantial number of clocks and navigational devices, he also involved himself in the political life of the community. He achieved a measure of fame and possibly an introduction to Benjamin Franklin with his experiments on electricity.[22] Claggett's heavy brass movement, (Fig. 1-3) one of over 50 surviving mechanisms,[23] illustrates his superb craftsmanship and understanding of metal. The expert casting and engraving of the dial (Figs. 1-4 and 6-13) were probably undertaken by Claggett himself, whose skill as an engraver and founder is documented in 1738 and 1742 by credits in an anonymous day book for making the plates to print Rhode Island's paper currency. He was evidently capable of the difficult tasks of casting and cutting copper.[24]

William Claggett's son, Thomas (ca. 1730-1797), followed in his father's footsteps as a clock maker with broad interests in science. Thomas rented space in 1765 from John Bannister in Bannister's Row in Newport, where several artisans had their shops. Two years later, he advertised "All sorts of Goldsmiths Work" and indicated that his shop offered the latest fashion by employing as a journeyman, "a Person from London who makes and mends all Sorts of Clocks and Watches in the neatest Manner."[25]

In 18th-century Newport, customers received their clocks already cased and did not contract for the cabinetwork themselves. The clock (Pl. 1) sold by Thomas Claggett to Abraham Brown of Tiverton, Rhode Island, in 1772 illustrates how business was conducted in the community where the Townsends and Goddards dominated the production of fine Baroque furniture without completely monopolizing the market. Claggett movements are mounted in cases made by several Newport cabinetmakers, including Benjamin Baker, John Cahoone, and Jonathan Swett.[26]

The date of Thomas Claggett's warranty indicates that he arranged directly with Baker for the case. Baker's account book includes two entries with Claggett between 1772 and 1774.[27] (Claggett purchased one mahogany clock case and had another one polished.) On December 30, the clock maker sold the finished product directly to his customer, Abraham Brown. The label inside the clock is the cabinetmaker's: "Made and Sold by Benjamin Baker in Newport 1772." These transactions and the hierarchy of materials invested in clocks illustrate that urban clock makers ranked above cabinetmakers. Nevertheless, the costly imported mahogany and Baker's craftsmanship, rather than the workmanship of the Claggett clock shop, dominate its overall appearance.

Abraham Brown focused on the clock mechanism and was shrewd enough to include Claggett's written assurance that it would keep time in the purchase price. He pasted the warranty given on December 30, 1772, inside his new clock. (Fig. 1-5)[28] Though costly, Brown's clock proved to be a good investment: it kept good time and proclaimed his status as a prosperous merchant.[29]

THE WORKSHOP AND MARKETPLACE were adapting to the complexity imposed on life by the perceived need for punctuality. "Remember that TIME is Money" was Benjamin Franklin's *Advice to a Young Tradesman, Written by an Old One*[30] in 1748. We should not imagine that the past was a slower-paced age, as the drive for accurate timekeeping during the second half of the 18th century was burdensome. All occupations became more specialized and city tradesmen increasingly worked in shops away from home. Time off for a meal implied a punctual return to the workplace. Farmers produced surpluses for distant markets and became more aggressive consumers. By the middle of the 18th century, timekeeping and clock making were going hand in hand. The rhythm of the household in every city, town, and farm was governed by the pressure of measured time. As 'Patience Meanwell' wrote to *The Newport Mercury* in 1772:

> The new regulation of ringing a bell at sunrise, one o'clock...and nine in the evening, is very agreeable in several respects; the first tells us

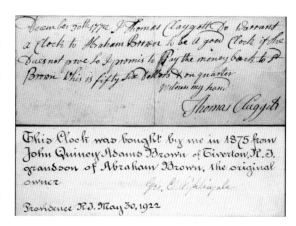

Fig.1-5. Bill of Sale, Tall Clock, Thomas Claggett, Newport, R.I., 1772. 57.1.92

that it is time to rouse from our beds; the second that dinner ought to be ready; and the last, that it is time for people to prepare for taking their repose; but as inconveniences many times arise from things well intended, so it has happened to me. ...My husband is a labouring man, and ringing bell at one o'clock brings him home for his dinner; and when he finds it is not ready, he fumes, frets, and abuses me; Wrangling often takes away both our appetites....Now you must know that before the bell was rung at one o'clock, if my husband came home, and his victuals was not ready as neither he nor I really know the time of day, I could easily make an excuse....Now, Sir I beg that you would inform the gentlemen who direct those matters, that is absolutely necessary, for the sake of family peace, that they either desist from ringing the one o'clock bell, or that they will direct a bell to be rung at eleven in the forenoon, in order that the housewife, whose task it is to cook the dinner may know when to begin her work.[31]

Clock making was not strictly a condition of city living in New England before the Revolution. Whether a clock's movement was made of brass, iron, or wood, the prestige of setting it up at home was just as significant away from the busy seaports.[32]

Rural clock makers were also skilled craftsmen who performed a variety of metalworking chores.[33] Many of them worked in iron as well as brass and precious metals and could provide their neighbors with most of the metalwork and repair required for house, farm, and shop. They were jacks-of-all-trades, who could also make clocks. Although sometimes crude by the standards of contemporary Boston, rural clocks often document eccentric ingenuity

Fig.1-6. Tall Clock, Isaac Blasdel, Chester, N.H., ca. 1763. 57.1.127

and their cases illustrate the woodworking traditions of rural cabinetmakers.

Before the Revolution the clock-making trade was conducted in several agricultural towns along the coast and even a few communities farther inland. The presence of navigational and scientific instruments used at sea may have inspired some of these coastal clock makers who competed for the patronage of the rural elite.[34] David Blasdel (1712-1756) of Amesbury, Massachusetts, and his brother Jonathan (1709-1802) of East Kingston, New Hampshire, were the first generation of this extensive family of metalworkers to exhibit a talent for clocks. More than 59 clocks made by this family have been identified.[35] David's sons, David, Jr. (1736-1794), Isaac (1738-1791), and Nicholas (1743-ca. 1800), and grandson, Isaac's son Richard (1762-1790), made clocks in Amesbury, Chester and Newmarket, New Hampshire, and Falmouth, Maine, into the 1790s. David, Sr. appears to have made more clocks than any other family member, despite the shortness of his career. Blacksmiths were recruited to serve as armorers during wartime, accompanying military units to keep their firearms and other equipment in good repair and David was killed near Lake George while serving in the last French and Indian War.[36]

Blasdel clocks show their makers' broad knowledge of both black and whitesmithing in the forging of iron, drawing of wire, and casting of pewter, brass, and lead. As blacksmiths they worked at a forge with wrought iron. As whitesmiths they worked with copper, tin, and their alloys, including brass and pewter. A founder casts metal objects and might specialize in iron or copper alloys like bronze and bell metal. Blasdel's brass dials show that he was also a brazier. These skills, separated by both tradition and law in Britain,[37] were joined by rural necessity in New England.

The similarity of Blasdel clocks over three generations demonstrates how families perpetuated specific designs in the conservative barter economy of the Yankee hinterland. (Fig. 1-6) The heavy iron movements confirm that they were smiths who worked with knowledge of traditional English clock making. Their 30-hour, posted-frame mechanisms are reminiscent of 17th-century house clocks, as well as 18th-century tall clocks from southern England. (Fig. 1-7) This movement is especially crude: most of the arbors are not horizontal! Not only does it keep time, it is actually Blasdel's advanced model with the extra features of a calendar wheel, two hands rather than one, and a striking mechanism mounted within the posted movement.

Another related group of eastern Massachusetts clocks was made in the extended circle of the Mulliken family in Bradford, Newbury, and Lexington. Daniel Balch and even Benjamin Willard of Grafton and Roxbury fame also came into their orbit. When clock maker Samuel Mulliken, of Newbury, died in 1756 at the age of 36, he was in the prime of his life. His property was appraised at £ 191/17/11, of which the dwelling house and land were £ 80 and the shop, on a separate parcel, was £ 8. The inventory of his estate provides a peek into an 18th-century clock maker's shop in which Mulliken cast, forged, finished, and engraved the parts of the clocks that he made, and repaired the clocks and watches of others. His stock of parts valued at almost £ 8 suggests that he expected a significant proportion of his work to include repairing the imported watches of his Newbury neighbors. Too distant from Boston suppliers, Mulliken applied his tools and experience to making all of the metal parts of his weight-powered clocks: his "engin," used to cut the teeth in the wheels of a clock movement was appraised at £ 4/13/4. The contents of the shop were:

Grindstone 4/ an engin 9 3/4 pair brass flasks 18/ Graving tools 6/2 turning laiths 18/ small do 6/ 3 hammers 2/8 2 pr forging tongs 2/5 old files 10/2 burnishers 16 new files 3/ 2 clocks partly done £ 7 1/4 2 saw frames 6/ 2 scrapers 1/ 1 bitt stock & 6 bits 5/8 clock spring 1 Froster [possibly to create a matted surface on brass] 2/ 6 bean compasses 3/4 1 clock bell 4/ 2 dividers 34 5 arbors 2/ Canadersticks 1/ 5 chisels 1/ 20 brass stocks 3/ 3 scew plates & taps 4/ borax box 1/ 2 handvices 3/ 4 pr pliers 6/ 4 gravers 1/ 4 small files 1/ 4 lead 1/4 wire brush 2/ brass plate hair spring 2/ magnifying glass 3/ Patterns for buckles 2/ clock wheels 6/ 72 watch springs 52/6 72 watch keys 25/ 12 watch springs 30/ 6 files 3/4 4 old brushes 10/ 4 buckles 4/9 107 crystals 21/5 42 watch seals 12/ 40 watchkeys 13/4 22 ditto 3/ 1 watch spring 2/ 1 brush 6/ 1 salver 1/ cash for acc 6/ 2 bottles aquafordy 4/5 small bottle varnish 1/8 pendulum wyer 1/ glass case 1/ parcel of potts 1/6 1 stake 12/8 small ditto 1/ 2 vices 42/ 4 qts sand 2/8 34 bushels charcoal 9/ cream of tartar 2/ [38]

The clock-making tools and materials in his estate inventory were valued at £ 31/14/10. This important capital investment, slightly less than half the value of his house and land, was evidence that Newbury was a promising business location. When Mulliken died, his sons were only five and ten years old, and although they would eventually follow their father's trade, his death provided an opportunity for someone else.

Daniel Balch (1735-1789) was just completing his apprenticeship in Bradford, where Mulliken had grown up and learned clock making,[39] and through the fraternity of masters and apprentices, Balch was able to succeed him in Newbury. Clocks by Balch in the OSV collection reveal that he was trained in both the blacksmith's tradition of posted-frame, 30-hour movements made substantially of iron, and the more modern whitesmith's tradition of brass mechanisms supported by vertical plates. Balch's clocks illustrate the ability of rural clock makers to adapt their methods to their clientele and, in contrast to stylish contemporary urban clocks, his workmanship illustrates an inventive blend of ver-

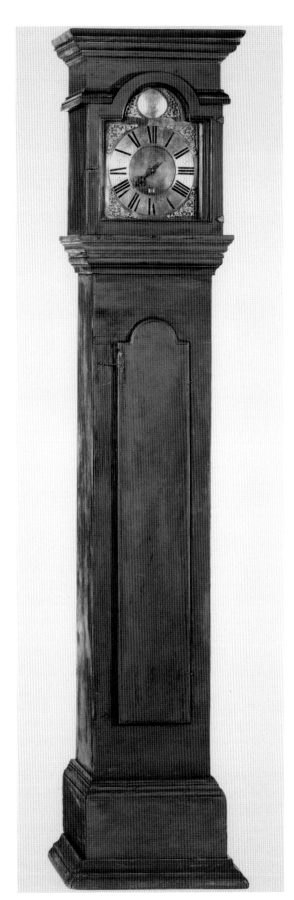

satility with craft specialization.

A tall clock marked "2" is presumably the second made after Balch completed his apprenticeship, (Fig. 1-8) although by the mid-1750s this design was outmoded. The movement runs for a day on a pull-up weight that descends on a rope with a counterweight at the free end. There is no striking train, and the clock is fitted with a single hand and calendar wheel.[40] The eye-catching brass dial has cast spandrels, applied name boss, and chapter ring made with distinctive crosses and drilled dots that mark the half- and quarter-hours.

Balch's notions about the proper appearance of a tall clock were apparently defined by an older master familiar with early English clock making. Its pine case by an unknown cabinetmaker is as comfortably old-fashioned as the movement and, like it, the sophisticated origins of its design fool the eye. The squat base of the case, its long waist, and flat hood had been stylish in England a century earlier. Its hood, which is removed by lifting straight up rather than by sliding forward, illustrates a feature of the most advanced London tall clocks of the late 17th century.[41] (Fig. 1-9)

But these clocks are not an accurate reflection of the level of Balch's training. A clock in a private collection, dated "Newbury 1756,"[42] shows that he had the technical competence to function successfully in a more fashionable arena. Balch obliged this patron, presumably one with more money to spend, with a brass eight-day movement fitted with a rack-and-snail strike, two hands, seconds and calendar dials, and winding posts through apertures in the dial. The case has a fashionable sarcophagus hood.

When Newburyport was set off from Newbury in 1764, Balch and his business were part of the new town, where expanding commerce offered great potential for business. His reputation was enhanced by the dozens of commissions that followed. On the seacoast the earth's natural clock so obviously governs the tides and navigation. A clock customer might well need a way to track the difference between apparent or sun time and mean or clock time through one season. A tall clock in the collection contains a movement signed by Daniel Balch that dates to the third quarter of the 18th century. The movement and dial are housed in a later Newburyport case, in which the 1766 manuscript label by Balch and James is pasted.

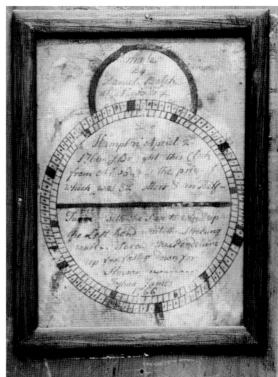

While the date of the label corresponds to the style of the movement and dial, like the mechanism, it may have come from another source. The label reads:

> made/ by /Daniel Balch at /Newbury/ / Hampton [New Hampshire] April 2nd 1766. I/ Brought this Clock from Newbury the price of / which was 32 dollors & an Half—/ Turn with the Sun to wind up —the Left Hand/ wait the Striking wait. Screw the Pendulum up/ for faster Down for Slower — Joshua James [1740-1809]."[43] (Fig. 1-10)

Balch made a clock in 1766 which may reflect an attempt to provide someone engaged in navigation with a method to track the equation of time. A hand-written chart suggests that instruction in the science of time may have been part of his training.

A circle intersects a smaller arc at the top resembling an abstract clock dial with the tympanum above the chapter ring. The ring is composed of a two-tiered border of squares (some with dots) that may represent days. Both tiers are divided into six sections by black squares. Each section contains 14 to 17 squares, which may be keyed to the number of days between the recurrence of high tide at the same time and place. The difference between clock time and sun time may be represented in the sum of the outer tier–94 and of the inner tier—93. The instructions in the center are written in a different hand.

Samuel Mulliken's brother Nathaniel, Jr. (1722-1767) was also trained by his uncle Jonathan (b. *ca.* 1710), and chose to establish his business in Lexington in about 1751.[44] The dial and movement of the clock by Nathaniel Mulliken, Sr. made in his shop about 1760, are equal to fine London workmanship.[45] (Fig. 1-11) The heavy brass dial is mounted with expensive, well-cast spandrels and engraved elements. The movement features heavy brass plates that support deeply cut wheels and pinions with ample room for the operation of the escapement and the strike-lifting levers in the typical English way. (Fig. 1-12) Nathaniel was capable of making well crafted high-style clocks, a skill which in 1766 attracted a young man, whose apprenticeship experience until then had failed to equip him with the skills he desired. Benjamin Willard (1743-1803) of Grafton, learned from him the knowledge of clock making he had failed to find with Benjamin Cheney (1725-1815) in East Hartford. Nathaniel Mulliken's death the following year left Willard in charge of the shop.[46] Willard, whose forte was brass clocks, remained in Lexington until

December 21, 1771, when he advertised "that he has removed from Lexington to Roxbury." The storm clouds of conflict with England were already on the horizon, but Willard advised his patrons that they could continue to expect work of the quality to which they were accustomed. "His Workman at Grafton, where clocks are made as well as at Roxbury" was still at his bench.[47]

CLOCKS MADE BY BROWN, THE CLAGGETTS, AND MULLIKENS, then by Benjamin Willard, had heavy brass movements, requiring a large and steady supply of imported metals. By 1770 it had become apparent that the colonial relationship with the mother country was going to impede importation of these materials through the ports of Boston or anywhere else in America. To continue to do business, inventive clock makers sought alternatives and found two: to make clock movements with a more readily available material or to make them smaller.

Wooden clocks by Jonas Fitch (1741-1808) of rural Pepperell, Massachusetts, have been viewed as a curiosity. (Fig. 1-13) How could this man about whom so little is known, but who called

Fig.1-11. Tall Clock, Nathaniel Mulliken, Lexington, Mass., ca. 1760. 57.1.48

Fig.1-12. Tall Clock movement, Nathaniel Mulliken, 57.1.48

Fig.1-13. Tall Clock, Jonas Fitch, Pepperell, Mass., ca. 1765. See pl.25. 57.1.237

Fig. 1-14. Tall Clock movement, Jonas Fitch. A large count wheel for the hour strike mounted on the back plate, simple pillar posts to separate the plates, and a small, domed bell to sound the hours characterize the 30-hour clocks by Fitch. See pl.25. 57.1.237

himself a clock maker, produce 30-hour wooden movements (Fig. 1-14) which he mounted behind composite brass dials? His neighbors wondered the same thing back in 1764. The son and brother of wealthy landowners, Jonas Fitch was a victim of his own uniqueness, but was exonerated by the Pepperell selectmen, who certified that, "he is a person compos mentis and standeth in no need of a guardian ... but never having his hearing so perfectly as people commonly have, appears a little odd." Fitch was described as not only being of sound mind, but also "Remarkably Ingenious about any Craft."[48] A century after his death, it was still remembered that "in the winter season, before and during the Revolution he made a few clocks. They are lettered on the dial 'Jonas Fitch.' They are well made and good timekeepers."[49]

Like all of the half-dozen known clocks by Fitch, a fanciful and highly stylized phoenix is engraved in

Fig.1-15. Tall Clock, John Bailey, Hanover, Mass., ca. 1765. The massive width and depth of this case are a clue that it houses an unusual eight-day, wooden movement. 57.1.230

Fig.1-16. Tall Clock movement, John Bailey. This wooden movement is the only known eight-day example from this period, the earliest known in Massachusetts, and the only known example by this maker. 57.1.230

the typanum and the dial is embellished with cast pewter spandrels in an elaborate open-work pattern retaining traces of gilt varnish. The calendar dial window is centered below the hands. The steel hands help to identify his work.(Pl. 25) The work of clock makers in the Ashby, Massachusetts, area later in the century suggests that Fitch trained them in the style and layout characteristics of his clocks, but working alone he was unable to take advantage of the opportunities presented by large and clever families like the Blasdels, Mullikens, Baileys, or Cheneys.

A clock made by John Bailey (1730-1810) of Hanover, Massachusetts,[50] during the 1760s reveals how he, like the Cheneys, used elaborate details to mask the economy of the movement hidden within. (Fig. 1-15) The dial with calendar wheel and two winding arbors inside the chapter ring surmounted with the fashionable sarcophagus hood suggests an expensive, brass, eight-day movement. Removal of the hood, however, reveals that Bailey had constructed a wooden movement that runs for eight days like a brass mechanism. (Fig. 1-16) A clock with a brass mechanism made by him in about 1785 reveals his versatility as a clock maker in the 18th-century tradition. (Fig. 1-17)

Likewise contemporary clocks by Benjamin and Timothy Cheney (1731-1795) of East Hartford, Connecticut, reveal that they were able to develop a considerable market for their wooden clocks which only used a small quantity of brass. Despite the wealth found in some of New England's rural valleys, these people could not be customers for clocks as emblems of their presumed place in society without access to them.[51] A sample of 113 probate inventories taken in Hartford County, Connecticut, and Hampshire County, Massachusetts, between 1754 and 1777 yields only seven references to clocks, all in estates valued at more than £600. (Seven other households listed a watch, but none listed both a clock and a watch.) Only Caleb Ely of Springfield (1755) owned two timepieces, non-striking mechanisms appraised at £1/10/0 each.[52] Wealth and the ownership of clocks correlate in the Connecticut River valley after 1750 when the Cheneys established themselves.

Wooden clocks by the Cheneys gave consumers of the lower Connecticut Valley the opportunity to monitor time at about half the cost of a brass clock, had they been able to obtain one. Except for a brass escape wheel mounted on a wooden arbor, the entire movement was made of wood. Until 30 hours have passed and it is time to pull up the weights inside the case, no one is the wiser that within it, ticks a cheaper, wooden movement.

Sons of a cabinetmaker,[53] the Cheney brothers built clocks with oak or chestnut plates, cherry wheels, and maple arbors that ran for 30 hours. These heavy movements were hidden behind brass-sheathed wooden dials and housed in hardwood cases like expensive eight-day clocks.[54] From across the room, a clock with a brass or wooden movement appears the same: costly. Only the discerning eye notices the hood's added depth to accommodate the deeper, wooden thirty-hour movement. The Cheneys may also have built their remarkably consistent cases, like this fashionable walnut example with a pagoda-style hood.[55] (Figs. 1-18, 1-19)

Ready access to large quantities of brass was not a factor in their clocks, as revealed by an apprentice's recollection of Benjamin's shop in 1761. Impressed by Cheney's imposing clocks, John Fitch, later the

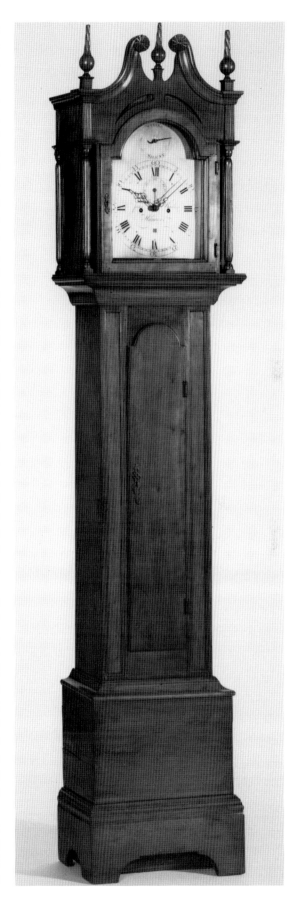

Fig.1-17. Tall Clock, John Bailey, Hanover, Mass., ca. 1785. 57.1.88

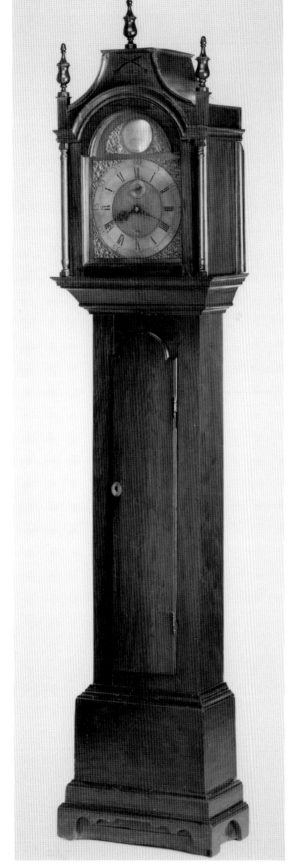

Fig.1-18. Tall Clock, Benjamin Cheney, Hartford, Conn., ca. 1760. 57.1.117

Fig.1-19. Tall Clock movement, Benjamin Cheney. Thirty-hour, wooden movement with chestnut plates, cherry wheels, and maple arbors and pinions. The thin brass dial plate and applied components are attached to a pine board. 57.1.117

inventor of the steamboat, had selected that shop as the place to learn the craft. He was disappointed to learn that Cheney was using local materials. "Benjamin Cheaney," John Fitch discovered to his surprise, "followed nothing in the shop but wooden clocks and small brass work, and my indentures was ambiguously exprest that he ws to learn me clockwork and brass foundering." At the end of his time and still "almost ignorant of clockwork," Fitch turned to Timothy Cheney and "followed making brass and wooden clocks" for a year. He got no further with Timothy either. "I was not put to one single clock, neither wood nor brass during that time."[56]

Wooden-wheeled clocks became so common in Connecticut that in 1797 the state legislature introduced a tax on them. The rate was $3.34 on wooden-wheeled clocks, compared to $10 on brass movements. Not only were all these clocks a potential source of revenue for the state, but the tax lists record the growth in clock ownership. By the end of the century the proportion of clock-owning households had risen to one in twelve. In East Hartford

and East Windsor alone, the 1798 tax assessments listed more than 200 wooden clocks, most of which contained wooden mechanisms.[57]

But the marketplace needed to develop, too. Before timekeeping could become more accessible, Americans had to perceive a need for accuracy close at hand. Advances in manufacturing moved the craftsmen of colonial America away from traditional habits of looking to Britain for manufactured goods of all sorts, including clock parts and clock-making tools. Although they were adequately trained to make the components of a clock, the colonists simply were not fully capitalized to invest nor legally free to transform raw materials into finished products. At the end of the century it became equally logical for the Cheneys and Eli Terry to Americanize clock making by substituting native woods for imported brass as it was for the Willard family to continue the urban tradition of combining English-produced parts into elegant clocks for the new republic.

NOTES

[1] John Winthrop, "A Modell of Christian Charity," *Winthrop Papers, 1498-1649*, ed. Allyn B. Forbes, 5 vols. (Boston: 1929-1947), 2:293-295. The authors thank Kenneth Hafertepe for bringing this reference to their attention.

[2] Will of Henry Packs (Parks?), Hartford, September 4, 1640. *A Digest of the Early Connecticut Probate Records, Vol. 1: Hartford District, 1635-1700.* Charles W. Manwaring, comp. (Hartford: R.S. Peck & Company, 1904), 29.

[3] Probate Inventory, The Rev. Thomas Hooker, Hartford, 1649. Hartford District, file 2841, Connecticut State Library.

[4] Massachusetts Bay Records (October 1, 1633, and March 4, 1633/1634), I:109,112.

[5] Chris H. Bailey, *Two Hundred Years of American Clocks and Watches*, 15; Penrose R. Hoopes, *Connecticut Clockmakers of the Eighteenth Century* (Reprint of first edition, 1930; New York: Dover Publications, Inc., 1974), 5; George Francis Dow, *The Arts and Crafts in New England, 1704-1775* (Topsfield, Mass..: Wayside Press, 1927).

[6] Thomas Badely (d. 1721), James Batterson (adv. 1707), James Bichaut (adv. 1729), John Brand (adv. 1712-1714 who returned to England), Elijah Collins (adv. 1727), William Davis (wkg. after 1683), Joseph Essex (adv. 1712-1715, d. 1719), David Johnson (wkg. ca. 1687), Robert Peasely (adv. 1735), and Isaac Webb (adv. 1708).

[7] David Hackett Fischer, *Albion's Seed: Four British Folkways in America* (New York and Oxford: Oxford University Press, 1989), 158-166.

[8] *Diary of Cotton Mather*, 2 vols. (New York: Frederick Ungar Publishing Company, 1957), 2:604. The sermon was printed that year in Boston by S. Kneeland for J. Edwards.

[9] James Asby (adv. 1769-1772), James Atkinson (adv. 1745-1757) who died in Nova Scotia, Thomas Clark (adv. 1764), Richard Cranch (adv. 1749-1789), and John McLean (adv. 1767-1773), all of London or Dublin, were trained watch makers who made their livings mostly in repair work, jewelry, and instruments.

[10] Proceedings of The Boston Clock Club, 1934-1940, Bulletins & Special Papers (unpublished typescript, 1968): 27-30, 32-33, 36-37, 76 (hereafter cited as Boston Clock Club); Dow, pp. 133-134, 143. Benjamin Bagnall, Sr., probably come from Staffordshire, England, where other Bagnall clockmakers are known to have worked. Clocks by Bagnall are discussed in Charles L. Venable, *American Furniture in the Bybee Collection* (Austin: University of Texas Press, 1989), 10-13;

Wallace Nutting, *Furniture Treasury*, 3 vols. (Framingham, Mass.: Old America Company, 1928), 2: fig. 3240; Albert E. Partridge, "Benjamin Bagnall of Boston, Clockmaker," *Old-Time New England* 26, no. 1 (July 1935): 26-31; Morrison H. Heckscher, *American Furniture in the Metropolitan Museum of Art. Vol. 2, Late Colonial Period: The Queen Anne and Chippendale Styles* (New York: Metropolitan Museum of Art and Random House, 1985), no. 187.

[11] William H. Distin and Robert Bishop, *The American Clock* (New York: E.P. Dutton and Company, 1976), 30; David Hansen, "Gawen Brown, Soldier and Clockmaker," Boston Clock Club, 108-115; David Hansen, "Gawen Brown, Soldier and Clockmaker," *Old-Time New England* 30 (July 1939): 109; Dow, 134-137. A tall clock in a private collection is inscribed "Gawen Brown/London." Brown's only child, Mather (1761-1831), became a renowned portraitist after training with Benjamin West in London. Dorinda Evans, *Mather Brown: Early American Artist in England* (Middletown, Conn.; Wesleyan University Press, 1982).

[12] *Boston Evening Post*, January 16 and February 6, 1749.

[13] Boston Town Records, October 22, 1766; Edwin Churchill, "Thomas Jackson, Clockmaker—Now There Are Two," *Maine Antiques Digest* 19, no. 4 (April 1991): 12B-13B; Brock Jobe, *Portsmouth Furniture: Masterworks from the New Hampshire Seacoast* (Boston: SPNEA, expected 1992). Two Thomas Jacksons made clocks in colonial New England. Until recently, Thomas Jackson (ca. 1741-1784) of Portsmouth, N.H., and Kittery, Me., has been confused with the Englishman Thomas Jackson (1727 or 1733-1806), who worked in Boston and in Preston, Conn.. This entry in the Boston records documents his arrival in Boston via Canada.

[14] *Boston Gazette*, May 8, 1769.

[15] *Boston Evening Post*, December 11, 1752; Hansen, 9. Brown's principal competitors were Benjamin Bagnall, Sr. (*ca.* 1689-1773), his sons Benjamin, Jr. (b. 1715), and Samuel (b. 1718), Moses Peck (adv. 1753-1800), and Joseph Pope (1748-1826).

[16] Dean A. Fales, Jr., "Boston Japanned Furniture" and Sinclair H. Hitchings, "Boston's Colonial Japanners: The Documentary Record," *Boston Furniture of the Eighteenth Century,* ed. Walter Muir Whitehill (Boston: The Colonial Society, 1974), 49-69, 71-75; Morrison H. Heckscher and Frances Gruber Safford, "Boston Japanned Furniture in The Metropolitan Museum of Art," *Antiques* 129,

no. 5 (May 1986): 1046-1061; John H. Hill, "The History and Technique of Japanning and the Restoration of the Pimm Highboy," *American Art Journal* 8 (November 1976): 59-84. Both Winterthur and Henry Ford Museum own japanned tall clocks by Gawen Brown, the latter dated 1766. The Metropolitan Museum of Art owns a tall clock by Brown housed in a Newport case. A clock made about 1740 by John Doane (1664-1755) of Scituate, Mass., survives in a japanned case made by Peter Stelling (or Stallings) of Boston. See Sotheby's, Americana Auction, sale 6201, June 27, 1991, lot 354.

[17] Anyone who owned a good clock and a sundial noticed that the two only kept the same time toward the middle of April and June and at the end of August and December. From earth, the sun's daily path is elliptical and tilted, and the earth does not revolve evenly on its axis, making the solar days irregular. Sidereal time was more accurate because it focused on the consistent intersection of the earth's daily revolution and the location of selected stars that do not seem to move. Although mathematically more accurate, sidereal time can be charted only at night and loses about a day each year, or about four minutes each day, if compared to the segmented mean time kept by a clock for practical living. Resolving the relationship between the two times was important to the Enlightenment mind and is still significant in practical navigation.

[18] Gawen Brown, "Calibre Book," 1753-1757, Massachusetts Historical Society. A photocopy is available at the Winterthur Museum.

[19] Albert L. Partridge, "William Claggett, of Newport, Rhode Island, Clockmaker," *Old-Time New England* 27 (January 1937): 110-115.

[20] *News-Letter* (Boston), December 26, 1715, as quoted in Richard Champlin, "William Claggett and his Clockmaking Family," *NAWCC Bulletin* Supplement 11 (Summer 1976): 5; The advertisement includes the suffix "jun." after Claggett's name. His father's name was Caleb, but his uncle, William, also lived in Boston. The term junior was probably used to differentiate the two generations rather than to denote strictly father and son. A businessman as well as a clock maker, Claggett sold luxury goods that were not of his make nor specialty (like fashionable imported bed hangings) to the same clientele.

[21] William Claggett, *A Looking-Glass for Elder Clark and Elder Wightman, and the Church under Their Care* (Boston: James Franklin, 1721); Champlin, 6-8.

[22] "Diary of Nathaniel Ames," *Dedham Historical Register* 3 (July 1892): 133, as

quoted in Champlin, 10; Arthur A. Ross, *A Discourse, Embracing the Civil and Religious History of Rhode Island* (Providence: H.H. Brown, 1838) 36; *Boston Evening Post*, August 24, 1747.

[23] Champlin, 14. The movement by William Claggett at OSV is housed in an early 19th-century case. A tall clock by Claggett, fitted with dials to record the tides, is owned by The Metropolitan Museum of Art. See Heckscher, *American Furniture*, 294-295. A similar tall clock by James Wady, Claggett's son-in-law, is in the collection of the Winterthur Museum. See Joseph Downs, *American Furniture, Queen Anne and Chippendale Periods in the Henry Francis duPont Winterthur Museum* (New York: Macmillan, 1952), fig. 202. Other clocks by William Claggett are illustrated in Nutting, figs. 3245, 3246, 3248, 3249, and 3319; Luke Vincent Lockwood, *Colonial Furniture in America.* 2 vols. (Rev. ed., New York: Charles Scribner's Sons, 1926), 2:282-286; Barry A. Greenlaw, *New England Furniture at Williamsburg* (Williamsburg, Va.: Colonial Williamsburg Foundation, 1974), 96-98; Michael Moses, *Master Craftsmen of Newport: The Townsends and Goddards* (Tenafly, N.J.: MMI Americana Press, 1984), 31; Oswaldo Rodriguez Roque, *American Furniture at Chipstone* (Madison, Wisconsin: University of Wisconsin Press, 1984), 87-89; Robert P. Emlen, "A Masterful William Claggett Clock: A Short Story in a Tall Case," *Antiques* 118, no. 3 (September 1980): 502-507. Tall clocks by William Claggett are also in the collections of Greenfield Village and Henry Ford Museum and the Redwood Library, Newport.

[24] Anonymous, Day Book, 1733-1734, Newport Historical Society, no. 703, as quoted in Champlin, 14. See also, 10-12.

[25] *Newport Mercury*, August 24 and 31, 1767; Richard L. Champlin, "High Time: William Claggett and His Clockmaking Family," *Newport History* 47 (Summer 1974): 159-190; Richard L. Champlin, "Thomas Claggett: Silversmith, Swordsman, Clockmaker," *Newport History* 49, Part 3, 163 (Summer 1976): 57-68.

[26] Margaretta M. Lovell, " Such Furniture as Will Be Most Profitable': The Business of Cabinetmaking in Eighteenth-Century Newport," *Winterthur Portfolio* 26, no. 1 (Spring 1991): 27-62; Sloane, "John Cahoone and the Newport Furniture Industry," 88-122. A Goddard-Townsend style high chest of drawers with the inscription, "Benjamin Baker," is owned by the Newport Restoration Foundation.

[27] Benjamin Baker, Account Book, Newport Historical Society, 1904. Baker made furniture in Newport between 1751 and

1792.

[28] The OSV clock is one of ten examples known by Thomas Claggett. Two short clocks are in The Metropolitan Museum of Art and the Winterthur Museum.

[29] For a discussion of monetary values, see John J. McCusker, *Money and Exchange in Europe and America, 1600-1775: A Handbook* (Chapel Hill: University of North Carolina Press, 1978).

[30] Benjamin Franklin, *Advice to a Young Tradesman. Written by an Old One* (Philadelphia: Benjamin Mecan, 1748), 1-4.

[31] *The Newport Mercury*, July 27, 1772. The authors thank Glee Krueger for bringing this reference to our attention.

[32] For studies of rural society and craftsmanship that examine the dynamics of design selection and consumerism in the northeastern United States, see Roderic H. Blackburn and Ruth Piwonka, *Remembrance of Patria: Dutch Arts and Culture in Colonial America, 1609-1776* (Albany: Albany Institute of History and Art, 1988); Edward S. Cooke, Jr., *Fiddlebacks and Crooked-backs: Elijah Booth and Other Joiners in Newtown and Woodbury, 1750-1820* (Waterbury, Conn.,: Mattatuck Historical Society, 1982); Dean F. Failey, *Long Island Is My Nation: The Decorative Arts and Craftsmen, 1640-1830* (Setauket, NY: Society for the Preservation of Long Island Antiquities, 1976); Charles F. Hummel, *With Hammer In Hand*; *Agreeable Situations: Society, Commerce, and Art in Southern Maine, 1780-1830*, ed. Laura F. Sprague (Kennebunkport, Me.: The Brick Store Museum, 1987); Robert Blair St. George, *The Wrought Covenant: Source Material for the Study of Craftsmen and Community in Southeastern New England, 1620-1700* (Brockton, MA: Brockton Art Center, 1979); Scott T. Swank et al., *The Arts of the Pennsylvania Germans* (New York: W.W. Norton & Company, 1983); Robert F. Trent, *Hearts & Crowns: Folk Chairs of the Connecticut Coast, 1720-1840* (New Haven: New Haven Colony Historical Society, 1977); *The Great River: Art & Society of the Connecticut Valley, 1635-1820*, eds. Gerald W.R. Ward and William N. Hosley, Jr. (Hartford: Wadsworth Atheneum, 1985).

[33] For a discussion of the working life of an 18th-century rural metal worker, see Susan R. McGowan, "Agreeable to His Genius: John Partridge Bull, 1731-1813, Deerfield, Massachusetts" (unpublished master's thesis, Trinity College, Hartford, Conn., 1988).

[34] Bailey, 46-47, 60; e.g. Charles S. Parsons, "An Early Clock Made by Richard Manning in Ipswich, Massachusetts." *NAWCC Bulletin* 9, no. 3, whole number 85 (April 1960): 194.

[35] David W. Hoyt, *The Old Families of Salisbury and Amesbury* (Providence, R.I.: Snow and Farnham, 1897), 65; Joseph Merrill, History of Amesbury (Haverhill, Mass.: Franklin P. Stiles, 1880), 203, 224; Benjamin Chase, *History of Old Chester from 1719-1869* (Auburn, N.H.: Benjamin Chase, 1869), 67, 140, 254, 375, 437, 456-457, 474; "Blaisdell Papers," Proceedings of the Blaisdell Family Association 2, no. 7 (Summer 1944): 2-21;. Charles S. Parsons, *New Hampshire Clocks and Clockmakers* 18, 64-67, 158-159. Parsons recorded 59 Blasdel clocks: two by Jonathan, 33 by David, 19 by Isaac, two by Richard, and three by Nicholas and several more have been discovered since his 1976 publication. OSV also owns an uncased, non-striking, thirty-hour timepiece ("wag-on-the-wall") by Isaac Blasdel (57.1.113). The similarity of many cases with Blasdel movements leads to speculation that family members may have done the cabinetwork.

[36] M.L. Brown, *Firearms in Colonial America: The Impact on History and Technology, 1492-1792* (Washington, D.C.: Smithsonian Institution Press, 1980), 149-150, 157, 248, 283; Merrill, 224. Like his father, Isaac Blasdel served as an armorer at the Battle of Bennington in 1777 and in Rhode Island in 1780.

[37] Clock making in Britain was advanced by the immigration of skilled Protestant tradesmen from northern Europe during the Thirty Years War (1618-1648). The earliest clock makers became members of the Blacksmith's Guild because they worked primarily with iron. The growing demand for domestic clocks led to the charter of the London Clockmakers' Company in 1631. Rupert Gentle and Rachael Field, *English Domestic Brass, 1680-1810, and the History of Its Origins* (New York: E.P. Dutton, 1975), 1-28; Percy G. Dawson, C.B. Drover, and D.W. Parkes, *Early English Clocks* (Suffolk, U.K.: Antiques Collectors Club, Ltd., 1982), 42; *Britten's* 317-319.

[38] Probate Inventory, Samuel Mulliken, Newbury, 1756. Essex County Registry of Probate, Salem, Mass.

[39] Galusha B. Balch, *Genealogy of the Balch Families in America* (Salem: Eben Putnam, 1897), 34-35, 55. Daniel Balch was born on March 14, 1735, the son of the Rev. William and Rebecca Stone Balch of East Bradford.

[40] Although two-handed clocks were well known in urban England during the last quarter of the 17th century, the use of a single hand to provide adequate accuracy lingered with more frugal and provincial customers on both sides of the Atlantic through most of the 18th century.

[41] Dawson, 166.

[42] The clock is illustrated by Distin and Bishop, 24.

[43] See Joseph Dow, *History of the Town of Hampton, New Hampshire*, 2 vols. (Salem, Massachusetts: Salem Press Publishing and Printing Company, 1893), 2:762-763.

[44] Edwin S. Burt and Fraser R. Forgie, "Clockmakers of the Concord, Massachusetts Community," *Bulletin NAWCC*, Supplement 1967 3-8; The Rev. Gideon Tibbetts, *History of the Families Millingas and Millanges of Saxony and Normandy* (Lewiston, Maine: 1907), passim. The Mullikens came from Bradford in Essex County. It is no coincidence that the Balch family and Michael Carleton (1757-1836) also had roots there. The importance of family ties to understanding American craftsmanship is underscored by the genealogical gymnastics required to learn just which Mulliken has put his name on the dial of a clock. The senior metalworking Mullikens were the brothers John (1690-1737) and Jonathan (born about 1710), sons of Robert, a weaver probably from Glasgow, Scotland, who lived in Boston before moving to Bradford. The elder son was a blacksmith. His younger brother, Jonathan, recorded as a clock maker in Bradford and for a time at Falmouth, trained his brother's sons: Samuel (1720-1756) and Nathaniel, Jr. (1722-1767), maker of the clock illustrated here. Samuel moved to Newburyport after 1740, and Nathaniel went to Lexington after 1751. Jonathan II (1746- 1782) [possibly Samuel's son] and Samuel II (1761-1847) [possibly Samuel's nephew], became clock makers in Newburyport. (Samuel II worked earlier in Salem and Lynn.) In the next generation, Samuel III (b. 1769) made clocks for a time in Hallowell, Me, with his brother, Nathaniel (1776-1847).

[45] The maple clock case was locally made and is missing its most stylish feature: a sarcophagus-shaped roof removed to accommodate a low ceiling. A similar clock with a sarcophagus hood made by Nathaniel Mulliken, Sr., in 1765 is illustrated in *American Antiques from the Israel Sack Collection* 9 vols. (Washington, D.C.: Highland House Publishers, Inc., ca. 1891-1990), 1:100. The Museum of Fine Arts, Boston, owns a clock by Nathaniel that is housed in a later Roxbury-style case. See Richard H. Randall, Jr., *American Furniture in the Museum of Fine Arts, Boston* (Boston: Museum of Fine Arts, 1965), 243-244. See also, Christie's auction catalogue, sale 7368, October 19, 1991, lot 187, for a clock by Mulliken dated 1754.

[46] Nathaniel III [1752-1776] and Joseph [1765-1802] eventually followed in their

father's footsteps and John [b. 1754] became a cabinetmaker who supplied clock cases. John Ware Willard, *Simon Willard and His Clocks* (1911; New York: Dover Publications, 1968), 79-80;

[47] *Boston Evening Post*, December 17, 1771.

[48] Jonas Fitch, Docket 7700, First Series, Registry of Probate, Middlesex County Courthouse, East Cambridge, Mass.

[49] Ezra Stearns, "Old Clocks in Fitchburg," *Proceedings of the Fitchburg Historical Society*, 1907-1913, V:120.

[50] *Bailey Genealogy. James, John and Thomas and Their Descendants*, ed. Hollis R. Bailey, (Somerville, Mass.: The Citizen Company, 1899), 322, 333-334, 350-352; Jedidiah Dwelley and John F. Simonds, *History of the Town of Hanover, Massachusetts* (Plymouth: Memorial Press, 1910), 6-7, 9-10; Donald K. Packard, "The Baileys of Hanover, Massachusetts, Clockmakers" Boston Clock Club, 1940), 189-196; Chris H. Bailey, *Two Hundred Years* 48, 50-52, 94, 96. The Bailey network in Hanover began in 1700 when John III's grandfather, John (1673-1752), moved from nearby Scituate. John III was born in Hanover on October 30, 1730, the son of John, Jr., and Elizabeth Cowen Bailey, and died on October 27, 1810. He passed his clock-making skill to subsequent generations. His sons, John IV (1751-1823), Calvin (1761-1835), and Lebbeus (1763-1827), all followed in the trade. In the third generation, John IV trained his sons, Joseph (born ca. 1783) and John V (1787-1883).

[51] Richard D. Brown, "Regional Culture in a Revolutionary Era: The Connecticut Valley, 1760-1820," *The Great River*, 44; Zea, "Rural Craftsmen and Design," 64-67.

[52] Bailey. "Clocks and Instruments," in *The Great River* 341. Estate Inventory, Caleb Ely, Springfield, 1755. Hampshire County Probate Records, 8:129, Hampshire County Courthouse, Northampton, Mass.

[53] Charles H. Pope, *The Cheney Genealogy* (Boston: Charles H. Pope, 1897), 277-279; *The Descendants of Thomas Olcott, One of the First Settlers of Hartford, Ct.* by Nathaniel Goodwin, ed. Henry S. Olcott (Rev.ed.; Albany: J. Munsell, 1874), 42-43. Benjamin, Sr. (1698-1760), a joiner and wheelwright was partner in a sawmill. A chair in the collection of the Winterthur Museum inscribed "Cheney" in chalk has spawned speculation that it is his work. Benjamin, Jr., and his younger brothers, Abiel (born 1727), Timothy, Silas (1734-1791), and Asahel (1737-1763), worked with wood. Abiel became a boat builder. Benjamin, Timothy, and possibly Silas did clock making. (Distin and Bishop, 294)

Timothy lived in the section of East Hartford that become Manchester and was still an active clock maker when he died. Benjamin, moved from East Hartford to Berlin, Connecticut, near his son, Elisha, around 1800.

[54] Robert C. Cheney, "A Study of a Tall Clock by Benjamin Cheney, Hartford," *NAWCC Bulletin* 23, Whole No. 211, no. 2 (April 1981): 115; Bailey, "Clocks and Instruments," 349-351.

[55] Although the case and finials may seem awkward, the design was relatively modern and executed in a hardwood quite likely imported into Connecticut from Pennsylvania or Virginia. The finials are replaced. The incised firearms cut into the tympanum of the hood are a later addition.

[56] Roscoe Conkling Fitch, *History of the Fitch Family*. 2 vols. (Haverhill, Mass.: Record Publishing Company, n.d.), 2:209, 213-267; Thompson Westcott, *Life of John Fitch, The Inventor of the Steamboat* (Philadelphia: J.B. Lippincott and Company, 1878), 221. See also John Fitch, *The Autobiography*, ed. Frank D. Prager (Philadelphia: 1976), 75. Asahel Cheney (b. about 1758) made both brass and wooden clocks in East Hartford, Northfield, Mass., 1790-7, Putney, Vt. to 1808, Royalton to 1816 and then Rochester. Elisha (1769-1847), who remained in Connecticut moved to Berlin about 1793 and through marriage entered the firearms business of Simeon North (1765-1852) as did Benjamin Cheney. Elisha's clock-making career focused on wooden clocks. He and made shelf clocks with his son, Olcott (1796-1860), moving in 1835 to Lima, N.Y. and then Roscoe, Ill. The third Cheney son, Martin (1778-ca. 1830), settled in Windsor, Vermont, in 1803 where he made a tall clock now in the collection of the Constitution House. A Massachusetts-style shelf clock made with a brass dial (rather than enamel) in Windsor before Cheney moved to Montreal in 1809 is in the collection of the Henry Ford Museum and Greenfield Village. The fourth Cheney son, Russell (b. 1772), settled in Woodstock Vt. where he advertised as "from East Hartford" in 1806. He lived in Thetford until 1811 and then in Chelsea before apparently returning to Conn. Either Benjamin or Timothy Cheney probably trained their nephew, Daniel White Griswold (1767-1844) of East Hartford, who made clocks with wooden movements. See Pope, 277, 328-329; Hoopes, 58, 60-61; J.H. Temple and George Sheldon, *History of Northfield, Massachusetts* (Albany: Joel Munsell, 1875), 175, 352, 422; Carlisle, *Vermont Clock and Watchmakers*, 69-70, 91, 94-95; *The Great River*, 351, 361, 365-366; *Federal Galaxy*

(Brattleboro, Vt.), 1798 September 15; *Northern Memento* (Woodstock, Vt.) 1806; *Northern Sentinel* (Burlington, Vt.), 1827 June 29; Dexter North, *John North of Farmington, Connecticut and His Descendants* (Washington, D.C.: 1921), 45, 79-82; Catherine M. North, *History of Berlin, Connecticut* (New Haven: Tuttle Morehouse and Taylor Co., 1916), 288, 290.

[57] Connecticut Tax Returns for East Hartford and East Windsor, 1798, on deposit at The Connecticut Historical Society. See Bailey, "Clocks and Instruments," 342-3 fn., 351. Wooden movements by both Benjamin and Timothy are owned by the American Clock and Watch Museum, Bristol, CT. A wooden movement by Benjamin is also owned by Historic Deerfield, Inc. A brass movement by Timothy is owned by The Connecticut Historical Society.

"ELEGANT FACES AND MAHOGANY CASES"
Clocks by the Willard Family

THE WILLARD FAMILY dominated Boston-area clock making during the first half of the 19th century. In New England their clocks became emblems of status in an urbanizing society. The brothers, Simon (1753-1848) and Aaron (1757-1844) Willard, (along with Eli Terry's family in Connecticut), took what they had learned about traditional 18th-century clock making and began to make clocks on a larger scale than ever before. They applied principles of design, construction, inventory, and distribution to clocks. Their dealings with specialized workmen in factory settings transformed clock making into one of America's first industries.

The Willards produced clocks so efficiently, using precast parts which they mounted in elegant "Roxbury" cases, that they attracted the best apprentices to the family circle. Their success allowed them the luxury of making innovations with costly patent timepieces and later shelf clocks. By the second quarter of the 19th century, the Willard family had transformed the craft of clock making into a business that permitted diversion into the science of horology. This chapter reviews the Willard family of clock makers by describing the clocks in the Old Sturbridge Village collection which illustrate their developing business and scientific interests.

By his own reckoning Benjamin Willard (1743-1803) made and sold 253 clocks in Massachusetts before 1774.[1] Although he worked in Grafton, Lexington, and Roxbury, advertisements in Boston newspapers state: "all Branches of this Business are carried on at his Shop at Grafton."[2] Two tall clocks sold at Lexington were signed on their dials by Benjamin Willard in 1770 and 1771. These movements with lead pendulum bobs inscribed John Morris and S. Willard were made in Grafton and transported to Lexington.[3]

Morris, on record as Simon Willard's teacher,[4] is a shadowy figure with an uneven reputation in the clock business of the 1770s. In Simon's opinion this "Englishman then engaged in the manufacture of clocks in Grafton" did not teach him anything and family tradition holds that he "was heard to say that the man to whom he was apprenticed knew little or

Fig. 2-1. Tall Clock, Benjamin Willard, Grafton, Mass., ca. 1770. The concave and convex sunburst patterns are carved out of solid cherry lumber, instead of the easier method of applying the convex carving to the door. The replaced fretwork is incongruous with a composite brass dial; a simple scroll or pagoda top would be more appropriate. 57.1.98

Fig. 2-3.
Timepiece
movement,
Simon Willard.
Economical to
produce, the
30-hour, weight
powered
timepiece features
a fall-off or
"passing" strike
sounding one bell
on the hour, dead
beat escapement,
pendulum rod
attached directly
to the pallet arbor
without a
suspension spring
and an additional
wheel (far left) to
trip the moon's
age dial in the
arch. Willard
charged $10 for
this clock.
57.1.122

nothing of the art himself, and that his teacher was his brother Benjamin."[5] Preston, Connecticut, clock maker John Avery (1732-1794) later recorded "Mr Marises Rule for cutting Pinions to Clocks" inside the cover of his ledger.[6] In 1777 it was reported that "one John Morris a clock maker...well known to Hartford, Middletown, and Norwich [stole] a quantity of silver, in bullien, some cash, and several other

articles" from Elijah Yeomans (1738-1794) of Hadley, Massachusetts.[7]

The progress of the "workman" mentioned in Benjamin's announcement of his move to Roxbury, most likely 18-year-old Simon, may be traced through clocks and occasional references in other people's diaries. Simon may have made the "Grafton" tall clock about 1770 (Fig. 2-1) which lacks the finish of a master's hand. The brass dial of another clock, which is engraved "Benjamin Willard, Roxbury, Fecit" and "Warranted for Mr. James Mears, 1772," a tanner and shoemaker, has a different story scratched onto its movement. It is "number 9" ... "Made by Simon Willard in his 17th year [1770] — Cleaned by him in his 81st year, August 10th, 1833."[8]

Benjamin's move to Roxbury in 1771 may have been an attempt to guarantee a steady supply of imported materials. During colonial times most commodities, especially finished metals needed for clocks, had to be imported. England's unpopular decision that her colonies had to take on a greater burden of paying for its own defense threatened to close the port of Boston as early as 1769. Suppliers like John Welch who advertised in 1772 that he "Imported from England... and sold at his shop No. 6 Union St. Boston, a general assortment of English goods...cutlery, Jewelry, goldsmiths, clock and watch articles" were vital to Willard's ability to do business. Welch advertised,

Watches, clock dials, plates, ornaments, &c. all sorts of clock and watch files, musical bells, Clock gut, gilt balls, brass and iron scratch brushes, clock and watch Riveting hammers, clock and watch hands, watch crystals, mainsprings, pendants, verges, silk springs, steel chains, seals and keys, watch dial plates, clock and watch screw drivers, broaches, endless screw keys, turkey flips, Bohemia stones, &c. [9]

Was this advertisement an act of defiance to the British Crown or an attempt to sell old stock? Whichever it was, the result would be the same: soon there was a shortage of materials for making and repairing elegant clocks. The only metal wares produced profitably in the colonies were hand-forged iron implements or heavy cast objects belched forth from rural blast furnaces.[10] Obtaining brass, bronze, and other copper alloys was problematic. Mines for copper, zinc, and tin had not yet been exploited in the New World and investment in manufacturing was slow to develop since the Crown controlled local manufacture. Clearly Benjamin Willard had to make some changes.

In one of his last recorded actions in Boston, in the summer of 1774, Benjamin contracted with Rea and Johnston, painters and japanners, for "pt [painting] a clock face 0.6.0."[11] Soon afterwards Benjamin left New England.[12] While his politics are unknown, the boycott of English goods made the necessary brass and clock parts difficult to obtain.

Simon Willard remained in Grafton during the Revolution, did clock and watch repairs, and tinkered.[13] He addressed the increasing scarcity of imported raw materials for clocks by experimenting with new forms, which reduced the size of clock movements. Simon found prototypes for a smaller timepiece among the European spring-powered bracket clocks,[14] which would have come into his shop for repair. It was obvious that they functioned successfully with much smaller movements than the tall clocks that his brother was making. Simon developed a small wall clock that gives the appearance of a complicated device, but it runs only for a day and strikes once on the hour. (Figs. 2-2, 2-3) Resembling a portable, spring-powered clock sitting on a bracket,[15] it has a kidney-shaped dial,[16] tells time, and gives the moon's age both on the lunar dial and an inner ring of numerals at the top. (Pl. 16) A steel

Fig. 2-4.
Timepiece, Aaron Willard, Grafton, ca. 1780. 57.1.68

hand points to the date on its outer ring of numerals. Like other early Willard wall and shelf clocks, it is a timepiece with a fall-off striking mechanism. Willard advertised these clocks on his labels, which read in part: "Time pieces which run 30 hours and warranted, price 10 dollars." While relatively costly, it was only one-fifth the price of a tall clock. For Simon Willard the new clock was a stepping stone to success, although less than two dozen have appar-

Fig. 2-5. Detail, Timepiece dial, Aaron Willard. The hands are large versions of those found on 18th-century English watches. The bell and hammer allow a single ring on the hour. 57.1.68

Fig. 2-6.Detail, Timepiece movement, Aaron Willard.The 30-hour timepiece movement is attached to the brass bezel by extensions of the round plates. The pendulum is mounted directly to the pallet arbor. 57.1.68

ently survived with dials engraved "Simon Willard/ Grafton," "Willard/Grafton" or "A/Willard." None are known marked Roxbury.[17] Aaron Willard also made a Grafton wall clock about 1780. (Figs.2-4,2-5,2-6) The movement is in the standard round format. The round dial, which confuses (or perhaps combines) the visual appeal of both the bracket clock and the watch, was also popular on European bracket clocks.

Benjamin spent the war years in York,Pennsylvania,[18] "with," he reported, "the best approved clock and watchmakers on the continent, in order to obtain further knowledge of the different branches of said business." He returned to Grafton in 1782 intending to resume his former specialties of tall and musical clocks and also to make his brother Simon's "New invented clock jack for roasting meat."

BENJAMIN WILLARD, Clock and Watch-Maker, ... is determined to work on the most reasonable terms, and as he lives on a farm and his expenses are much less than if he lived in a seaport, he can afford to work cheaper....In order the better to accommodate the publick, he has engaged with Mr. [Isaiah] Thomas to receive and forward all commands left at his printing office....Said Willard informs those who have purchased clocks of him before the war ... that those which need it, he is ready to repair, and warranted ones gratis.[19]....

To relaunch his business, Benjamin also advertised for "two or three active sprightly BOYS about fourteen years of age, as apprentices." A distant cousin, Gardner Parker (1772-1816)[20], may have been one of these youths.

Among the varied and complex clocks, which Willard advertised, were "Musical CLOCKS playing different Tunes, a new tune every Day in the Week, and on Sunday a Psalm Tune...without any Obstruction in the Motion...of the Clock—A new Invention for picking Barrels to perform this Musick." He seems to have found some takers. Willard's name is inscribed on a clock of this description made in Grafton between 1788 and 1790. The dial was imported from England, where it was made by Thomas Osborne of Birmingham.[21] Despite the promising number of clocks made, his attempt to restart business in Grafton was short lived, and by 1790, he moved to Worcester. Before the end of the century he had left New England.[22]

By this time his younger brothers, Simon and Aaron, had followed his early path to Roxbury, where their names first appeared on the tax list in 1783. On January 15, 1784, Simon advertised that he had "opened a shop in Roxbury Street, nearly opposite the road that turns off to Plymouth, where he carries on the CLOCK MAKING BUSINESS in all its branches." He also advertised Clock Jacks, his new invention, which "may be had of Paul Revere."[23]

Simon's struggles to get on his feet in Roxbury led to his association with Revere, who offered Willard an outlet for manufactured jacks, supplies of brass, and a source for "a large and valuable assortment of hardware goods, ...Clock, Watchmakers, Goldsmith, Jeweler's files, tools, & ...Enamelled Clock Faces." To support his family Willard repeatedly begged Revere for advance payment and frequently noted his need for tin and brass.[24]

Simon told Revere on February 7, 1785 that his workmen were already making more than jacks. The following October when he went to Newburyport to set up a Turret Clock for the North Church,[25] he asked Revere to dispatch "one of my time pieces" to a customer he had found there. What kind of clock was this? The work that Simon—and Aaron—had been doing suggests that it was one of the 30-hour timepieces developed in Grafton during the war, or an eight-day clock now known as the Massachusetts shelf clock.

This fascination with a compact, miniature clock survived the difficult economic transition from Grafton to Roxbury. Three shelf clocks dating from the 1780s demonstrate advancements in case and mechanical design. Simon created an eight-day, weight-powered movement mounted above a cabinet.[26](Fig.2-7) Similar to the wall clock, a base

conceals the weight as it descends. A fall-off strike, which produces one strike on the hour, replaces a more costly and elaborate rack-and-snail striking mechanism. (Fig. 2-8)

Simon's technical progress in making shelf clocks by the mid-1780s is shown by a weight-powered example with a pinwheel escapement, a feature seen on spring-powered clocks in France at the time. Previously displayed and illustrated on what appears to be a three-part cabinet, examination of the bottom section reveals that it is a later addition, probably made to increase weight fall to a full week's duration.[27] (Fig. 2-9) The features of its complex eight-day movement, in addition to the pinwheel escapement, include a rack-and-snail strike, strike/silent attachment, pendulum regulator, seconds hand, and calendar dial. (Pl.7) The rate of the pendulum is adjusted by the small regulator at the 12 o'clock position without opening the back of the clock. As in shelf clocks made later, the movement is not screwed to the backboard, but mounted on a seat board. (Fig. 2-10)

Aaron's French-style shelf clock was probably inspired by the popularity of Montgolfier's balloon ascensions begun in 1783 and extensively reported

Upper left: Fig. 2-7. Shelf Clock attributed to Simon Willard, Grafton, ca. 1780. See Fig. 6-17. 57.1.103

Fig. 2-8. Detail, Shelf Clock movement attributed to Simon Willard. It is mounted to the backboard, has wheel work with no crossings, a pendulum directly attached to the pallet arbor, and a dead beat escapement. 57.1.103

Fig. 2-9. Shelf Clock, Simon Willard, Roxbury, Mass., ca. 1785. Glue lines suggest placement of ogee feet on the base of the original section. See pl.7. 57.1.120

Fig. 2-10. Detail, Shelf Clock movement, Simon Willard. The movement and seat board slide into recesses in the sides of the case. Adjustments required access through the back door of the case. Note the difference in coloration between the original upper section and the lower addition. 57.1.120

Fig. 2-11. Shelf Clock, Aaron Willard, Roxbury, Mass., 1784. A kidney-shaped bracket clock on a cabinet to provide weight fall is a rare American interpretation of a European form. 57.1.79

During the 1790s the Willards began to develop a standard, streamlined design for the shelf clock. An early example retains the appearance of a bracket clock standing on a cabinet. The handles on the sides of the base suggest that the clock is portable.(Figs. 2-14, 2-15) Like the movement of a tall clock, its small weight-powered mechanism with a rack and snail strike rests on a seat board.(Fig. 2-16) The white enamelled, kidney-shaped dial is painted with a beautiful cartouche.[31] By 1795 a popular basic model had emerged with hood and base integrated to look like a condensed tall clock, a style produced into the 1830s. (Figs. 2-17, 2-18) This clock had evolved in tandem with the Willards' elegant tall clocks as an efficiently made and economical alternative.[32]

in the *Columbian Centinel* around the time the Willards moved to Roxbury.[28] The period label affixed to the backboard claims that the clock is "The 1st short/time piece/made in/America/1784," although it is more likely to have been the first made in Roxbury.[29] (Fig. 2-11) Aaron borrowed the time-train layout from the tall clock, altering the wheel count to shorten the pendulum length and to accommodate a shorter weight fall.(Fig. 2-12) A shallow case was then used because the pendulum is mounted directly to the pallet arbor between the plates. This design created high friction and so, early in this clock's history, it was altered. The pendulum was moved to the back of the movement with a suspension spring. The added depth of the movement due to this alteration required cutting away the backboard to allow the pendulum to swing.[30](Fig. 2-13)

Fig. 2-12. Detail, Shelf Clock movement, Aaron Willard. The extra holes through the front plate indicate either experimentation or an early replacement dial. 57.1.79

Fig. 2-13. Detail, Shelf Clock backboard, Aaron Willard. The period paper label below the cut-out reads: "The first short timepiece made in America, 1784." 57.1.79

Fig. 2-14. Shelf Clock, Simon Willard, Roxbury, Mass., ca. 1790. Access to the weights and pendulum on some early shelf clocks was gained through the back of the clock. The door was cut into the front of the case in the early 20th century for convenience. 57.1.82

Fig. 2-15. Detail, Shelf Clock backboard, Simon Willard. The sliding backboard is original and allowed access to regulate the pendulum and attach the weights. The movement rests on a seat board which slides into the case. 57.1.82

Fig. 2-16. Detail, Shelf Clock movement, Simon Willard. Standardized at this point, the eight-day movement was a small, efficient and well made version of the typical tall clock mechanism. 57.1.82

Weight-powered adaptations of the bracket clock by the Willards mark the first effort in America to capture the world market for clocks dominated by England. Spring-powered clocks are shown on Aaron's label (see Fig. 2-31) and Simon's label noted, "Spring Clocks of all kinds, price from 50 to 60 dollars." A striking eight-day, spring-powered bracket clock with a calendar attachment was sold by Aaron Willard about 1795. The Willards were fully capable of making bracket clocks, but they are extremely rare. Evidently the difficulty of obtaining coiled springs and the cost of manufacture was beyond the means of their clients.[33]

Fig. 2-17. *Shelf Clock, Aaron Willard, Jr., Boston, ca. 1810. Remaining evidence suggests a central finial plinth, finial, and fret on the top of the hood. The ogee feet are replacements. 57.1.18*

Fig. 2-18. *Detail, Shelf Clock movement, Aaron Willard, Jr. An eight-day timepiece of standard design and quality like this represents the end of shelf clock experimentation by the Willards. 57.1.18*

IN THE LAST DECADE OF THE 18TH century, Simon increased his production of tall clocks and made a hit with a design that was evidently well priced. Lacking shop records for either brother, their careers are best analyzed through their clocks. In 1792, Simon's engraved label was printed by Joseph N. Russell of Boston. Willard invited customers to his "Clock-Manufactory at his Clock Dial in Roxbury." A large two-dial clock installed between the second-floor windows of his neighbor's house made the sign hard to miss. Willard emphasized that these clocks were "elegant," using the word three times in the text to promote his public and domestic clocks. His offerings included "Common eight-day Clocks, with very elegant faces and mahogany cases, price from 50 to 60 dollars" like one warranted for Josiah Temple (1742-1824) of Framingham.(Fig. 2-19) He also offered "clocks that will run one year with once winding up, with very elegant cases, price 100 dollars;[34] Chime clocks that will play six tunes, price 120 dollars."[35] Willard provided his wealthy clientele with instructions for running the clock, a written guarantee, a public statement of ownership on the dial, and personalized service. In 1796 Isaiah Thomas, Jr. reprinted the label with virtually the same text, which Willard used until about 1805. (see Fig. 2-29)

Simon expected to meet with his customers to discuss the personalizing features of their purchase. He further recommended that when the clock was

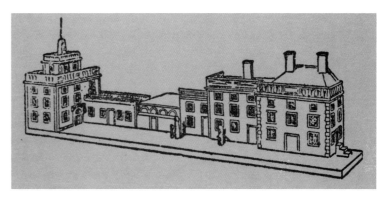

delivered, his workman stay overnight to ensure that all was in working order. One customer received a letter from Simon when his clock was delivered.

> I have Sent you one of my best clocks with a Very good bell—I put brass wire round the face which I forgot to mention when you was here. I thought you would like it as most every person does. I charge nine shillings [$1.50] for doing it, but as I did it without your agreement I shall ask but one dollar—The case is a hier price one than I put to a fifty dollar clock, I could not afford Such a Clock under fifty-three dollars.....NB. It will be well enough to have the boy tarry the night to see how the Clock goes. [36]

For a price roughly equivalent to a half-year's salary for hired agricultural labor, his customers could purchase beautiful tall clocks like many already ticking in fashionable homes. Despite the high price, each time the buyer opened the waist door of his clock, he was reminded by reading the label that: "it is much cheaper to purchase new, than old and second-hand Clocks."

Working in separate Roxbury locations, the Willard brothers rode the crest of a consumer market which sought to keep time in parlors, offices, churches, and other public spaces. The Willards' success in manufacturing was based on their work places, which were quite different from the traditional tiny shops of the 18th century. Aaron relocated across the Boston line about 1792, still only a quarter mile away from Simon in Roxbury. The 1798 Boston Directory lists "Aaron Willard, clock maker on the Neck." His estate is depicted in a painting by John Ritto Penniman (1783-1837) showing a wing that was larger than the dwelling house attached to it.[37] (Fig. 2-20) Here were the large workshop, storerooms, and bench space rented to independent craftsmen who worked in all phases

Fig. 2-19. Tall Clock, Simon Willard, Roxbury, ca. 1795. Inside the waist door is a label printed by Isaiah Thomas, Worcester. 57.1.64

Fig. 2-20. "Model of the Willard Clock Factory" from John Ware Willard's book.

of clock making, especially the shelf clocks in which Aaron specialized. He employed up to 30 people. By 1807, some 21 clock makers, cabinetmakers, dial and ornamental painters, and gilders worked within a quarter-mile radius of Simon's and Aaron's factories. The concentration of related craftsmen was exceptional, but had precedent in Boston.[38] At this point in their careers, the Willards were making their tall clocks, continuing to refine the shelf clock, and had introduced the stylish patent timepiece.

Willard clocks were in the mainstream of urban clock making on both sides of the Atlantic. The elegant cases mentioned with pride by Simon were inspired by mid-century London styles with grand moldings and one-piece feet.[39] The cases were made in Roxbury by such cabinetmakers as Samuel (1769-1797) and William Fisk (1770-1844). In all, 10 cabinetmakers had their shops in the vicinity of Aaron Willard's house and factory.[40]

Simon Willard continued to make tall clocks until about 1815 and Aaron made this style for about ten years longer. Roxbury cases were made in either restrained or architectonic styles used by at least seven other clock makers.[41] Precise attribution of these cases to specific cabinetmakers is difficult. The Willards employed several cabinetmakers over the years and maintained such control that the woodwork varied more by style than by craftsmanship.

Opulent cases masked standardized production. The hoods and cases had to be constructed to receive parts of regular sizes. The human proportions of the clock bodies were finished with enameled English faces or dials, featuring painted classical designs. Dials imported from James Wilson or Osborne's Manufactory of Birmingham, England, (see front cover) were mounted with a false plate. (See Fig. 6-14.) The movements were made in standard dimensions to fit them.

Each case incorporates figured mahogany, brass fluted quarter columns, and pierced fretwork with three plinths surmounted by brass finials. The arched door is protected by a molding applied around its perimeter. Early examples have ogee bracket feet; later cases have French feet. (see Figs. 2-22, 2-35) Production of these elements and the movements used by the Willards were speeded by templates and jigs. For example, the fretwork on the hood was laid out with a master, drilled, and cut with a fret saw.

Fig. 2-22. Tall Clock, Aaron Willard, Boston, ca. 1800. Inside the waist door is a label engraved by Paul Revere. French feet reflected the current fashion in Federal furniture. 57.1.7

(See Fig. 6-2.) The other parts of the hood were also predetermined. (See Fig. 6-7.) The woodwork was highlighted with cast brass bases, capitals, escutcheons, hinges, and finials, all of which were likely imported. Iron locks secured the case doors.

The columns on the waist were made by sawing a billet into fourths, gluing them together with shims between, turning them to shape, planing the flutes, removing the billet from the lathe, and separating it into four sections, enough for use on two clocks. The case is supported by rounded glue blocks stacked behind the quarter columns.(Fig. 2-21 and see Fig. 6-6) Vertical blocks behind the bracket feet support the mass of the clock. In the style of 18th-century Boston case furniture, the front brackets are mitered while the rear sections are diagonal and the supporting glue blocks are set in from the rear of the case. (see Fig. 6-3) Other details, like the paper applied to the roof to keep the movement dust-free, were extra touches that made a better product. Even the white pine glue blocks were standard in their shape, application, and species.

Although the Willards were capable of making their own clock movements, (see pl. 14) they also evidently relied on English-made products, in part because of the scarcity of materials like copper in New England. Makers' signatures found within the clocks indicate that entire movements might be imported, eliminating the time and expense of casting and assembling each clock individually. The movement of a clock signed by Aaron Willard (Fig. 2-22) was made by Robert Roskell of Liverpool, England, an exporter of complete clock movements to the American market. Made with small brass plates and superior wheel work, Liverpool movements are very similar to those made in urban America.[42] (Figs. 2-23, 2-24) But in 1815, short of brass castings while the nation was still in a war time economy, Simon was debited "for 2 setts of large brass Clock works $93.50" by Boston founder William Hunneman (1769-1856), who made everything from andirons to fire pumps.[43] When imported iron wire was scarce, the Willards used wooden pendulum rods,[44] often painted red, blue, green, or black to match the weights.

FOUR TALL CLOCKS ILLUSTRATE most of the options offered by Simon Willard's shop. The clock purchased by Josiah Temple of Framingham, Massachusetts, has the fewest embellishments. (See Fig.

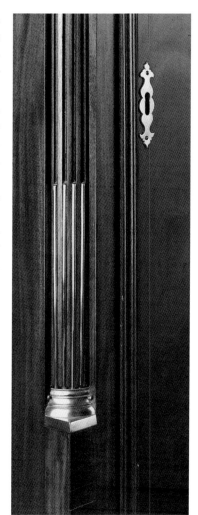

2-19) The case is constructed of straight-grained mahogany without inlay, stringing, or carving. The enamelled Wilson dial is painted with a reclining shepherdess in the arch and gold spandrels at the corners.[45] The movement, as the dial reveals, simply has a seconds hand and calendar wheel. There is no moon's age dial or rocking ship.

Temple's neighbor Thomas Nixon, Jr. (1762-1842) bought a more costly model in 1801.(Pl.11) It has a lunar dial and a case of figured mahogany with stringing around the doors and base. The bill of sale tacked inside the case indicates the price. It reads: "Roxbury, February 17, 1801/Mr. Tho. Nixon bout of Simon Willard/ one Warranted Eight day clock $60./ Received pay in full/ Simon Willard." (Figs. 2-25, 2-26)

A flamboyant mahogany case inlaid with oval and quarter-round fans (Fig. 2-27) suggests that a third clock by Willard was more expensive than either Temple's or Nixon's clock. The movement

Fig. 2-21. Tall Clock case, Simon Willard, Roxbury, 1801, showing the quarter column, brass stop fluting, and Doric capital. See pl.11. 57.1.144

Fig. 2-23. Tall Clock movement, imported by Aaron Willard. 57.1.7

Fig. 2-24. Tall Clock movement, Aaron Willard. The stamp: "Roskell, Liverpool" (England) reveals the source behind the Willard name on the dial. 57.1.7

Fig. 2-25. Tall Clock dial, Simon Willard, Roxbury, 1801. See pl.11. 57.1.144

Fig. 2-26. Detail, Tall Clock, Simon Willard. See pl.11. 57.1.144

Fig. 2-27. Tall Clock, Simon Willard, Roxbury, ca. 1800. 57.1.6

resembles the latter, with calendar and moon attachments. The dial was made by Osborne and the label printed by Isaiah Thomas, Jr., is pasted inside the waist door. (Figs. 2-28, 2-29)

The clock inscribed "1585/Simon Willard" was owned by Richard Johnson of Kingston, Massachusetts. Its case was the top of the standard line. (See back cover.) The beauty of the contrasted veneers and cross banding is balanced by fluted columns in the hood and waist mounted with brass stop-fluting, bases, and Corinthian capitals. (Doric capitals are more common.) Its substantial case, with a label by Isaiah Thomas, Jr., inside the waist door, is supported by fully developed ogee bracket feet. The dial

Fig. 2-28. Tall Clock dial, Simon Willard. Delicate steel hands, cut out with a fret saw and filed to shape required about two days work to complete. The imported dial made by Osborne in Birmingham, was signed with Willard's name. 57.1.6

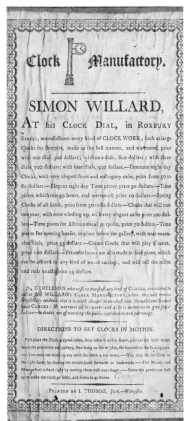

Fig. 2-29. Tall Clock, Simon Willard. Label printed by Isaiah Thomas, Jr., Worcester. 57.1.6

is animated with seconds, minutes, hour, and calendar hands. The corners are guarded by personifications of the Four Seasons and the moon traverses overhead. (See front cover.)

Simon and Aaron Willard patronized the same workmen and merchants for dials, parts, brass castings, ornamental painting, and cases. The brothers regularly sold clocks with attractive features that did not significantly increase their investment of time or materials. Calendar wheels, moon dials, and rocking ships were popular. The calendar wheel, for example, only required fitting a pin on the hour wheel and mounting the 30-tooth wheel to the back of the dial. These features made the clocks more saleable, while masking their ultimate simplicity.

With their movements standardized, the cases, which range from plain to fancy, distinguish the clocks. Tall clocks by Aaron in the collection reveal that they had become very standardized. He even used the same label for more than a quarter of a century.[46] A tall clock made about 1810 (Figs. 2-30, 2-31) makes a bold statement by using a 13" dial

Fig. 2-31. Label engraved by Paul Revere, Boston, early 19th century. See pl.5. 57.1.74

Fig. 2-30. Tall Clock, Aaron Willard, Boston, Mass, ca. 1810. See pl.5. 57.1.74

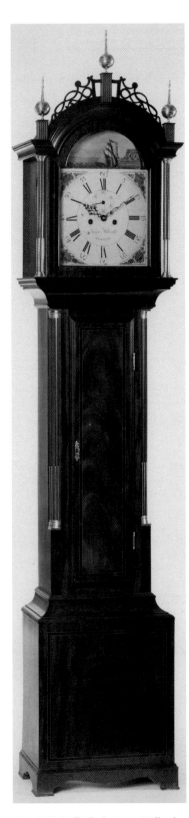

Fig. 2-32. *Tall Clock, Aaron Willard, Boston, ca. 1810. 57.1.67*

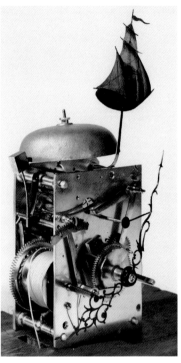

Fig. 2-33. *Detail, Tall Clock dial, Aaron Willard. The flags flying above the ship or on the coastline often provide clues to the origin of the dial. "Generic" flags may be found on imported dials, which are otherwise unmarked. 57.1.67*

Fig. 2-34. *Tall Clock movement, Aaron Willard. The rocking ship is mounted to the pallet arbor and moves back and forth with each swing of the pendulum. A painted seascape on the arch of the dial was a popular addition to tall clocks providing mechanical fascination as well as telling the owner at a glance that the clock was running. 57.1.67*

rather than the standard 12-inch square. The cabinetmaker used the same template to make the fretwork on the hood in the following example. (See Fig. 2-32.) This case probably also had French feet, but when restored prior to acquisition, inappropriate ogee feet were added. The dial, which does not bear the hallmarks of the imports, may be the work of Spencer Nolen, who had been in partnership with Aaron, Jr. in 1805. (Pl.5) The turbulent seascape in the arch gives the impression that the ship is rocking, but it is at anchor. Without the animation, the clock was slightly less expensive. The simple, elongated hands are extended versions of the type found on Aaron's shelf clocks. (See Fig. 2-55.)

After the War of 1812, new fashions and the need to control cost caused the Willards to alter their formula for a beautiful tall clock. (Fig. 2-32) Keeping up with current furniture styles, the cases became a hybrid of old and new. French feet (here shortened) weakened the bold design still dominated by the s-curves of the 18th century. The waist door became a simple rectangle, lacking the arched top that echoes the dial's shape on earlier clocks. The dial itself is beautifully rendered, but its design visually separates the tympanum from the square below.

The rocking ship was merely a distraction: behind the scenes, the movement was still a workmanlike product assembled by rote in Willard's factory. (Figs. 2-33, 2-34; see Fig. 2-23 for comparison.)

The details of a fourth tall clock by Aaron date its manufacture to the 1820s, near the end of his career. (Fig. 2-35) His cabinetmakers had adopted an English practice of using mahogany veneer on mahogany. The columns are reeded rather than fluted. The expensive, brass stop-fluting on the columns has been eliminated. The blocky French feet and shaped skirt parallel trends in late Federal period furniture. The batch number "45" is stamped on the principal parts of the case. The spandrels are stencilled, rather than painted freehand on the dial.[47] The clock is elegant, but the crisp design of earlier tall clocks by both Simon and Aaron has been eroded by tired repetition.

A WALL CLOCK WITH A PATENTED DESIGN replaced tall clocks as Simon's bread and butter. The precise dates of its development and introduction, with its innovative styling and compact movement, are impossible to trace without account books and correspondence. Willard had unprecedented skill in modifying design without sacrificing quality in order to meet fashion or need. Although expensive, at $25 to $35, its creation coincided with the birth of modern American consumerism and made the "banjo" shape the most famous in American timekeeping. Its inspiration was not the musical instrument, but rather an adaptation of European technology.

It may never be known if Willard intended to patent this design or whether it was a result of his journey to Washington D.C. in 1801. He went to the Capitol to install the gallery clock commissioned for the United States Senate Chamber. He received a handsome fee for the clock ($750), but as was apparently his custom when he journeyed, he took one or more of his newest domestic clocks with him. Willard's patent application, filed on November 25, 1801, hastily describes its features. "The height of it is two feet and the diameter of the face about seven inches," he wrote. "The power of motion is a weight [which falls fifteen inches in eight days] instead of a spring which is the case in all regulators and time pieces smaller than the clock." The external details of the case must have been a priority with him. Its shape and the decorated glass required different

Fig. 2-35. Tall Clock, Aaron Willard, Boston, Mass., ca. 1820. 57.1.70

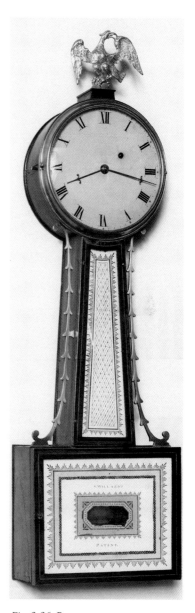

Fig. 2-36. Patent Timepiece, Simon Willard, Roxbury, ca. 1805. The unusual side pieces are generally found on the earliest examples. See Pl. 17. 57.1.8

Fig. 2-37. Patent Timepiece movement, Simon Willard, Roxbury, ca. 1810. Shown from the front, the patent timepiece has a trapezoidal "keystone" (the section of the pendulum rod which circumvents the hand arbor), "T-bridge" suspension of the pendulum mounted at the top of the front plate, and "through" bolts (upper right and lower left corners) passing through both plates of the movement and into the backboard to attach the movement to the case. 57.1.83

Fig. 2-38. Detail, Patent Timepiece movement, Simon Willard. The front plate is removed to show the four wheel, "step train" (all the wheels except the escape wheel mounted toward the rear plate), dead beat escapement and well finished brass and steel work. 57.1.83

skills from the fine mahogany cabinetwork of tall and shelf clocks. "The cace [sic] is thick glass painted, varnished and gilt in a manner than can never fade and is more durable as well as beautiful and cheaper than common china enamelled or any other kind of cases."[48] Finally Willard had produced a clock which required "much less labor and expense than any other kind of regulator." This description was written at the behest of President Thomas Jefferson, who was possibly intrigued by the novelty of Willard's technology. The fourteen-year patent was granted on February 8, 1802.[49] Writing to his wife Mary from Portland, Maine, the following summer, Simon said, "I dont know how many large clocks will sell here but my timepieces are Very much liked. I have ingaged one to go to Salem for fifty dollars. I expect to sell the other one I brought here."[50]

IN ORDER TO ACHIEVE PLEASING PROPORTIONS and control cost, the early models are timepieces and lack striking mechanisms. Simon Willard shrewdly predicted that the American public would concede sound for show, satisfied by its ticking and the pendulum action visible through the lower tablet. His inspiration for the lightweight design (Fig. 2-36) may have been the European wall regulator[51] and English barometers[52] for which he reordered the skills of existing specialists. He reduced an eight-day movement to fit the clock by eliminating the striking mechanism and by placing the pendulum on the front of the movement for easy adjustment. A trapezoidal attachment to the pendulum rod, called the keystone, circumvents the hour and minute wheels behind the dial. Willard made the movement with either a dead-beat or recoil escapement. The former is often found in early patent clocks.(Figs. 2-37, 2-38, 2-39) It is theoretically more accurate, but the clock with the recoil escapement is less apt to stop if it is out of plumb or needs cleaning. The suitable pendulum length was attained by altering the standard tall clock time train to place the swinging bob in the base.[53] The pendulum suspension spring terminates at a "T" and rests in a bridge mounted at the top of the front plate.

In the 'step train', all of the wheels, except the escape wheel, are mounted on arbors toward the back plate of the movement, similar to the time train of a tall clock. The mechanism itself is fastened to the case with two bolts that pass through the upper right

Fig. 2-39. Patent Timepiece movement, Simon Willard. Right side view showing front plate motion work (left), internal four wheel train and one of the long bolts which pass through both plates of the movement into the backboard (upper section of the movement, just below the pillar post). 57.1.83

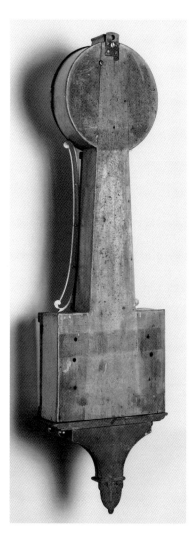

Fig. 2-40. Patent Timepiece backboard, Simon Willard. Unlike most of his patent timepiece backboards which are constructed with one piece of mahogany, this example is birch and made in five pieces, more commonly found on Concord, Massachusetts clocks. 57.1.9

and lower left corners of both plates and into the backboard. The rear plate fits flush against the backboard. Some plates are rounded at the top. Plate measurements are approximately 2 3/4" wide by 4 5/8" high.

The back of the timepiece is often made of one piece of mahogany.[54] (Fig. 2-40) The clock is suspended on the wall by an iron hanger at the top. Inside the head, canvas is glued at the top to secure the joint. A block of wood on the outside further supports the joint and the finial. Most patent clocks were topped with a gilded wooden acorn or eagle finial. Cast brass eagle finials were also used. The sheet-iron dial is affixed to the outer edges of the head with two or three L-hooks that permit the wood to expand and contract behind the dial. The hands are beautifully filed spears, heat treated to a bluish color.(Pl.17) A brass bezel secures the glass over the dial and is attached to the case with a long, brass hinge set into the side of the head.

The sides of the case run into the head to support the movement and down through the pendulum box to the bottom of the case. The long throat and box permit an adequate descent for the rectangular weight, which is tapered and hung from an attenuated hook. Long glue blocks secure the assembly. Inside at the upper left of the throat, a screw or nail stops the weight from encroaching on the movement when fully wound. Below, a divider of sheet iron inside the box, called a weight baffle, keeps the weight from interfering with the pendulum bob. A brass strip behind the pendulum bob serves to tie down the pendulum assembly when the clock is moved. The dovetailed box is strengthened with chamfered glue blocks. Since the parts are small, imported mahogany was often used as the secondary wood.(Fig.2-41) The lower door is hinged at the right and locked by the winding key.

Because the form of the clock was a new idea, Willard had to turn to local sources for parts, rather than importing movements and decorative elements. As the patent indicates, the ornamental painter, rather than the founder or the cabinetmaker defined the appearance of the new clock. The skills of decorative painters of dials and glass tablets, like Charles Bullard (1794-1871), Spencer Nolen, and John Ritto Penniman[55] included understanding pigments and varnish and how to conceive their work "backwards," in the opposite order from the shapes and colors applied to a canvas. Like an

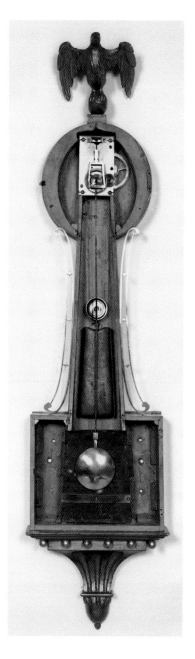

Fig. 2-41. Detail, Patent timepiece, Simon Willard. The efficient and economical design of the patent timepiece is seen in this view with the dial, bezel, and glasses removed. 57.1.9

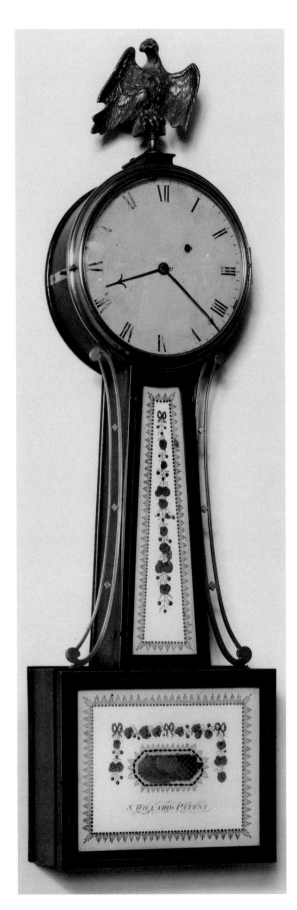

Fig. 2-42. Patent Timepiece, Simon Willard, Roxbury, ca. 1810. 57.1.3

engraving, the detailed foreground was done first (sometimes copied from a master on which the glass was laid) and covered by the background layers.[56]

The earliest style of ornamental painting on patent timepieces is delicate, geometric, and non-pictorial. (See Fig. 2-36.) Floral motifs were featured later (Fig 2-42), followed by romantic imagery framed by linear borders: then biblical, mythological, and military. Not surprisingly the same themes were painted on the upper tablets of contemporary looking-glasses. The obituary of the painter and gilder Charles Bullard noted his artistic contribution to "the beauty of the old eight-day clock manufactured by those worthy old pioneers in the clock business, the Messieurs Willard." His renderings of "blushing Aurora or the rising sun added their magic charm to this aperture of which the pendulum was visible."[57]

The reverse painted tablets conceal the pendulum rod and weight. On early clocks, the tablets are secured with tiny glue blocks in cross-banded mahogany frames inlaid with stringing. The throat glass is generally attached to the case with two or four screws. Willard also offered reeded frames or gilt with rope molding. Rope-molded frames are attached with two screws concealed by the dial and with two more hidden in the box below. There are rare examples of patent clocks with a thermometer mounted behind the throat glass. Stencilled frames are also rare and found on later clocks.[58]

JOHN DOGGETT (1780-1857) OF ROXBURY supplied gilded eagles, brackets or pedestals, balls, swags, and painted tablets for patent pieces.[59] (Fig. 2-43) Specifically for Simon, Doggett gilded "swircles [sic] for clocks $4 ea." probably referring to the circular bezel. His "time piece cases" were $9.50. Aaron Willard, Jr., completed his training during the initial production of the new form and worked for Doggett at times between 1804 and 1807. In 1804, he was credited: "By painting lightening spear 3 points $1.50;" in the summer of 1807: "By painting 6 tablets at 4/6"; "to Gilding 40 timepiece doors 53.33," and "to 4 Pedestals Part painted @ 3.25." Simon Willard also bought "pedestals for patent timepieces" at four dollars each (with or without balls and in different sizes), "round glasses for timepiece" at 28 cents each, and complete clock cases—sized for public and domestic clocks—from William Viles, a cabinetmaker who worked for Doggett.[60]

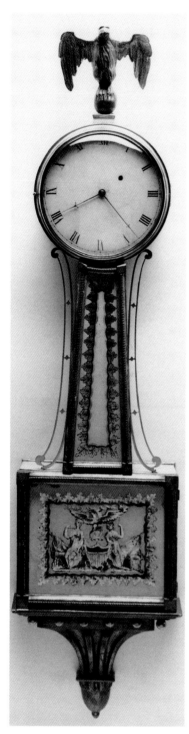

Special orders aside, the timepiece cases that Doggett provided were standardized to the point of numbering the models. Aaron Willard, Jr.—apparently assembling clocks on his own account in 1806, rather than for Doggett—was billed for half a dozen cases which illustrate the range of prices. Case "No 1 Gilt at the side" was the most costly at $80. "No 2 Common" was priced at $42, with "Eagles & Swags of Balls" attached for an additional $.52. "Common No 3" cases were $25 for Willard and if made for someone else, in this instance, the clock maker Jabez Baldwin (1777-1809), they were priced at $28. For the work, Doggett's bill to Aaron Willard added up to $228.[61]

William Hunneman provided castings of "side pieces"[62], bezels for the round glass, and wheel blanks. In 1815 he charged Simon $.33 per pound for brass castings and $.50 per hour for making finished clock parts. In addition, he supplied Aaron with "12 Setts of brass time piece works" at one dollar apiece. [63]

Demand for the patent clock was so great that around 1810, Aaron Willard and William Cummens were authorized to produce their own versions.[64] Aaron promoted one improvement that his brother did not undertake: a striking patent clock.[65] Several examples by Aaron, Jr., have survived, one with its original packing box.[66]

A variety of striking mechanisms with alarms were devised after the patent expired. Aaron, Jr. made a wall clock about 1830 which was fitted with an alarm set by the brass disk behind the hands. (Figs. 2-44, 2-45). A place for the bell was found by mounting it as a finial. He probably used the depthing tool (Pl.13) to lay out the wheel work for this clock. The expense of the case was reduced by eliminating fancy painting and gilding. The dial and glasses are framed by a half-round mahogany moldings. A variant of the clock made by Simon, Jr. (1795-1874), at the same time uses reverse painting on glass as an ironic simulation of panels of mahogany veneer. (Fig. 2-46)

While the patent was still in force, Simon adapted the timepiece by enlarging it for public spaces,(Pl.29) a possibility he had anticipated in the original patent: "the dial and case could be expanded." Genius lies in simplicity. Willard knew that a domestic-scale movement, with the addition of a bell, fall-off strike, and counter balance for the long hands, could be housed in an enlarged case. The gallery clock is

Fig. 2-43. Patent Timepiece, Simon Willard, Roxbury, ca.1805-10. This white-painted case is a decorative option found on other early 19th century Federal furniture. Commonly called "bride's" clocks, they cannot be firmly documented as wedding gifts. The carved and gilded eagle finial is an appropriate replacement. 57.1.9

Fig. 2-44. Wall Clock, Aaron Willard, Jr., Boston, ca. 1830, 57.1.128.

oversized: complete with finial, round dial, beautifully cut hands, reverse painted tablet in the base and pedestal. A gilt wooden bezel gives the effect of brass. The wooden dials were made of two or three glued boards of either lightweight poplar or sometimes mahogany, turned on the endstock of a lathe to a tapered edge. These woods are less prone to warp. Doggett sold "Meeting house" or gallery clock cases at $28 each, and provided "1 Clock Case Woodwork & Gilding complete for the Old South Church $70" in November 1805. After the patent expired, Simon Willard ceased making gallery clocks. Both Aaron Willards, Abel Stowell (1752-1818), and John Pierce Sawin (1801-1863) produced this form.[67]

The Willards also adapted the basic timepiece movement for use in schools, workshops, and offices. (Figs. 2-47, 2-48, 2-49)[68] With simpler cases and recycled ideas, they were probably less expensive. In 1823 Simon Willard and Son created a clock for commercial use which was mounted in a dovetailed mahogany box with a painted mahogany dial surrounded by a brass bezel. They altered a patent-alarm timepiece movement by eliminating the alarm, mounting the pendulum on the front plate and changing the wheel count for suitable pendulum length and weight fall. (Figs.2-50, 2-51, 2-52, 2-53)

Late in his career, Simon Willard produced wall regulators intended for precision timekeeping. A large version of the patent timepiece, the regulators used seconds-beating pendulums and dead-beat escapements with maintaining power to ensure accuracy. (Pl. 30, Fig. 2-54)

In 1816, when the patent expired, the Willard enterprises marked the epicenter of American clock making. Later developments focused on materials rather than on design or mechanics. The Aaron Willard shelf clock on Empire-style lion's paws incorporates a popular concave dial and two reverse-painted glass tablets, features generally associated with the patent timepiece. (Fig. 2-55) One of these clocks was purchased for $50 as a gift for Louisa Adams (d. 1876) of Quincy, Massachusetts, in 1817, when she married William Wilson (1793-1863). It conceals a simple timepiece. (see Fig.6-9)

Several years later, Simon warned that many clocks claiming to be Willard's Patent were not his work:

> I believe the public are not generally aware,
> that my former Patent Right expired 6 years

Fig. 2-45. Wall Clock movement, Aaron Willard, Jr. Willard enlarged the standard plates and added an alarm attachment in the upper left corner. Powered by a separate weight, the alarm is wound through the dial at the ll o'clock position. 57.1.128

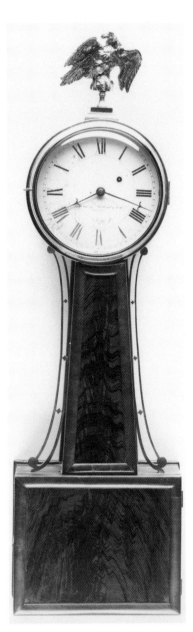

Fig. 2-46. Patent Timepiece, Simon Willard and Son, (Simon Willard, Jr.), Boston, Mass., ca. 1830. This late form of patent timepiece is also found with mahogany panels, instead of glasses and without brass side pieces. The eagle finial is an inappropriate replacement. 57.1.97

Fig. 2-49. Wall Clock movement, Aaron Willard, Jr. Simon Willard's patented movement, still retaining the "T-bridge" and through bolts to attach the movement to the case, was altered by the addition of an alarm mechanism (left) which when released would rap two hammers against a mahogany glue block. 57.1.80

Fig. 2-47. Wall Clock, Aaron Willard, Jr., Boston, ca. 1820. Commonly called "coffin" clocks by collectors, the timekeeper housed in a simple, dovetailed mahogany box probably served in a commercial setting. The third hand sets the alarm. 57.1.80

Fig. 2-50. Wall Clock, Simon Willard and Son, probably Boston, 1823. 57.l.109

Fig. 2-48. Wall Clock label, Aaron Willard, Jr. "DIRECTIONS FOR PUTTING UP THE TIMEPIECE" were provided to the new owners of a patent timepiece to aid in the installation of the clock. Aaron, Jr., utilized the same label in this wall clock to provide basic instructions. 57.1.80

Fig. 2-51.Wall Clock movement, Simon Willard and Son. 57.1.109

Fig. 2-52. Wall Clock, Simon Willard and Son. Shown with the dial removed, the movement utilized a double compounded pulley system to provide a short weight fall for a week's duration. 57.1.109

Fig. 2-53.Wall Clock weight, Simon Willard and Son. The weight is inscribed: "Simon Willard and Son, September 25, 1823". 57.1.109

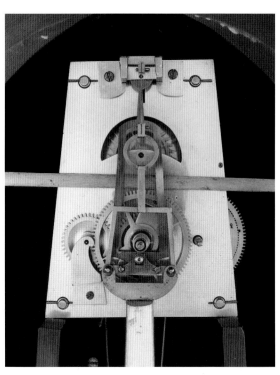

Fig. 2-54. Regulator movement, attributed to Simon Willard, Roxbury, ca. 1832. Willard's patented "T-bridge" provides pendulum suspension and the movement is secured in the case by a horizontal, brass strap. The back plate is faintly scratched, "1832". See pl. 30 for the large scale of these clocks. 57.1.87

ago [1816]; which induces me to caution them against the frequent impositions practiced, in vending spurious Timepieces. It is true, they have "Patent" printed on them, and some with my name, and their outward appearance resembles those formerly made by me: Thus they are palm'd upon the public. Several of them have lately been brought to me for repairs, that would certainly put the greatest bungler to the blush. Such is the country inundated with, and such, I consider prejudicial to my reputation; it therefore disclaim being the manufacturer of such vile performances. [69]

Simon, nevertheless, continued to produce these clocks after the patent had expired. Elihu Hoyt of Deerfield, Massachusetts, purchased the "Brass eight day time piece" (valued at eleven dollars in his 1833 probate inventory) from the patentee in January 1823 and sent instructions to his wife, Hannah.

I yesterday put on board Mr. Lucius Tuttle's sleigh a *Willard Timepiece* in a box to you. I wish you to let it remain untill I come home. I charged him to take good care of it as it is a very tender thing to handle. I hope that it will arrive safe. I bought it of Mr. Willard the original patentee. It is new & I hope will prove good.[70]

Willard also established the pattern of appointing agents to sell these clocks. For example in 1804, he engaged Payton and Dana of Providence, Rhode Island, to retail the timepieces, and in 1822, "authorized L. Goddard & Son to sell his new Patent Alarm Time Pieces" in Worcester.[71]

By 1819 Willard was moving into more experimental waters. His inspiration for the alarm clock which he patented that year was probably the

Fig. 2-56. Mantel Clock, maker unknown, Paris, ca.1845. Willard was aware of earlier alabaster clocks and drew on this design for his Patent Alarm Timepiece of 1819. This clock was owned by Squire Bowman (1771-1852) of New Braintree, Mass. 57.1.218

Fig. 2-55. Shelf Clock, Aaron Willard, Boston, ca. 1825. Half round, mahogany frames, cast paw feet and stenciled decoration on the glasses characterize Willard's work in the Empire period. 57.1.66

spring-powered, Empire style mantle clock, widely imported from France and commonly called "French," "Paris," "alabaster," or "chimney clocks."[72] (Fig. 2-56) Fashionable households like the one depicted in Henry Sargent's painting of "The Dinner Party"[73], placed these clocks on mantels. They were costly, but several examples are recorded in early 19th-century Boston. For instance, the auctioneer, G.G. Channing, advertised the sale of "Beautiful Gilt and Alabaster Paris Clocks and Timepieces" in 1822 and the next year a wealthy Bostonian, David Hinckley, died leaving in "the finest private house in Town....1 French time piece and Glass [$] 30....1 alabaster Clock and Glass [$] 35 ....1 Alabaster Clock & Glass 35.00" respectively in the Dining Room, First Drawing Room, and Second Drawing Room.[74] Willard was influenced by the porcelain dials, pressed or cast brass dial bezels and pendulum bobs, cast brass case furniture, exposed mechanisms, and glass domes of the French mantel clock. His weight-powered clock is a reconfiguration of the spring-

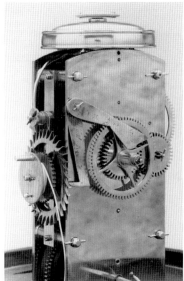

Fig. 2-58. Patent Alarm Timepiece movement, Simon Willard. The alarm weight was wound by removing the glass dome and turning the crank on the left side of the movement. An alarm bell is mounted above the movement. 57.1.16

Fig. 2-57. Patent Alarm Timepiece, Simon Willard, Roxbury, ca. 1825. 57.1.16

powered French clock.

Simon wed the popularity of these clocks with punctuality. Since he did not make patent wall clocks with an alarm, Willard may have planned this design to fill the void.[75] (Fig. 2-57) Having learned from his success with the patent wall clock that Americans are deluded by practicality, his patent for the alarm clock promises that it "strikes on the top of the case...and makes a noise like someone rapping at the door, and it will wake you much quicker than to strike on a bell in the usual way."[76] By the time the clock went into production, Willard had scrapped the rap-on-wood idea and mounted a bell above the movement.[77] (Fig. 2-58) He built the clock around the industrialized character of the visible movement, the added appeal of the popular Empire design, and America's 1825 love affair with our nation's guest, Lafayette.[78] Likely sold into the 1840s, later models are short and less classical in their appearance. However, the clock was received as expensive and eccentric. With its fire-gilt brass castings, glass dome, veneered column, porcelain dial, and specialized mechanism, the alarm timepiece probably retailed at about the cost of a fine, imported French clock.

The experimental quality of the alarm clock was not conducive to standardized production. Variation in the cases and movements suggests that they were either commissioned or manufactured over a long period of time. Their fussiness invited continual tinkering, and Simon was still making modifications at the end of his career.[79] One is inscribed: "Made by Simon Willard in 1833 — in his 80th

Fig. 2-60. Patent Alarm Timepiece, Simon Willard. The brass disk which supports the movement is engraved: "Made by Simon Willard in 1833—in his 80th year". 57.1.15

Fig. 2-59. Patent Alarm Timepiece, Simon Willard, Roxbury, 1833. 57.1.15

Fig. 2-61. Patent Alarm Timepiece movement, Simon Willard. He returned to a more traditional movement after discovering the mechanical flaws inherent in the standard design as shown in fig. 2-58. 57.1.15

year."[80] (Figs. 2-59, 2-60, 2-61) At this advanced age, he was still active in the workshop. Complicated to make, the patent alarm clock was one Willard's few horological Edsels, and about 50 examples are known today.[81] Its experimental nature evidently appealed to Willard.

Years before in 1807, Willard had proudly commissioned "My portrait by Stuart."[82](Pl. 10) The picture shows a prosperous tradesman whose steady gaze illustrates the nation's confidence before the War of 1812. His skilled hands hold a scientific instrument, which cannot be identified, rather than a clock. Portraiture often includes emblems of occupation and symbols of identity[83], and Willard's choice of an instrument reveals his self-perception.

Clocks and instruments were traditionally made by the same craftsmen. Clock maker Joseph Pope (1748-1826) of Boston, for example, made an orrery to illustrate the movement of the planets and their moons around the sun.[84] As early as 1784, Simon Willard advertised a:

> new-constructed astronomical time-keeper, ascertaining the 60th or 120th part of a minute, by a second hand, from the centre of the large circle, made upon a most simple plan, in which the friction and influence of the oil is almost

Fig. 2-62.
Heliostat, Simon Willard, Roxbury, 1816. The front plate of the clock movement is engraved: "Simon Willard, Fecit, Roxbury, Mass, 1816".
4.7.5

annihilated, and has proved to keep time with the greatest accuracy, with a new constructed pendulum from the center of the ball, shews the different degrees of expantion (sic) of the oars, and answers in some degree as a thermometer, &c. those that ossillate half seconds are portable and are easily moved to any part of the room, or where it is convenient for to make observations, to the pedestal of which is affixed (without obstructing the movement) a perpetual callandar, newly engraved, which shews at one view, the day of the month, the true and comparative time of the sun's rising and setting forever, as well as the age, increase, decrease, rising and setting of the moon, time of high water, &c. the whole globe with its rotation every twenty-four hours, shewing the longitude, latitude, the hour and minute upon the most [____] on the globe.[85]

Simon Willard continually experimented with the layout and efficiency of gear trains and escapements, but his keen sense of design, machinery, and mathematics went beyond clocks. A heliostat, with an attached solar microscope, is signed "Simon Willard, Fecit Roxbury, Mass. 1816." (Fig. 2-62) It incorporates a clock mechanism that aligns the mirror with the sun to reflect the light into a lens.[86] Simon Willard sold this device in July 1819 to Harvard University for students to use in the "new philosophy" room.[87] The transformation of clock maker to scientist was nearly complete.

Simon's genius for making instruments was inherited by the next generation. His sons, Simon, Jr., and Benjamin Franklin (1803-1847), made astronomical clocks.[88] Simon, Jr.,finally entered the family trade relatively late in life. He called himself a watch maker, but advertised that he repaired chronometers (a navigational device for ascertaining longitude), which he had learned to make in New York. Benjamin patented an improved lighthouse mechanism in 1839[89], and was awarded a gold medal by the Massachusetts Charitable Mechanics Association in 1844. Between 1842 and 1844, Benjamin made a spring-powered skeleton clock with an exposed mechanism probably for a craft competition. (Fig. 2-63) Inscribed "Rich & Willard, Boston," it has a beautiful symmetry that comes to life.[90] A rarity and a marvel in its own time, the clock shows a complete mastery of concepts and materials.

Benjamin's skeletonized movement was the cul-

Fig. 2-63. Skeleton Clock, Benjamin Franklin Willard, Roxbury and Boston, 1842-44. The spring powered, exposed movement with skeletonized plates features a silvered brass dial and a fall-off strike. Signed on the chapter ring: "Benj. F. Willard, Roxbury" and on the plate below the dial: "Rich & Willard, Boston". 57.1.112

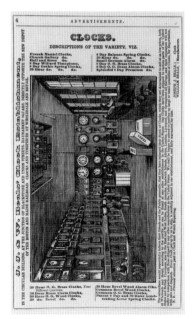

Fig. 2-65 Advertisement, J.J. & W. Beals' Clock Establishment, Boston, 1846-47. Beals advertised "French mantle, church gallery and 8-day Willard timepieces".

mination of the intellectual dominance of clock making by Simon Willard's family. The artfulness of the machine for the machine's sake propelled the new generation far beyond the old trade of clock making. The Willards confirmed Boston as the first major center of clock making in the new republic. In 1832, when they were no longer in the forefront of the industry, there were still 14 men and six boys directly employed in making clocks, mostly patterned on the old patent timepiece. Some may have been working for the Willards. Another 40 or 50 were engaged in repair work. Production was estimated at 1200 clocks per annum valued at $20,000. (On hand were 600 pounds of brass castings, 1200 mahogany clock cases, and 10,000 pounds of lead.) Their makers expected to sell 600 of them in Massachusetts, 300 in New York, 150 elsewhere in the United States, and the rest in South America. [91]

Simon Willard's patent timepiece had become a generic product. The name on the dial was sometimes that of a retailer who might have purchased the clock from any source, rather than the makers, whose names were now unimportant. The name of William Grant, a Boston jeweler, is on a wall clock which strikes on the hour and was retailed by him about 25 years after the patent was obtained.[92] (Fig. 2-64) The proportions of the case are adjusted to accommodate the larger movement, bell, and two weights. J.J. & W. Beals's Clock Establishment advertised clocks of 20 different types in their Haymarket Square showrooms in Boston in 1847.[93] (Fig.2-65) Among them were "8 Day Willard Timepieces." As late as the 1860s, Simon, Jr., and his son, Zabdiel (1826-after 1898) still made the basic timepiece. George Hatch of North Attleboro, Massachusetts, "Manufacturer of Fine Eight-Day Willard Clocks," was selling a variant for $15.00 in 1877.[94]

The standard of innovation and elegance conceived by Simon Willard succeeded in part because sophisticated tall clocks, shelf clocks, and patent timepieces were also made by apprentices and imitators. Since then, the name Willard has been routinely applied to modern adaptations of his famous timepiece, which have been made almost continuously since he received the patent. With the deaths of the Willards their property "was broken up and disposed of,"[95] but the accuracy, attractiveness and availability of Willard clocks have left an enduring name in American craftsmanship.

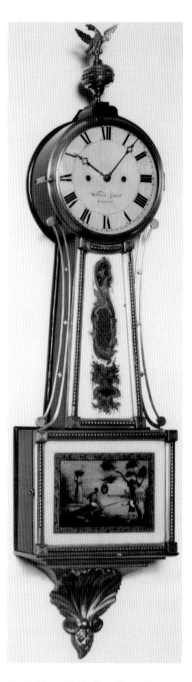

Fig. 2-64. Wall Clock, William Grant, Boston, ca. 1825. Adding the hour strike feature to the patent timepiece required a clock case with heavier proportions to allow for the fall of two weights. Note the differences in the proportions of this clock and Fig. 2-43. The gilded pedestal is a probable replacement. 57.1.105

NOTES

[1] Data collected by Robert C. Cheney shows that numbered clocks by Benjamin Willard are chronological. No. 16 is dated 1768 and marked Grafton. No. 18 is also dated 1768, but inscribed Lexington. Nos. 105 and 114 are marked Grafton. No. 131 (Metropolitan Museum of Art) is dated 1772 and marked Roxbury. Also inscribed Roxbury are Nos. 132, 138, 142, 153, 155, 163, 198, 209, 213, 219, 232. No. 275 was built back in Grafton. All of these clocks are mounted with composite brass or sheet brass dials. With painted dials, nos. 282 and 295 have no place name. No. 345 is Grafton. Nos. 348, 427, 470, 508, 580, and 604 have no place names.

[2] *Boston Gazette*, July 22, 1773; *Boston Gazette and County Journal*, September 5 and October 3, 1774; *Massachusetts Spy* (Boston), October 15, 1774.

[3] A clock by Benjamin marked "Grafton" and "Warranted for Mr. Benj'n Piper" is owned by Greenfield Village and Henry Ford Museum. See *The Antiquarian* 15 (October 1930), 12; Brooks Palmer, *A Treasury of American Clocks* (New York: Macmillan, 1967), figs. 8-11. A clock by Benjamin inscribed "Roxbury" is owned by The Metropolitan Museum of Art. See note 8 below. A third clock in a private collection is signed "Benj. Willard/Lexington." The OSV clock is similar to one inscribed "Benj. Willard/Grafton" with comparable carved rosettes on the waist door that "Belonged to the First Minister of Leicester, Mass. [the Reverend Otis Converse] in 1814...." See Sotheby's Americana auction, sale 5883, June 21, 1989, lot 274.

[4] *Boston Transcript*, September 4, 1857.

[5] John Ware Willard, *A History of Simon Willard, Inventor and Clockmaker*, (1911; Repr. as *Simon Willard and his Clocks*, New York: Dover Publications, 1968) 2, 100-103.

[6] Account Book, John Avery (1732-1794) and Amos Avery (1774-1840), Preston, Conn., 1762-1810. The Connecticut Historical Society, as cited in Amos G. Avery, *Clockmakers and Craftsmen of the Avery Family in Connecticut* (Hartford: The Connecticut Historical Society, 1987), 22-23.

[7] *Connecticut Courant* (Hartford), April 21, 1777.

[8] Daniel J. Steele, "The Clocks of Simon Willard," *Antiques* 1 (February 1922): 69; Charles Messer Stow, "Simon Willard, Maker of Clocks," *Antiquarian* 6 (April 1926): 36-41; Morrison H. Heckscher, *American Furniture in the Metropolitan Museum of Art* II *Late Colonial Period: The Queen Anne and Chippendale Styles* (New York: Random House, 1985), 299-300.

[9] *Boston Gazette*, January 3, 1774.

[10] *America's Valley Forges and Valley Furnaces*, eds. J. Lawrence Pool and Angeline J. Pool (Dalton, Mass.: The Studley Press, 1982). The word "profitably" is used here in relative terms. Most of the blast furnaces in the colonies struggled to survive.

[11] Account Books, Rea and Johnston, Boston, VI:1. Baker Library, Harvard Business School. Sinclair Hitchings, "Thomas Johnston," *Boston Prints and Printmakers*, 1670-1775 (Boston: Colonial Society of Massachusetts, 1973), 83-131. This ledger entry may refer to painting a moon dial rather to decorating a white enamel dial.

[12] John Ware Willard, 3-4, 85; Benjamin was last taxed for real estate in Roxbury in 1774. Tax List, Volume 5, 1774, Roxbury, Mass.

[13] *The Diary of Rev. Ebenezer Parkman, of Westborough, Mass.*, ed. Harriette M. Forbes (Westborough Historical Society, 1899), 163; John Ware Willard, 6, 83-84, 86-67.

[14] Richard Husher and Walter W. Welch, *A Study of Simon Willard's Clocks* (Nahant, Mass.: Husher and Welch, 1980) 7-12; 31-32; 39-45.

[15] For a visual survey of English and European bracket clocks, see Percy G. Dawson, C.B. Drover, and D.W. Parkes, *Early English Clocks* (Suffolk, England: Antiques Collectors' Club, Ltd., 1982); Cedric Jagger, *The World's Great Clocks and Watches* (New York: Hamlyn 1977); Eric Bruton, The *Wetherfield Collection of Clocks* (London: N.A.G. Press, Ltd., 1981); *Britten*, 90-107, 156-7, 160-4; Herbert Cescinsky, *English Long-Case and Bracket Clocks, Being a Collection Made by the Late Frank Garrett...To Be Sold at Auction* (New York: Anderson Galleries, 1926). Spring making was a specialty built on mastering tempered steel and unleashing its power with consistency. Compensation for the uneven release of tension from the relaxing spring was achieved with a fusee, which was also costly to make.

[16] This clock is the only known example by the Willards with a kidney-shaped dial.

[17] See Lockwood Barr, "The Forerunner of the Willard Banjo," *Antiques* (March 1959)75: 282-285; Lockwood Barr, "Willard's Experimental Banjo Models," *NAWCC Bulletin* 9 (June 1951): 370-377; Heckscher, 309-310; Husher and Welch, 7-30. Lockwood Barr, "Willard Thirty-Hour Wall Clocks" (unpublished ms. on file at the Edward Ingraham Library, American Clock and Watch Museum, Bristol, Conn.) The two OSV clocks are described by Husher and Welch, 12-13, 20-23, 28. Aside from the two OSV examples, Grafton wall clocks are owned by: Historic Deerfield, Inc.; The Metropolitan Museum of Art; Museum of Fine Arts, Boston; Willard House and Clock Mu-

seum, Grafton; and the Winterthur Museum. A similar clock inscribed "Timo[thy] Sibley/Sutton" is owned by the Chipstone Foundation, Milwaukee, Wis.

[18] According to unpublished research by Dr. Roger Robinson, Willard lived in York, Penn. during at least some of this period. His relocation raises the probability that Willard was exposed to German-American clock making.

[19] Joseph Willard, 69-70; *Vital Records of Grafton, Massachusetts* (Worcester: Franklin P. Rice, 1906), 375; Deed, John Goulding to Benjamin Willard, Grafton, February 5, 1782. 88:533. Worcester County Registry of Deeds, Worcester, Mass.; Another agent in the sale of clock jacks was Thomas Learned, Jr., a Roxbury clock maker, who advertised them in the *New-Hampshire Gazette* (Portsmouth), March 18, 1785. *Massachusetts Spy* (Boston), September 2, 1784.

[20] Parker is discussed on pp. 63-65.

[21] Edwin A. Battison and Patricia E. Kane, *The American Clock: 1725-1865* (Greenwich, Conn.: New York Graphic Society, 1973), 54-57.

[22] Benjamin lost a law suit and served time in prison in 1798 before moving to Baltimore where he died in 1803, leaving a modest estate of $75. U.S. Census, Worcester, County, Mass., 1790, 1800.

[23] *Massachusetts Spy* or *Worcester Gazette*, March 11, 1784 in Mabel M. Swan, Simon Willard's Clock Jacks, Boston Clock Club, March 2, 1940.

[24] *Independent Chronicle and the Universal Advertiser* (Boston), January 15, 1784, *ibid*.

[25] Willard's tower clocks were held in high regard. Rare examples are owned by the First Parish Church of Portland, Me., where it was installed in 1802 and Willard House and Clock Museum, Grafton, Mass. See Husher and Welch, 244-57, 262-264.

[26] Husher and Welch, 31-56. They report that "No. 2" also appears on a similar clock, location now unknown.

[27] Husher and Welch, 42-44. The lower section of the OSV clock is a modern fabrication from old lumber.

[28] A similar clock appears in Israel Sack's advertisement, *Antiques*, 127(February 1985).

[29] Aaron Willard must have made other short clocks by 1784. The label may refer to the first clock of this design.

[30] For a related shelf clock by Aaron Willard with the same scalloped molding, see Husher and Welch, 35. This molding is similar to the type found on some tall clock cases made in south-central Mass. and in the Norwich, Conn. areas.

[31] A similar shelf clock by Simon Willard with a reverse-painted coat of arms on the lower case is in the collection of Historic

Deerfield, Inc.

[32] Although Aaron, Jr., did not own his father's business until 1823, many clocks signed by him are in designs that had been popular many years earlier. As an experienced craftsman, family member, and possibly as a foreman, he may have inscribed his own name on clocks.

[33] American bracket clocks are in the collections of: The Chipstone Foundation, Colonial Williamsburg Foundation; Greenfield Village and Henry Ford Museum; Historic Deerfield, Inc.; Independence National Historical Park; Rhode Island Historical Society; The White House; and Winterthur Museum. The origin of the movement of the Willard bracket clock at Winterthur is unclear. Some parts may have been imported and assembled here. See Charles Montgomery, *American Furniture, The Federal Period in the Henry Francis DuPont Winterthur Museum* (New York: Viking Press, 1966), 209.

[34] About 1792 Simon Willard examined a year-running clock that had descended in the Oliver family of Boston and then made one. A year-running clock made by Simon Willard about that time was given to the Harvard Medical School in 1950 by Mrs. Robert Sampson.

[35] A musical clock by Simon Willard is in the collection of the Willard House and Clock Museum.

[36] Letter, Simon Willard to Abijah Hawkes, Roxbury, April 2, 1796, reproduced in *Antiques* 120(September 1981): Sack advertisement inside front cover.

[37] *Boston Directory* of 1798; an illustration of a model of the complex appears in John Ware Willard, 87. The Penniman painting is in a private collection and unavailable for photography.

[38] See Brock Jobe, "The Boston Furniture Industry," *Boston Furniture of the Eighteenth Century* (Boston: Colonial Society, 1974), 3-48.

[39] See Husher and Welch, 208-213.

[40] Charles Stimpson, *Stimpson's Boston Directory* (Boston: Charles Stimpson, 1816); John Ware Willard, pp. 89-90, 117-119; Pieter Roos, "Summary of Research on 12th Ward Clockmakers and Associated Artisans" (unpublished report, Old Sturbridge Village, January 1989), passim. Among the craftsmen near Simon and Aaron were clock makers Aaron, Jr., William Cummens, and Elnathan Taber; the cabinetmakers Nehemiah Munroe, William Fisk, Pratt and Walker, Thomas Bacon, Spencer Thomas, Thomas Dudley, James Blake, and later Charles Crane Crehore and Henry Willard (Aaron's son); the turner Thomas Ayling; the carver Thomas Wightman; the ornamental painters Charles Bullard, John Ritto Penniman,

Samuel Washburn, and John Green, Jr.; the dial painters Spencer Nolen, Samuel Curtis, Jr., and John Minott; the looking glass maker John Doggett; the gold beater Lewis Lauriat; and brass founders Simeon Gilson and William Abbot. "Lead works and mahogany mills were close by." Bullard and Pratt and Walker are listed on Washington Street in a section of the 1816 edition entitled "Residents in Streets not numbered." Also listed as having a shop is a John Bullard whose trade and association with Aaron is unknown. "Willard, Henry, clockcase maker, rear 843 Washington," appears in 1831. This was Aaron's address after the street was numbered in 1825. *Stimpsons' Boston Directory*, 1831, 335.

[41] Elnathan Taber, William Cummens, Daniel and Nathaniel Munroe, Joseph Mulliken, Zacheus Gates, James Doull, and John White.

[42] Liverpool was a major clock and watch making center. Allied tradesmen also prospered, including toolmakers John Wyke (about 1770), Peter Stubs of Warrington (about 1800), and James and Thomas Jones of Prescott. These men supplied complete clocks, watches, castings, and tools to other craftsmen in England and America. See Brian Loomes, *Lancashire Clocks and Clockmakers* (North Pomfret, VT.: David and Charles, Inc., 1975), 12.

[43] Quoted from the account books of William C. Hunneman, Boston, in Mabel M. Swan, "The Man Who Made Brass Works for Willard Clocks," *Antiques* 17, no. 6 (June 1930): 524-526.

[44] Husher and Welch, 218.

[45] Brian Loomes, *The White Dial Clock* (New York: Drake Publishers, 1975), 45-48. James Wilson was one of more than 70 dial makers and painters advertising in Birmingham, England, between 1772 and 1800. Forty-eight firms competed between 1770 and 1815. He and one-time partner, Thomas Hadley Osborne, ran the two largest dial making firms in the world.

[46] The Revere labels on clocks by Aaron and Aaron Willard, Jr., are found with three variations—the first with "Roxbury," the second with "Boston," and the third with "Boston" followed by the instruction: "to make it go faster, screw the pendulum up, slower, screw down." On some examples "Jr." is found penned in after "Aaron Willard." Presumably the "Roxbury" label is the earliest. An entry in Revere's day book in July 1781 indicates that he also printed watch papers for Aaron. See Clarence S. Brigham, *Paul Revere's Engravings*, (Worcester: American Antiquarian Society, 1969), 176-179.

[47] For late tall clocks by Aaron Willard, see *Sack Collection*, 5:1318, 1378. An example

made by Aaron for Joshua Seaver in 1806 helps to understand the chronology of workmanship. See *Sack Collection*, 2:345.

[48] Robert C. Cheney interprets the patent description as follows: The cace [read: face] is thick glass [read: brass] painted, varnished....as beautiful and cheaper than common china enamelled or any other kind of cases [read:faces]. Although no patent timepiece is known with a painted brass face, he may have intended to use them as he had used silvered brass faces in his earlier wall clocks. Iron was a much more suitable material for a painted dial.

[49] John Ware Willard, 14-15, Pls. 5,6; the original patent document is at the Willard House and Clock Museum. Willard's patented improvements were: 1) generally, a new and useful regulator or timepiece; 2) a weight fall of 15" in eight days; 3) a height of two feet and a face diameter of seven inches; 4) the placement of the pendulum forward of the weight; 5) suspension of the pendulum from pivots to minimize wobble; 6) graduated plate in an arc to measure the oscillation of the pendulum; 7) a case highlighted with thick glass, paint, gilt, and varnish and an oval to view the pendulum.

[50] Letter, Simon Willard to Mary (Bird) Willard, Portland, Me., July 6, 1802 (location unknown); see John Ware Willard, pl. 7.

[51] See Peter Heuer and Klaus Maurice, *European Pendulum Clocks* (West Chester, Penn.: Schiffer Publishing, Ltd., 1988), 326.

[52] For a technical discussion of early patent timepieces and of the barometer as the origin of Willard's design, see Husher and Welch, 57-102.

[53] The time train of the standard tall clock was adapted by substituting a seven-leaf pinion (rather than eight) on the intermediate and escape-wheel arbors. This alteration is discussed by Husher and Welch, 84.

[54] Some patent clocks, particularly those made in Concord, Mass., have five-part back board. The central board is a long trapezoid.

[55] A patent timepiece in a private collection is signed: "Painted by John R. Penniman, Boston, 1803," on the back of the lower glass.

[56] See also Chapter 6, "Spurious Timepieces."

[57] Obituary of Charles Bullard, *Suffolk County Journal* (Boston, Mass.) August 5, 1871. Thanks to Carol Damon Andrews for sharing her unpublished research.

[58] Advertisement, New England Gallery, *Antiques* 127, no. 6 (June 1985):1257; Northeast Auctions Catalog, (Hampton, N.H.) August 1-2, 1992, shows two patent

timepieces, one with a thermometer and one with stencilled frames.

[59] Day Book, John Doggett, Roxbury, 1802-1809, Winterthur Museum.

[60] Doggett offered "Mahogany furniture at the above place by WILLIAM VILES" in the Columbian Sentinel (Boston), February 8, 1806, see Betty Ring, "Check List of Looking-glass and Frame Makers and Merchants Known by Their Labels," Antiques 119 (May 1981): 1183. Doggett dealt with other Boston and Salem furniture makers whose work may also have been found in the Willards' finishing room. The daybook reveals the names of his uncle, Stephen Badlam, Sr. (1751-1815), Lemuel Churchill (working 1805-circa 1828), [Isaac] Vose & [Joshua] Coates (partnership 1805-1818) as well as looking glass makers Paul Cermenati (working 1805-1809), in partnership with John Bernarda (working 1807-1808), and G. Monfrino. The authors thank David L. Barquist for sharing research on Cermenati, Bernarda, and Monfrino.

[61] Doggett, 135. Aaron Willard, Jr., had already contracted with or was debited to Jabez Baldwin, who received two of the finest No. 3 cases. See also 1, 48, 61, 72, 81, 135, 168, 171.

[62] The authors thank David Wood, Curator, Concord Museum, for sharing this terminology from the Hunneman account book.

[63] Quoted from the account books of William C. Hunneman, Boston, Antiques (June 1930)

[64] John Ware Willard, 110-112; Husher and Welch, 95. Cummens's timepieces are illustrated in Randall, 252; Battison and Kane, 198-99. An example in a private collection states, "S. Willard's Patent" on the box glass and "Warranted by W. Cummens" on the dial.

[65] Battison and Kane, 200-201.

[66] Sack Collection, 7:1930-1931.

[67] Other gallery clocks by Simon Willard are in the collections of Greenfield Village and the Henry Ford Museum; Museum of Fine Arts, Boston; the Supreme Court, Washington, D.C.; The Time Museum, Rockford, Ill.; and the Willard House and Clock Museum. See Randall, 247-248; Husher and Welch, 129-170, esp. 137-142.

[68] Husher and Welch 111-128.

[69] Columbian Centinel, August 10, 1822.

[70] Letter, Elihu Hoyt to Hannah Taylor Hoyt, Boston, January 17, 1823. Hoyt Papers, Box 8, Folder 6, Pocumtuck Valley Memorial Association, Memorial Libraries, Deerfield, MA.; Estate inventory, Elihu Hoyt, December 9, 1833, Deerfield, MA., Docket 7/283. Franklin County Registry of Probate, Greenfield, Mass.. A patent timepiece by Aaron, Jr., that descended in the Hoyt family is in the collection of Historic Deerfield, Inc. Dean A. Fales, Jr., The Furniture of Historic Deerfield (New York: E.P. Dutton, 1976), fig. 525.

[71] Providence Gazette, February 1804; Worcester National Aegis, September 25, 1822.

[72] Husher and Welch correctly identify the French skeleton clock with a porcelain dial as a possible inspiration for the patent alarm clock (p. 172), but they incorrectly refer to the "Paris," "Alabaster," or "chimney" clocks as French skeleton clocks on the basis of their exposed movement and glass dome. Unlike the "chimney" clock, true French skeleton clocks were extremely rare in America and were probably not often seen by Willard and his clientele. These authors also cite the English skeleton clock as a source for this design; also unlikely, since they are normally fitted with engraved brass dials, were not widely imported, and are generally later than the patent alarm timepieces. To compare skeleton and mantle clocks, see Heuer and Maurice, 16-97; Antiques (August 1991) 140: 212.

[73] The painting and its companion, The Drawing Room, are in the collections of the Museum of Fine Arts, Boston, Mass. See Jane C. Nylander, "Henry Sargent's Dinner Party and Tea Party, Antiques (May 1982) 121: 1175.

[74] The Columbian Centinel (Boston), October 22, 1825; Estate Inventory of David Hinckley, Boston, 1826. Suffolk Co Courthouse, Boston.

[75] Three patent alarm clocks were stolen in 1972. Only the mechanisms were retrieved and two are now mounted in reproduction cases made at OSV.

[76] Schedule of claims for the patent alarm clock, Simon Willard, 1819, reproduced in John Ware Willard, Pl. 9.

[77] Antiques (May 1990) 137: 1040; Husher and Welch, 191, 195; Sack Collection, 4:1098, 6:51; John Ware Willard, 66-69. Some alarm clocks are signed "SIMON WILLARD & SON," like one in the collection of Historic Deerfield, Inc. The pendulum supports reverted from a yoke, hinge pin, and knife-edge suspension to the T-bridge found on the original patent timepiece. Simon, Jr., was trained by his father as well as by John Pond (wkg. 1809-1811) in Portsmouth, N.H. He entered West Point in 1813, but left the army in 1817 to engage in the crockery business. When that failed, he worked for his father between 1823 and 1826. Simon, Jr., then went to New York for two more years to train as a chronometer and watchmaker with a Mr. Eggert. He established himself independently in Boston in 1828. Four years later, Simon, Jr., made an astronomical clock, now owned by Harvard University. Simon, Jr., and his son, Zabdiel, were also in partnership between about 1850 and 1870. Willard patent alarm clocks are also found at The Metropolitan Museum of Art; Museum of Fine Arts, Boston; Society for the Preservation of New England Antiquities; The Time Museum; The Willard House and Clock Museum; and the Winterthur Museum.

[78] A clock at the White House is mounted with a sulphide bust of Lafayette who toured the country in 1824 and 1825.

[79] According to Husher and Welch, the first so-called lighthouse clocks have brass or painted iron dials and incorporate the alarm mechanism between the plates. When production increased, Willard put a conventional bell above the movement, placed the alarm on the left side, and lengthened the plates to accommodate one more wheel and pinion in order to reduce the length of the weight's descent. Willard designed the movement to run for eight days with a weight fall of only twelve inches. The cases of the early patent alarm clocks are a box with a door that supports the low, glass dome. Later, they were cased in mahogany columns with brass fittings. Painted tinned sheet iron was also used for the cases.

[80] The engraved inscription on Simon Willard's last alarm clock copies a faint pencil notation in the original case. Willard used a patent timepiece movement and placed the winding arbor at the two o'clock position. The wheel count and the shortened pendulum are different, and the clock must have been powered by a heavy weight suspended from compound pulleys in order to run for eight-days. The added mass of the weight explains the projection of the pendulum behind the movement to clear the weight below. See Husher and Welch, 187.

[81] For a technical discussion of patent alarm clocks, see Husher and Welch, 171-205.

[82] 70. Richard McLanathan, Gilbert Stuart (New York: Harry N. Abrams, 1986), passim; Dorinda Evans, Benjamin West and His American Students (Washington, D.C.: The National Portrait Gallery, 1980), 52-59; Carol Troyen, The Boston Tradition: American Paintings from the Museum of Fine Arts, Boston (New York: American Federation of the Arts, 1980), pp. 76-81. The portrait of Simon Willard is among Gilbert Stuart's earliest works in Boston and a rare example in pastel. The artist had returned from England and Ireland in 1793 after a stay of 18 years. He painted in the Mid-Atlantic until about 1805 and

relocated in Boston. Stuart lived in Roxbury between 1813 and 1816 and then moved back to Boston where he died on July 8, 1828. Although the attribution of the portrait to Stuart has been debated, the label affixed to the back is in the handwriting of Simon Willard.

[83] See essays by David Jaffee and Jack Larkin and catalog entries by Jessica Nicoll, *Meet Your Neighbors: Portraits, Painters and Society in New England 1790-1850*, ed. Caroline Sloat (Sturbridge, Mass.: Old Sturbridge Village, 1992).

[84] It is among the scientific holdings of Harvard University; Aaron Willard, Jr., constructed an orrery in about 1826 for West Chester Academy in Pennsylvania.

[85] *Independent Chronicle*, January 15, 1784.

[86] Letter, Ebenezer Gay, Harvard University, to Frank White, Old Sturbridge Village, September 10, 1981. OSV Research and Collections files.

[87] Correspondence of William J.H. Andrewes, Harvard University, to Robert C. Cheney, March 27, 1992, with enclosed copy of material from the University archives.

[88] The astronomical clock was owned by Frank G. Macomber in Boston in 1911 and is now in the Collection of Historical Scientific Instruments, Harvard University. For a description, see John Ware Willard, 75.

[89] Benjamin Franklin Willard was trained by his father. See Joseph Willard, 140, 256; John Ware Willard, 74-78;
John Ware Willard, Pl. 25 and 71-72, 75-77; Husher and Welch, 277-281. While rotating lights were known in the 1820s, Benjamin's improvements permitted lighthouses to flash a distinctive pattern that would orient mariners during a storm.

[90] Benjamin was the partner of Obadiah Rich (wkg. ca. 1830-1850) in the jewelry business from 1842-1844. A second skeleton clock (57.1.119) was made by Edwin B. Horn in Boston for the exposition of the Massachusetts Charitable Mechanics Association in 1841. A "Patent Lever" was displayed at the exhibition, and Horn's clock is inscribed: "PATENT LEVER." The dead-beat escapement is fitted with a fork that gives an impulse to the balance wheel at the top to further animate the movement.

[91] Louis McLane, *Documents Relative to the Manufactures in the United States*, 2 vols (1833: repr. ed. New York:A.M. Kelley, 1969) I:442-443,

[92] Grant, Boston Directory; Other retailers like John J. Low of Boston and Benjamin Smith in New York City, also signed and distributed patent clocks. See *Sack Collection* 3:645, and Berry B. Tracy, *Federal Furniture and Decorative Arts at Boscobel*

(New York: Harry N. Abrams, 1981) 117.

[93] Advertisement, *Adams's New Directory of the City of Boston*, July 1846-7, 4.

[94] Brochure, J.B. Hatch, *Manufacturer of Fine Eight-Day Willard Clocks and Regulators*, North Attleboro, Mass. (Boston: Times Job Printing, 1877; repr. ed. Cranbury, N.J.: Adams Brown Company, n.d.) "J.B." was misprinted on the original document; George Hatch operated this business.

[95] Bullard obituary.

IN 18TH-CENTURY NEW ENGLAND, apprentices in clock making bartered labor for knowledge of the master's way. Apprentices expected to learn mechanical engineering and metallurgy, various hand skills, to use costly equipment and expensive raw materials, and to retail luxury goods. The good master imprinted his knowledge of patterns, templates, and products, so that the fortunate clock maker was able to make and repair clocks and watches as his life's work.

When the master was willing to teach or even share, 'the art, trade, and mystery' of clock making, the apprenticeship was a very satisfactory arrangement. When he was not, the relationship was a disappointment. Simon and Aaron, and probably Benjamin Willard, as well, took seriously the responsibility of training their apprentices. The apprenticeships described by Benjamin Willard and John Fitch, unsatisfactory as they were, give a glimpse of the expectations of a young lad who entered the shop of a proficient artisan. Both worked for Benjamin Cheney, whom Fitch described as a man "possessed [of] considerable genious," but also having a "great many oddities," not the least of which was his household. His wife, Deborah Cheney was silly, lazy, "extravagant in some things [and] ... penurious in others." Benjamin, "on the other hand was always willing that I should have a belly full of such as was going, but it frequently happened that it was very indifferent." As to learning how to build clocks, Fitch realized that his "indentures was ambiguously exprest that he [Cheney] was to learn me clockwork and brass foundering. ... Almost the whole of the time that I was in the shop [I spent] at Trifling pottering brass work, and was when I left him almost totally ignorant of clockwork."

To remedy this, Fitch tried an arrangement with Timothy Cheney, who "agreed to take me for one year and learn me the three branches." But that experience was not much of an improvement.

I was set to work at small brass work with the exception of being shortly put to clock work and going out once in a while to work on his place and at his shop which he was building

THE WILLARD LEGACY
Clocks By Their Apprentices

that summer, tending on masons, carpenters, &c. I was not put to one single clock, neither wood nor brass, during that time. It is true I did begin one wooden one, but never had time to finish it. As to watch work, I never saw one put together during my apprenticeship, and when I attempted to stand by him to see him put one together, I was always ordered to my work, and what was the most singular of all, it was but seldom that I could get to see his tools for watch work, as he had a drawer where he was always particularly careful to lock them up. He never told me the different parts of a watch, and to this day I am ignorant of the names of many parts.[1]

The known Willard apprentices represented in the collection form an honor roll of the makers of the most elegant clocks with the finest materials in the Willard mold. These apprentices were trained by the Willards in their earliest years in the trade. Once trained, Willard apprentices applied their knowledge and luck in new locations. Some found that even at some distance from Boston, Willard design and workmanship were constant. The journeymen who left Roxbury found it difficult to establish themselves as independent competitors. Willard marketing was apparently so thorough that many consumers simply went to the source.

Simon Willard's trainees in Grafton include Abel Hutchins (1777-1783), possibly his older brother Levi (1777-1780), and Luther Goddard. Gardner Parker was an apprentice in Grafton, sometime between 1786-90. Only Benjamin was still working there, but these were productive years for him. Apprenticeships with Simon in Roxbury include: Elnathan Taber, 1787-[1793], William Cummens, [?-1793?], Daniel Monroe [1789]-1796, and Lemuel Curtis, [1803]-1811; for Aaron: Stephen Taber [1792]-1799 and Zacheus Gates [1798]-1804.

In the Willards' later years they apparently enlisted no apprentices. Standardization and efficiency aimed at selling more clocks for less money took clock making from the hands of the master and his boys. Apprenticeships became shorter, and ceased to be the route to mastery in clock making. Young craftsmen became even less equipped to beat the Willards at their game. No longer fluent in the "art and mystery" of the craft, the new worker applied a trade to someone else's end. Practical manufacture to create volume altered traditional craftsmanship and conditions of apprenticeship.[2]

The broad knowledge required of one person to make a clock was fractured. While the Willards could produce and market large numbers of clocks, others had to mix production with running a retail establishment, selling jewelry, and offering repairs.[3] These men's careers illustrate the evolution of clock making during the early 19th century. Those who were able to adapt, found a market that would support the development of a lifetime career.

The stories of the Willard apprentices show that family was a driving force in clock making. Blood relationships brought apprentices to the door and sometimes led to marriages, but success in the Willard mold required more than family ties. Acumen and aptitude were also essential.

Taken together the work of the apprentices sheds light on many aspects of the business. Simon Willard was still a Grafton clock maker and brass founder when Abel Hutchins (1763-1853) was apprenticed to him. The six-year indenture, dated December 6, 1777, was witnessed by Aaron and Daniel Willard. Abel bound himself to good behavior, while Simon pledged to "teach & Instruct or Cause the said apprentice to be taught and Instructed in the Art or Trade or Calling of a Clock & Watchmaker by the best way or means he may or Can." Abel was to be cared for as a member of the household and, at the end of his term he was to be able to read, write, and cipher and to be provided with "one Full Sute of Cloaths."[4] Abel then joined his brother as a clock maker in Concord, New Hampshire. In 1786 he married Elizabeth Partridge, whose sisters also married up-and-coming members of the clock-making fraternity: Samuel Curtis (1785-1879), Elnathan Taber (1768-1854), and Aaron Willard.

Levi (1761-1855) and Abel Hutchins established one of the first clock businesses in Concord, New Hampshire, at the junction of the Merrimack River and the roads from Boston, Portsmouth, and the Connecticut valley.[5] They were partners from 1786 until 1806. In 1788, the Hutchinses advertised that they had indeed absorbed the current Willard way:

CLOCK MANUFACTORY.
Levi & Abel Hutchins,
Clock and Watch-makers,
(CONCORD)
Hereby inform the public, that they...carry on said business in its various branches,—and

make the following Clocks, viz. CHIME—REPEATING,and PLAIN EIGHT DAY CLOCKS——TIME PIECES of all sorts—equal to any manufactured in America.—The Cases are made in the genteelest taste, by one of the first artists in the state....[6]

True to their training, the brothers made fine clocks: some with silvered, multi-part, sheet brass dials and others with painted dials.(Fig. 3-1) They may not have rivaled "any manufactured in America," but they were certainly unrivaled in Concord, where they advertised for apprentices and journeymen.[7]

Sometime after ending the partnership with his brother, Abel Hutchins evidently went to England to arrange for a consignment of "Clock Materials," which he intended to wholesale in Concord. His instinct and training doubtless told him that it was the right thing to do. He imported "Zink, Grain Tin, Clock Balls, Clock Case Capitals, Quarter do., Hinges; Clock Hands, Clock Pinions, Clock Bells and Glasses, Clock Faces with moon, plain and ship arches." In short, supplies to make tall clocks in the prescribed manner and style that he had learned from Simon Willard.[8]

Lured by the promise of the textile industry during the Embargo and war period, Levi took a sabbatical from clock making between 1813 and 1818, but then returned for another two decades. (Abel withdrew from the business in 1819 and operated the Phoenix Hotel across from the State House until 1832.) Levi appears to have placed his last advertisement in 1824, although he claimed that he did not retire until 1838.[9] While Abel's name appears only on tall clocks, Levi also made short clocks, shelf clocks, and patent timepieces. His shop also sold a few New Hampshire mirror clocks.[10] In his autobiography Levi proudly recalled that "there are eight-day clocks or timepieces of our manufacture in all the original thirteen states of the Union."[11]

FAMILY TRADITION HELD that Gardner Parker (1772-1816) received some training from the Willards in Grafton, where he lived briefly before settling in Westborough.[12] Since he would have been barely 12 when Simon and Aaron Willard moved to Roxbury, he may have trained with Benjamin Willard, whom Simon credited with his own instruction in clock making.[13] 'Uncle Gardner' apparently liked to joke that he did not spend much time with the Willards, but they still made pretty good clocks.[14]

Fig.3-1. Tall Clock, Levi and Abel Hutchins, Concord, N.H., ca. 1800. Now refinished, tiger maple cases were usually stained a dark color to simulate mahogany. 57.1.142

Fig.3-2. Tower Clock, Gardner Parker, Westborough, Mass., ca. 1808-1816. Essentially made of iron, the wheel work of this clock is laid in a line along a bed; the time train on the left, the strike on the right, separated by a bridge that supports the pendulum (now gone). The frame is a reconstruction to display the mechanism. 57.1.185

Fig.3-3. Tall Clock, Elnathan Taber, Roxbury, Mass., ca. 1800. Willard apprentices used the same cabinetmakers as their masters and produced nearly identical clocks. 57.1.2

The tall clock (Pl. 18) made for Solomon Este of Southborough, Massachusetts, justifies his confidence. It has an added mechanism for recording the day of the month with a hand and dial rather than with a calendar wheel. Fitted with a rocking ship, the dial lacks a false plate and is mounted with an American-made tympanum for the rocking ship. The cabinetwork is a handsome variation on the "Roxbury" case made of cherry with oval veneers of mahogany. Parker had learned well from the Willards and was also familiar with the shelf clock form.[15] He drew apprentices and employed journeymen who helped produce eight-day brass movements for his clocks at his Westborough shop.

Parker also left his mark on big projects. He built organs and made one for the town of Westborough in 1809.[16] His attempt to build a dam to support a mill, perhaps conceived to apply water power to clock production, left an unintended name on the map. After the dam was built, the brook proved too small, and it was named, "Parker's Folly."[17] But Gardner continued to work on a grand scale, and made at least three tower clocks: for meeting houses at Westborough in 1801, Arlington (West Cambridge) in 1808 that cost $796.80, and Shrewsbury between 1808 and 1816. (Fig. 3-2)[18] This last movement was a costly undertaking that required superior casting. All wheels and pinions are iron. The wheel work has decorative crossings, or spokes, and utilizes a pinwheel escapement and rack-and-snail strike system. Despite his ability to make clocks like those by Simon Willard, Parker's personal and financial problems eventually overwhelmed him and on a cold February night in 1816, he took his own life.[19]

Simon's Roxbury apprentices illustrate that Willard designs and workmanship were immutable. Elnathan Taber (1768-1854) and William Cummens (1768-1834) established themselves in Roxbury and continued the tradition in which they had been trained. Apprentices between 1787 and 1793, they were taught the kind of work then on the bench: assembling the parts of movements and casing them to yield a conventional product that looked like a luxury item.

Elnathan Taber, from Dartmouth, Massachusetts, entered Simon's Roxbury shop at age 19 to begin an apprenticeship in the traditional European manner. When Willard retired in 1839, he sold Taber his shop and tools.[20] William Cummens is known best through his clocks. He had evidently completed his apprenticeship before March 10, 1793, when he married and established his home and shop in Roxbury.[21] At his death in Roxbury on April 20, 1834, Taber appraised his estate.[22]

The Willards' apprentices became conduits of consistency that popularized their name. The Roxbury tall clocks made by Elnathan Taber and William Cummens are remarkably similar, although they never entered a formal partnership. Their tall clocks are only distinguished by superficial differences.(Figs. 3-3, 3-4) Taber and Cummens clearly frequented the same cabinetmakers and hardware dealers and the cases of their clocks differ only slightly in their construction and in optional ornament, like the patera in the base of the Taber example. The movement of the clock by Taber has a calendar wheel and shows the phases of the moon, while the Cummens clock has neither. Instead, a rocking ship with an American flag races against time, a favorite Cummens ornament. There are no false plates behind the enamelled dials, which may have been locally manufactured. The well-made, eight-day brass movements have deeply cut teeth, highly polished plates, rack and snail strike systems, and the dependable recoil escapement. (Fig. 3-5) In the Willard tradition, the profiles of the fretwork, moldings, feet and, indeed, the way that the parts relate to the clocks' final beauty signal that these distinctive luxury items are conventional products. Both men are known to have made most Willard forms, including patent timepieces with T-bridge

Fig.3-4. Tall Clock, William Cummens, Roxbury, Mass., ca.1800. 57.1.191

Fig.3-5. *Tall Clock movement, Elnathan Taber. The movements of Roxbury-area clocks with painted dials are all of comparable quality. There are no particular features which identify a specific maker's work. 57.1.2*

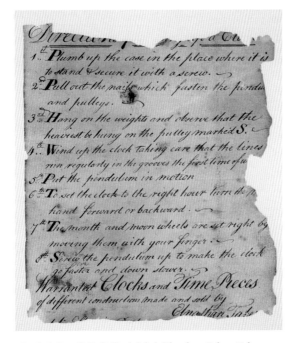

Fig.3-6. *Detail, Tall Clock label, Elnathan Taber. Taber combined and paraphrased the printed labels of Simon and Aaron Willard in his handwritten version. 57.1.2*

pendulum suspension and simplified wall clocks with alarms for use in shops and offices.[23]

Willard standardization obscured the actual origin of the mechanism and increased the importance of the name on the dial. The names of Taber and Cummens and their references to Willard quality were guarantees to consumers that they were purchasing traditional clocks. Like his master, Taber pasted directions inside the case, providing a brief 'apprenticeship' for the consumer in setting up the clock. Although not printed in the decorative Willard way, the intent of the eight handwritten steps was identical: to inform about the care and handling of the clock and to provide confidence. (Fig. 3-6) The concluding statement, "Warranted Clocks and Time Pieces of different construction made and sold by Elnathan Taber," suggests that his shop had kept abreast of the introduction of the patent timepiece even though it postdates his apprenticeship. "Of different construction" alludes to the availability of tall clocks and timepieces with optional attachments and case designs—the offer of variety within the successful Willard canon, rather than deviation.

The products of the Willards and their apprentices are so similar that it is often difficult to distinguish between them. The consistency of clockmaking practices within the Willard sphere is illustrated by shelf clocks made about 1805 by Elnathan Taber in Roxbury and by his brother, Stephen (1777-1862), 75 miles away in New Bedford. (Figs. 3-7, 3-8) The clocks vary only slightly in measurement, fretwork, inlay around the door of Elnathan's, and the pattern of the stringing at the base of both clocks. The moldings, feet, and templates used to construct the cases are similar. The painting of the dials on a bluish ground was apparently done by the same hand. The movements follow the same rules of standardization: both are eight-day timepieces with recoil escapements, identical wheel counts, and pendulum length. They differ only in the decorative turning of the pillars that separate the brass plates (Fig. 3-9).

Even though Elnathan and Stephen learned from different Willards and despite the fact that Stephen, then 22, was only ten years old when Elnathan had left home for Roxbury, their clocks are virtual duplicates.[24] Stephen's first newspaper advertisement upon moving to New Bedford in 1799 notes that he is "Late Apprentice to Mr. Aaron Willard, Clock-maker, in Boston."[25] Stephen apparently

*Left: Fig.3-7.
Shelf Clock,
Elnathan Taber,
Roxbury, Mass.,
ca. 1805. 57.1.73*

*Right: Fig.3-8.
Shelf Clock,
Stephen Taber,
New Bedford,
Mass., ca. 1805.
The painted iron
dial has several
features
characteristic of
the painter, John
Ritto Penniman:
Arabic numerals
at 15-minute
intervals, a gilded
border around the
chapter ring with
a "dot, dot, dash,
dot, dot, dash"
decoration, and
delicate floral
leaves. The
central finial is
missing. See pl.8.
57.1.46*

contracted for cases, dials, and perhaps clock parts through the 'home office.'[26] Although he made beautiful clocks, he could not succeed in New Bedford and left the trade altogether early in the new century.[27] The reminiscence of a grandson of Taber's first patron describes the clock maker's attempt to establish a business.

The first clock he made here was for my grandfather, Daniel Ricketson....Soon after his arrival, he...inquired for a place to board where he could pay in making a clock. My grandfather...said he would take a clock of him....For this clock, he [Taber] received a year's board....At the expiration of the time, Mr. Taber said he supposed that he should be obliged to leave....'Well,' replied my grandfather, 'I will take another clock of thee,' having engaged one to Captain James Howland in the meantime. At the end of the second year, the clock maker thought that he must certainly leave, but a third clock his host had engaged to Henry Tucker, of Dartmouth...[and he] continued his board for another year. So he [Taber] said, 'I received three years board for three clocks.' The value of these clocks was, I think, at the time of their manufacture, about $85 [each]....No clock stands higher in our community than those of Stephen Taber, and as he only worked at his trade about four years, there are probably less of his make than those of most manufacturers of his time.[28]

Despite the quality of his work, Taber was unable to develop a market. Roxbury was only two days' journey away. By the time he gave up, Simon Willard had already patented the timepiece. Whether it was cost or distance from the supporting network of craftsmen, in the end it was apparent that he could not succeed out at the rim of the Willards' reputation.

The name of Zacheus Gates (1770-1831) appears on a variety of Willard forms, and through family relationship, he is also considered to have been an Aaron Willard apprentice. In 1783 his second cousin married the clock maker, the first of a series of intermarriages involving the Gates family.[29] But Gates, like Stephen Taber was unable to establish himself outside of Boston. Described as a clock maker and goldsmith at Harvard between 1804 and 1810, Gates also lived briefly in nearby Shirley in 1809 and 1810.[30] The case of a shelf clock made in Worcester County is distinctively the work of a rural cabinetmaker. (Fig. 3-10) Finally Gates moved to Charlestown,[31] where he made clocks until after the War of 1812.

The case of a tall clock he made at Charlestown also differs from customary Willard patterns in the fretwork on the hood, the band of inlay across its base, and the tall French feet. The style of the painted enamelled dial, which lacks a false plate, is occasionally found on dials used by Aaron Willard. (Pl. 19) In both clocks, however, the movements follow the Willard way to a "T," but that aspect of the workmanship does not show. Unable to compete with the Willards so close to their own home turf, he specialized in repairing watches.

Daniel (1775-1859) and Nathaniel Munroe (1777-1861) grew up in Roxbury near the Willard manufactory. Daniel trained with Simon Willard and Nathaniel with Abel Hutchins in Concord, New Hampshire. Daniel received a solid letter of recommendation on July 13, 1796:

> This is to certify that Daniel Munroe, Jun.has served an Apprenticeship of seven years with me the Subscriber, that he has been uncommonly faithful, honest, and industrious,and that I hereby acknowledge him capable of making any work that I manufacture and that I do pronounce him as one of the best workmen in America. Simon Willard.[32]

After completing their training, the entire family

Fig.3-11. Tall Clock, Daniel Jr. and Nathaniel Munroe, Concord, Mass., ca. 1805. The dial of this clock has no decorative painting in the corners. The use of a sweep-center second hand and dead-beat escapement possibly suggests a special order for use in a non-domestic setting. 57.1.134

Opposite page:

Left: Fig.3-9.Shelf Clock movement, Elnathan Taber. Clock repairmen often scratched repair dates on clock plates.This movement has 16 notations, from 1821 to 1940, including six made by E. Taber. From this record, it is apparent that the clock was cleaned about every seven years prior to museum accession. 57.1.73

Right: Fig.3-10. Shelf Clock, Zacheus Gates, probably, Harvard, Mass., ca. 1810. The use of cherry as a primary wood supports a rural origin for this case. Mahogany was generally used in urban areas as a primary wood on shelf clock cases. 57.1.90

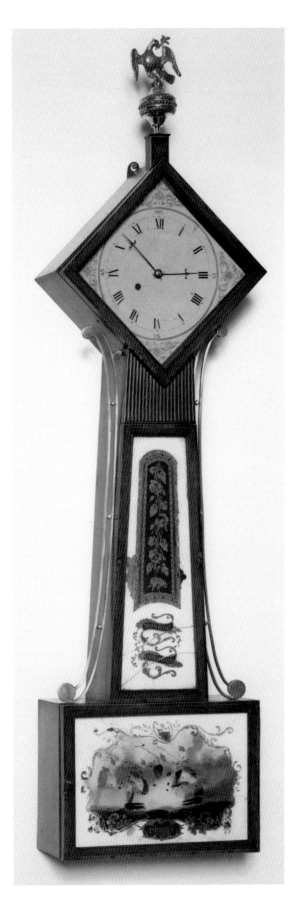

Fig.3-12. Wall Clock, Nathaniel Munroe, Concord, Mass., ca. 1815. The diamond-shaped head with removable hood and longer case evaded Simon Willard's patented design for a wall clock. See pl. 9. 57.1.102

Fig.3-13. Detail, Wall Clock movement, Nathaniel Munroe. The Willard patent was adapted mounting a standard movement upside down on a seat board, suspending the pendulum from the bottom of the plate (requiring added case length), and adding a fall-off strike. Munroe wall clocks are commonly found with broad, barbed hands. 57.1.102

moved to Concord, Massachusetts,[33] where they worked independently, joined forces as "D. Munroe & Company," and then broke up the partnership to do business separately. For a time the Munroes followed the Roxbury pattern—clocks similar to the Willard prototype, division of labor within the family, manufacture in batches, and sales individually or at wholesale—as they competed in the world of Boston clock making.[34] (Fig. 3-11) Emulating the Willards, Nathaniel gave his guarantee on the dial and supplied printed directions in the case. Their "Terms" were set forth in the label.

> By the Dozen, at a reduced price. If for exportation—boxed and delivered at any place within thirty miles of their Manufactory, (if requested,) and warranted well packed, and in good order for transportation....N.B. Orders for any of the above manufacture from any part of the country immediately attended to, and the least favor thankfully accepted.

Concord and Roxbury may have been too close to compete. The partnership was dissolved in 1808 and Nathaniel worked with Samuel Whiting (b. 1778, wkg. 1808-1836) until 1817. About eight journeymen and apprentices worked in their two-story shop, 15' by 30', on Concord's main street beside the mill dam. Across the way was a small brass foundry where Nathaniel cast brass sleigh bells and clock parts.[35] He and Whiting advertised in 1809 that the patent timepiece was in production.[36] Like Jabez Baldwin (1777-1819) of Salem, for whom, as shown, Doggett had made some elaborate clock cases, Munroe altered the case and movement apparently to skirt Willard's patent.[37] Some cases were

made with a diamond-shaped head. (Fig. 3-12) The mechanism was turned upside down with the escapement and pendulum at the bottom. The case was lengthened to accommodate the low suspension of the pendulum.[38] (Fig. 3-13) Inscribed "Munroe Concord," the clock in the OSV collection depicts the Battle of Lake Erie. This event occured some four years after Daniel had ceased doing business in Concord, so this clock is considered the work of Nathaniel.[39]

When Nathaniel moved to Baltimore, where he continued to make and sell clocks until 1840, he left the shop to Whiting.[40] After leaving the family partnership in 1809, Daniel returned to Boston, where he conducted business until retiring in 1858. He continued to offer a variety of clocks in the Willard mold, including patent timepieces priced at all levels.[41] This example was inexpensively cased for a modest budget or use in a shop or office. (Fig. 3-14)

To remain viable, Daniel's business in Boston was broad-based. He was an agent for dials and imported tools, repairer of clocks and watches, and supplier of cast parts for clocks and timepieces from his own brass foundry:

> Clock dials of a superior quality direct from the Manufacturers, for sale by D. Munroe, 51 Newbury St., Boston. Timepieces and watch ditto, clock and timepiece cast work cheaper than ever before offered for sale in Boston....best kind of lacker and watch oil. Best Lancaster cast steel and Sheffield files together with a general assortment of clock and watch tools and materials as can be found....N.B. Clocks, Watches and Jewelry repaired...and warranted.[42]

ANOTHER APPRENTICE WHO selected Concord, Massachusetts as a venue for business was Lemuel Curtis (1790-1857). He advertised a full line of goods at his shop near Munroe and Whiting in 1811.[43] Since three of his aunts had married clock makers in the Willard circle, Aaron Sr., Abel Hutchins, and Elnathan Taber, it is assumed that Curtis was probably trained by one of them. His brothers, Samuel, Jr. (1785-1879), and Benjamin (b. about 1792), also worked in the trade as dial and ornamental painters in Boston.[44] Curtis's Concord shop was described as "thirty feet long and ten or twelve feet wide. In a room on the left side he did repairs and had a small jewelry store. The rest he used with his men and apprentices as a manufactory

Fig. 3-14. Patent Timepiece, Daniel Munroe, Boston, Mass., ca. 1815. Mahogany veneered panels in the waist and lower box provide a more durable, but less decorative alternative to reverse paintings on glass. 57.1.101

*Fig.3-15.
Girandole Clock
movement, Lemuel
Curtis, Concord,
Mass., ca. 1816.
Many Concord
movements have a
pallet cock [top
center of photo,
suspending the
pendulum] similar
to the shape of
those used on tall
clocks and a half
moon cut-out in the
lower right corner
of the keystone (see
fig.3-19). They are
fastened in the case
by one machine
screw which passes
through the
backboard and is
threaded into the
back plate of the
movement. "L.
CURTIS" is
stamped into the
front plate below
the pallet cock. See
pl. 27. 57.1.115*

*Fig.3-16. Plate, Mitchell and Freeman's China and Glass Warehouse.
Staffordshire, Eng., ca. 1827-1835.*

of his timepieces."[45]

The work of Lemuel Curtis, Joseph Nye Dunning, Joseph Dyar (1795-1850), and John Pierce Sawin (1801-1863) is linked by family ties, common training, and doing business in the same towns: Concord, Massachusetts, Burlington, and Middlebury, Vermont. From their shops came various adaptations of Willard's patent timepiece.

Curtis's clocks closely followed the Willards' principles, meshing craftsmanship with standardization and marketing skill, and he learned to innovate, or at least to vary design in an elaborate way. Curtis selected a specialty and hired specialized craftsmen. In 1816, the year that Willard's patent expired, Curtis took Joseph Nye Dunning as a partner and patented his own improved timepiece.[46] Called the "girandole," it is the most elaborate of early 19th-century, New England wall clocks. (Pl. 27) The name is derived from contemporary mirrors with convex glass and candle arms.[47] Its ornamentation capitalizes on the gilt and glitter of contemporary neo-classical looking glasses, a similarity which was was no coincidence. John Doggett, the looking glass and frame maker in Roxbury, made four sizes of girandole mirrors and several kinds of clock cases.[48]

Curtis's patent description probably featured the appearance of the clock, but its specifics are unknown because they were lost in the 1836 Patent Office fire. Its hallmarks are suggested by surviving examples. This patent timepiece looked bigger and better than Simon Willard's original, in which its design is clearly rooted. The components of the head, throat, and base are flanked by brass "side pieces." The movement differs in only minor ways from those made by Willard.[49] (Fig. 3-15) It is stamped "L.CURTIS" below the pallet cock.

Visual highlights of the girandole clock design are the hands of linked circles, a characteristic of Curtis's work, and the beautifully executed reverse painting on glass. The street scene on this example resembles a view of Mitchell and Freeman's China and Glass Warehouse on Chatham Street in Boston, which distributed wares for William Adams & Sons of Stoke-on-Trent between 1828 and 1832.[50] The Staffordshire pottery produced plates with this scene between about 1827 and 1835, postdating the clock by ten or fifteen years (Fig. 3-16) If the reverse painting is the same Boston view, the picture on the clock and the plates was inspired by earlier art work.[51] This elegant clock was made for Daniel Shattuck, a local banker, but there were not enough Shattucks in Concord to support two clock-making firms as Curtis's successor soon discovered.

Remaining at the former Curtis and Dunning shop in Concord, Dyar entered into a brief partnership with John Pierce Sawin, who was Curtis's first cousin. Sawin joined Dyar shortly after he reached the age of 21 and the probable end of his apprenticeship with another cousin, Simon Willard, Jr. (1795-1874). Like Lemuel Curtis they developed the patent timepiece concept and together, Sawin and Dyar reportedly patented the lyre clock. But their partnership was short-lived. Within a year Joseph Dyar had left Concord, moving to Middlebury, in the prosperous Champlain Valley of Vermont, where he advertised a line of clocks and fancy goods.[52] Sawin moved to Boston in partnership with Dyar's younger brother George (1801-1872) between 1823 and 1828. Their lyre clock style (Fig. 3-17) probably described as an "elegant Harp pattern Parlor" clock in Sawin's advertisement in the 1839 Boston Directory,[53] was made by several clock makers during the second quarter of the 19th century.

Between 1818 and 1821, Curtis and Dunning moved to Burlington, Vermont. The firm's reputation for making fine clocks preceded it. In his first year Curtis constructed a gallery clock for the Unitarian Church.[54] Obviously encouraged, Curtis and Dunning pursued their flair for clock designs in Vermont. In 1821 Curtis and Dunning announced that they would manufacture clocks and repair watches. They also offered jewelry, hair work, shell combs, and plated wares for sale.[55] Through the 1820s, the variety of goods sold by the firm ranged from clocks and silverware to military accessories and musical instruments.[56] In this era, the modern jewelry store was born.

The firm did sell expensive clocks in Burlington, although neither the manufacture nor ownership of girandole clocks can be documented in the Green Mountain State. It is likely that they continued to make them for their wealthiest customers and that some of these timepieces are misattributed as Concord work. During the summer of 1827, Curtis and Dunning did advertise eight-day timepieces "with mahogany or gilt cases $23.00 to $35.00 each,"[57] which had their origins in Concord like the lyre clock with alarm attachment. (Fig. 3-18) Containing less costly materials than the girandole clock,

Fig.3-17. Wall Clock, John Sawin, Boston, Mass., ca. 1835. Perhaps the most austere of the 'lyre' clocks, this example has a flat mahogany, lyre-shaped panel and a simple pedestal base. 57.1.36A

Fig.3-18. Wall Clock, Lemuel Curtis and Joseph Nye Dunning, Burlington, Vermont, ca. 1825. This lyre clock has a carved midsection with a reverse painting on glass and a carved pedestal. Without a lower box to gain access to the pendulum, it is regulated by removing the midsection glass and frame. Compare with figs. 3-17 and 4-8. 57.1.86

Fig.3-19. Wall Clock movement, Lemuel Curtis and Joseph Nye Dunning. The alarm mechanism is mounted on the left of the movement, powered by a separate weight, and is wound through the dial at the 10 o'clock position. The half moon cut-out on the lower right corner of the keystone is clearly visible. See fig.3-15. 57.1.86

Curtis and Dunning produced it about the same time as their former journeyman and his new partner were making this design in Boston. The carved mahogany contrasts with the richness of the reverse-painted figures of Time and Justice on the throat piece. The painting may be by Lemuel's brother, Benjamin, who worked in Burlington between 1828 and 1831.[58] The movement is a Willard-like timepiece with an added alarm mechanism. (Fig. 3-19)

In 1830, Curtis and Dunning agreed with Aaron D. Crane of Caldwell, New Jersey, to construct public clocks. Although they never produced any, their diverse interests led to overextension and the break up of the firm in 1832.[59] Curtis sold groceries and dry goods until 1837 when he resumed watch repair. After filing for bankruptcy in 1842, he went to New York City where he died in 1857. Dunning remained in Burlington and continued to make eight-day clocks and to advertise quality clocks with alarm attachments.

> [They] give the alarm at any hour required, a very convenient and desirable article for those who require to be called at a particular hour. Any other kind of brass clocks called for and not on hand will be made to order. All clocks are of the best materials, such as brass and

hardened steel and will be warranted to keep first rate time and without any expense to the purchaser, except that of cleaning for the term of 20 years and as much longer as desired.[60]

Despite or because of their quality these clocks were already out of date. Although Dunning had made his living in the clock-making business, times and fashions had changed as his widow discovered when she consigned the unsold clocks to silversmiths Amos Pangborn and James Edgar Brinsmaid of Burlington. Their advertisement simply noted: "Dunning's large old-fashioned brass clocks for sale quite low."[61]

Clock and watch work separated and were further divided into retail and wholesale businesses as the market for portable time grew after the Revolution. Watches coincided perfectly with Enlightenment fascination with machinery and miniaturization. In the public arena, men sported watches to show that time was valuable to them. Most early clock makers, as a matter of course, advertised themselves as watch makers. Some were trained to repair them, but few exercised truth in advertising. Watch making required special equipment, materials, and production costs low enough to compete with inexpensive products from abroad. Watches with mandatory chains, seals, and keys began to adorn male dress.

Only a small number of domestic watches were sold in Federal New England. The faltering economy of the Embargo period, which forced consumers to 'buy American,' provided a protected opportunity for American craftsmen to make and sell watches.

During the War of 1812, the search for alternatives to making and selling clocks with brass, eight-day movements became necessary. One alternative was to add jewelry and other accessories made of similar metals to the retail shop and so many men moved from manufacture to retail. Others probably stayed awake nights, hoping for some angle or sales pitch in perception or production.

Thomas Harland (1735-1807) of Norwich, Connecticut, is credited with applying his London training to the manufacture of a few watches.[62] When his shop and contents were sold at auction at his death, Luther Goddard (1762-1842) of Shrewsbury, Massachusetts, who had already been making clocks for 25 years, purchased several imported watches as well as a set of watch tools for $10.[63] Goddard was a cousin of Simon and Aaron Willard and was probably trained in Grafton.[64] He

may have already suspected that the Embargo would result in changes within his craft and found a niche in a product that did not interest the Willards.

Returning to Shrewsbury he set up Harland's tools and established "his manufactory of watches" in a "one story, hip-roof building, some 18 or 20 feet square, with a small addition in the rear for a forge room" across the road from his farm.[65] By 1817 Goddard was ready to take on 14-year-old William Keith as an apprentice.

> His outfit for tools, machinery, and material was in keeping with his shop....So, Mr. Goddard had to cast his potence and pillar plates, and the barrel, fusee, and cock and potence; and very good castings they were. The hands, dials, round and dovetail brass and steel wire, the main and hair springs, balances and fusee chains and pinion wire, were all imported material, picked up among importers at War prices. His tools consisted mainly of a tooth-cutting engine, a common foot lathe; brass pivot turns, an upright tool, and sinking, depthing, grooving and hair spring tools; and the usual variety of pliers, tweezer, files and other appliances in use by watch repairers. All of which were English manufacture.[66]

Goddard also trained his sons Daniel (1796-1884) and Parley (b. 1787) here, but their apprenticeships were different from his own. He may have been the first in America to offer training that focused on watches rather than clocks. The boys still learned the old skills, but gilding and engraving were done in nearby Marlborough.[67] Keith records assembly of imported parts with Luther's castings. The final product was not up to the standard of fine European craftsmanship, but it was the equal of watches available during the war. With peace the Goddards' success, like that of so many contemporary entrepreneurs was suspended, and to continue they redefined their business. Luther saw a large market in nearby Worcester and moved there in 1817 with Daniel to expand the line. Parley continued to make watches in Shrewsbury until about 1825 before joining them.[68] (Figs. 3-20, 3-21) The Goddards occupied the house and shop of silversmith Geer Terry (1775-1858).

> Luther Goddard with his son Daniel Goddard have taken and opened the shop opposite Mr. D. Waldo's Brick Store in Worcester [see p. 107], for the purpose of making and repairing

Fig.3-20. Timepiece, Parley Goddard, Shrewsbury, Mass., no. 621, ca.1820-1825. The use of a variety of English imported parts made Goddard's product appear to be a common, imported English watch. 57.19.13

Watches, where they keep many Watches & Eight Day Time Pieces — all warranted good — together with an assortment of Silver & Gold Ware, Chains, Keys, Seals, and Trinkets, for Cash or approved Credit.[69]

Here they continued their business and retailed clocks made by Simon Willard. Luther Goddard is due greater recognition than he has previously received. In his memoirs, Keith, who became president of the American Watch Company in Waltham in 1861, promoted the idea that Goddard (rather than Aaron Dennison, whose business he had bought out in 1857) was the father of American watch making, thereby attempting to place himself in a century-old tradition that stemmed from the Willards of Grafton, Lexington, and Roxbury.

Goddard's watch making business was the result of wartime economics and was eclipsed by more efficient manufacture after the fighting ended. The Goddards' manufacture of over 600 watches in rural Shrewsbury demonstrates Luther's skill as an inventive artisan and a shrewd speculator in the market for timekeeping and jewelry and shows that he was a catalyst in industrializing the new American marketplace. Goddard's removal to Worcester in 1817 to operate a different kind of business shows an insight lacking in most 18th-century craftsmen. Goddard may have been a decade too old to ride the crest of mechanization and marketing, but his vision during the upheaval of embargo and war was as accurate as his watches.

After the War of 1812 the distinction between a tradesman and a merchant blurred. The business of clock making, perfected by the Willards, was eclipsed by its own expense. Clever and elegant clocks designed by the cousinage of clock makers were too costly. Fewer people could afford $60 clocks. Further specialization in the creation of parts or in the sale of a single product was the only course for surviving the transition from craft to business.

Fig. 3-21. Detail, Timepiece, Parley Goddard. Goddard finished a standard fusee movement with a crown wheel and verge escapement, which he adorned with a special balance wheel cock, cast with an American eagle and shield. 57.19.13

NOTES

[1] Fitch, *History of the Fitch Family* 2:209, 213- 267; Westcott, *Life of John Fitch*, 21.

[2] Carl Bridenbaugh, *The Colonial Craftsman* (Chicago: University of Chicago Press, 1950, 1974), 130-134, 138. The traditional term of apprenticeship, based on the English guild system, was seven years, which was not enforced in America.

[3] W.J. Rorabaugh, *The Craft Apprentice: From Franklin to the Machine Age in America* (New York and Oxford: Oxford University Press, 1986), 31-36, 72-77, 97-112.

[4] Charles S. Parsons, *New Hampshire Clocks & Clockmakers* (Exeter: Adams Brown Company, 1976), 344.

[5] Parsons, 170-172, 320; Nathaniel Boutin, *The History of Concord, New Hampshire* (Concord: Benning W. Sanborn, 1856) 603, 670; Samuel Hutchins, *The Autobiography of Levi Hutchins* (Cambridge, Mass.: Riverside Press, 1845) 53-57; Hazel E. Cummin, "A Willard Clock of Unusual Interest," *Antiques* 16(1929):46-7.

[6] *New Hampshire Spy* (Portsmouth), July 3, 1788.

[7] Parsons, 35, 170-2, 186, Husher and Welch 54-56.

[8] *New Hampshire Patriot* (Concord), Nov. 23, 1812, in Parsons, p.276.

[9] *Concord Observer*, January 14, 1819; Boutin, 603.

[10] Although widely published, a recent examination by Robert C. Cheney indicates that the shelf clock engraved "L. Hutchins" in the OSV collection was probably made in the 20th century; Parsons, 25, 173, 186, 212-3, 176; Distin and Bishop, 97, 100, 225, 234. No Hutchins clocks with chime or repeating mechanisms are known.

[11] Parsons, 120-1.

[12] Theodore Parker, *Genealogy and Biographical Notes of John Parker of Lexington* (Worcester: Press of Charles Hamilton, 1893), 98-100, 180-181.

[13] Parker, 181.

[14] Parker, 330; Boston Clock Club, 60; Letter, Dr. Charles Reed, Westborough, undated transcription on file in the Research and Collections Department, OSV.

[15] Parker also made shelf clocks. See Distin and Bishop, 99.

[16] Heman P. DeForest and Edward C. Bates, *History of Westborough, Massachusetts* (Westborough, 1891), 209.

[17] *Ibid.*, 355; *The Diary of Rev. Ebenezer Parkman of Westborough, Massachusetts*, ed., Harriet M. Forbes (Worcester: Westborough Historical Society, 1899) 286 fn.

[18] Benjamin and William R. Cutter, *History of the Town of Arlington, Massachusetts* (Boston: David Clapp and Son, 1880) 126 fn. The Westborough tower clock was in the possession of Dr. Charles Reed in the early 20th century.

[19] He committed suicide; Reed letter.

[20] George L. Randall, *Taber Genealogy: Descendants of Thomas, Son of Philip Taber* (New Bedford, Mass.: Vining Press, 1924), 33-34, 76-7; John Ware Willard, 106-7. Elnathan Taber settled in Roxbury and married Catherine Partridge in 1797.

[21] Parsons cites Benjamin Chase, *History of Chester, N.H.* (Auburn, N.H.:1869) as the source for a "Cummings, who was an apprentice to the Willards" hired by Timothy Chandler to "set up clock making in Concord." However, Parsons notes, "no other similar reference can be found or in Simon Willard and his Clocks," 291. Cummens's Roxbury shop was at the corner of Winslow and Taber Streets, named for Elnathan Taber.

[22] Willard, 110-112.

[23] Willard-type patent timepieces by Elnathan Taber are illustrated in *American Antiques in the Israel Sack Collection*, 8 vols. (Washington D.C.: Highland House Publishers Inc., 1980-1989) 1:124, 258; 4:947; 5:1330-1331; 6:1574. A shelf clock is illustrated in 1:236. Patent timepieces by Cummens are owned by the Yale University Art Gallery and the Museum of Fine Arts, Boston. See Edwin A. Battison and Patricia E. Kane, *The American Clock: 1725-1865* (Greenwich, Conn.: New York Graphic Society, 1973), 198-199; Richard H. Randall, Jr., *American Furniture in the Museum of Fine Arts Boston* (Boston: Museum of Fine Arts, 1965), 252.

[24] Randall, 34, 77-78.

[25] *The Medley or Newbedford Marine Journal*, October 14, 1799.

[26] A tall clock by Stephen Taber is pictured in the Christie's auction catalog, sale 7294, June 25, 1991, lot 155; Brooks Palmer, *Book of American Clocks* (New York: Macmillan, 1974), 85.

[27] Other New Bedford clock makers were William (b. 1731) and Josiah Wood (1774-1849) and Alanson Gooding (b. 1789). Nathaniel Shephard and Ezra Kelley were in partnership at Dartmouth about 1810 and a clock by them is owned by the Yale Art Gallery. See Elton W. Hall, "New Bedford Furniture," *Antiques* 113(May 1978):1105-1127.

[28] Ricketson's clock is illustrated by Hall, 1107; "Old Clocks," *New Bedford Evening Standard*, January 23, 1885.

[29] Charles Otis Gates, *Stephen Gates of Hingham and Lancaster, Massachusetts and His Descendants* (N.Y.: Willis McDonald and Co., 1898), 56; Jeannine Falino, "Zacheus Gates (1770-1831) Massachusetts Clockmaker," (unpub. ms, 1989), 3-5, 10-16; Joseph Willard, Charles W. Walker, and Charles H. Pope, *Willard Genealogy: Sequel to the Willard Memoir* (Cambridge Mass.: Murray and Emery Co., 1915) 123, 140. Gates was born in Harvard, Mass. Catherine Gates Willard, who died in 1785, was the mother of Aaron Willard, Jr. (1783-1864) and Nancy Willard (b. 1785), who married Spencer Nolen. The second husband of Mary Gates, sister of Zacheus, was Joel Willard, a third cousin of the clock makers.

[30] Laurence L. Barber, "Massachusetts Shelf Clocks," *Antiques* 32(July 1937): 20-21. For patent timepieces by Gates, see Palmer, fig 1148;

[31] Falino, 25-26; Worcester County Registry of Deeds, Worcester, Mass., 154:132, 133; 162:211; 164:291, 292; 173:470; 175:194; 176:87; 189: 122; Middlesex County Registry of Deeds, E. Cambridge, Mass., 193:125; 186: 512.

[32] Letter, Simon Willard for Daniel Munroe, Jr., July 13, 1796, quoted in Bailey, *Two Hundred Years*, 27. The surname was spelled as both Munroe or Monroe during the early 19th century.

[33] Richard S. Munroe, *History and Genealogy of the Lexington, Massachusetts Munroes* (Holyoke, Mass.: Mansir Press, 1966), 61, 103-106; Edwin B. Burt, Sr. and Fraser R. Forgie, "Clockmakers of the Concord, Massachusetts Community," *NAWCC Bulletin* Supplement 1967 1-2, 9-14. Daniel, Jr. married Sarah Dakin of Lincoln, Mass., in 1804.

[34] For clocks by Nathaniel Munroe, see *Sack Collection*, 1:2, 5:1234; 6:1465. His clocks are owned by the Museum of Art, Carnegie Institute, Pittsburgh; The Maryland Historical Society (inscribed N. Munroe, Baltimore); and Yale University Art Gallery.

[35] Burt and Forgie, 15-27.

[36] *Ibid.*, 11, 32-33. For a patent clock inscribed by Munroe and Whiting, see *Sack Collection*, 2:306.

[37] Battison and Kane, 194-197.

[38] Philip Zea, "Clockmaking and Society at the River and the Bay: Jedidiah and Jabez Baldwin, 1790-1820, *1981 Annual Proceedings, The Dublin Seminar for New England Folklife* (Boston: Boston University Press, 1982), 53-59. The inversion of the Willard plan for a patent timepiece freed the clutch wire and the pendulum from conflicting with the time wheels on the front of the movement. On the negative side, the weight in Munroe's timepiece interfered with the unprotected escapement at the bottom of the mechanism if the clock were wound too tightly. Munroe also circumvented the patent by securing the movement to a seatboard, which was wedged into the lower vertex of the diamond head. Willard screwed the mechanism to the backboard. The square dial was mounted on the movement with dial

feet while Willard mounted the dials of his "Improved timepieces" on the front edge of the round heads. Munroe's clock rings once on the hour while Willard's, in the strict definition of a timepiece, is mute.

[39] Both brothers apparently used this clock design. For a patent timepiece with a diamond head inscribed "DANIEL/MUNROE.", see *Sack Collection* 5:1381.

[40] Monroe, 104. After a brief turn as a clock maker, their brother William (1778-1861) became a cabinetmaker. He probably made clock cases until about 1812 and then entered the pencil business, manufacturing 1212 gross valued at $5946 in 1814. A fourth brother, John, was a clock maker and retailer in Barnstable, Mass.

[41] Burt and Forgie, 9. Daniel Munroe was briefly in partnership with Ezekiel Jones (wkg 1813-1825), another Willard apprentice, after his return to Boston.

[42] Advertisement, *Columbian Centinel,* quoted in Boston Clock Club, 106.

[43] *Columbian Centinel*, November 2, 1811.

[44] Samuel C. Clarke, *Records of Some of the Descendants of William Curtis* (Boston: David Clapp & Son, 1869), 6.

[45] Edward Jarvis, *Houses and People of Concord*

[46] Burt and Forgie, 28-29.

[47] The French term "girandole" relating to mirrors is defined by the presence of candle arms rather than of convex glass.

[48] Day Book, John Doggett, Roxbury, 1802-1809, Winterthur Museum.

[49] Walter H. Durfee, "Clocks of Lemuel Curtis," *Antiques* 4, no. 6(December 1923): 281-285; *Sack Collection* 2:539.

[50] A.W. Coysh and R.K. Henrywood, *The Dictionary of Blue and White Printed Pottery, 1780-1880* (Woodbridge, Suffolk, U.K.: Baron Publishing, 1982), 16, 249.

[51] Carol Damon Andrews, "John Ritto Penniman (1782-1841), An Ingenious New England Artist," *Antiques* 120, no 1 (July 1981): 147-170.

[52] *National Standard* [Middlebury], November 12, 1822; Carlisle, 126.

[53] Sawin advertised in the *Boston City Directory* for 1839. He remained in Boston and was in business with George W. Dyar (1801-1871), Joseph's younger brother, between 1823 and 1828. The lyre clock patent is reported with reference by Carlisle, 126.

[54] The Shelburne Museum owns the movement of this clock. Its built-in case survives in the Unitarian Church at the corner of Pearl and Church Streets, Burlington.

[55] *Northern Sentinel* [Burlington], June 1, 1821.

[56] Carlisle, 107-9.

[57] *Free Press* (Burlington), July and August, 1827.

[58] Carlisle, 107. Benjamin Curtis later moved to New York City and Philadelphia.

[59] Carlisle, 109,

[60] *Free Press*, December 14, 1832.

[61] *Free Press*, August 26, 1842.

[62] Few watches made in America before 1840 have survived. An example by Thomas Harland of Norwich, Conn.,., ca. 1800, is in the collection of the Winterthur Museum. Other American clock and watch makers, like Effingham Embree of New York City, may have made a few watches, but they are also known to have imported them and added their names.

[63] Inventory, Thomas Harland, Norwich, Conn.., 1807, Docket 4863. Connecticut State Library; Chris H. Bailey, "Thomas Harland of Norwich: Forerunner of the Clock Manufacturing Industry," *Connecticut Historical Society Bulletin* 51(Fall 1986): 226-249. A tall clock by Luther Goddard is pictured in the Christie's, auction catalogue, sale 7146, October 19, 1990, lot 330. Another example is owned by a public library in Worcester County.

[64] Maust, 1:14-15; William Austin Goddard, *A Genealogy of the Descendants of Edward Goddard* (Worcester: Spooner, 1833,) 20; Letter, Chris H. Bailey to Robert C. Cheney, Bristol, Conn, January 20, 1992. Luther was the son of Daniel and Mary Willard Goddard and the second cousin of clock maker and founder Nichols Goddard.

[65] Watches made after 1808 are signed "L. Goddard," During the war, when Parley became a partner the watches were inscribed "L. Goddard & Son."

[66] William H. Keith, "A Family Tale," (ms., Waltham Watch Company, Waltham, Mass., 1883); Percy L. Small, "Luther Goddard and His Watches, Part Two and Part Three," *NAWCC Bulletin* 6 no. 2(February 1954) and 6 no.3(April 1954): 105-108, 126, 181-187.

[67] Keith, 106.

[68] Keith, 107. In Shrewsbury Parley continued his father's numbering sequence, beginning between No. 525 and No. 530. The example illustrated here is the Goddard watch 621 and among the last made there during the early 1820s, where Parley apparently made at least 90 watches on his own. In 1828 and 1830, Luther moved briefly to Preston and then to Norwich, Conn. Daniel Goddard continued the business in Worcester with his sons: Luther D. and Charles A., who in turn each developed their own firms with dozens of employees. Their businesses were eventually eclipsed by the machine-made watches constructed by the Pitkin family in Hartford and later New York and by Aaron Dennison (1812-1895) and what became the Boston Watch Company in 1853.

[69] *Worcester National Aegis*, July 16, 1817

COLOR PLATES

*Pl.1. Tall Clock,
movement by
Thomas Claggett,
case by Benjamin
Baker, both of
Newport, R.I.,
1772, 57.1.92.
OSV photograph,
Henry E. Peach.*

*Pl.2. Tall Clock,
Caleb Wheaton,
Providence, R.I.,
ca. 1790,
57.1.107. OSV
photograph,
Henry E. Peach.*

Pl.3. Composite brass dial, tall clock, Gawen Brown, Boston, Mass., ca. 1760-1770, 57.1.132. OSV photograph, Thomas Neill.

Pl. 4. Composite brass dial, tall clock, Daniel Balch, Bradford or Newbury, Mass., ca. 1760, 57.1.226. OSV photograph, Thomas Neill.

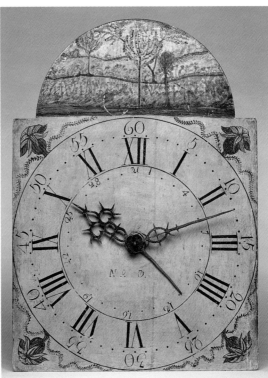

Pl.5. Painted iron dial, tall clock, Aaron Willard, Boston, Mass. ca. 1810, 57.1.74. OSV photograph, Thomas Neill.

Pl.6. Painted pine dial, tall clock, maker unknown, prob. northern Mass., ca. 1803, 57.1.147. See Pl. 15 OSV photograph, Thomas Neill.

Pl. 7. Silvered sheet brass dial, shelf clock, Simon Willard, Roxbury, Mass., ca. 1785, 57.1.120. OSV photograph, Thomas Neill.

Pl. 8. Painted iron dial, shelf clock, Stephen Taber, New Bedford, Mass., ca. 1805, 57.1.46. OSV photograph, Henry E. Peach.

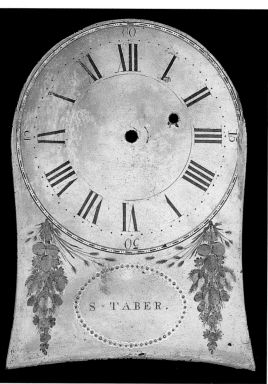

Pl. 9. Painted iron dial, wall clock, Nathaniel Munroe, Concord, Mass., ca. 1815, 57.1.102. OSV photograph, Henry E. Peach.

Pl. 10. Portrait of Simon Willard, Gilbert Stuart, pastel, ca. 1807, 20.9.30. OSV photograph, Henry E. Peach.

Pl. 11. Tall Clock, Simon Willard, 1801, 57.1.144. OSV photograph, Henry E. Peach.

*Pl. 12.
Wheel-cutting
engines used and
probably made by
(l.) Joshua
Wilder, Hingham,
Mass., early
19th-century,
57.12.3 and (r.)
John Avery,
Preston, Conn.,
ca. 1770,
57.12.4. OSV
photograph,
Henry E. Peach*

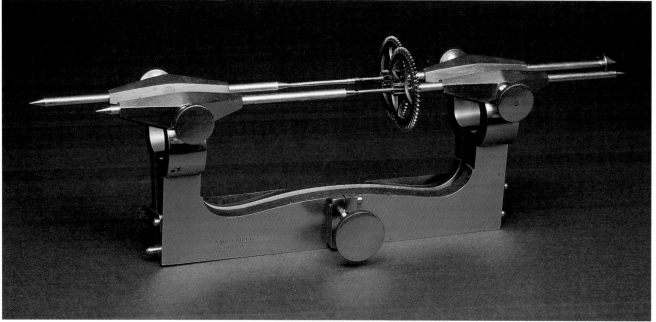

*Pl. 13. Depthing Tool (Compas Pouces), Switzerland, used by Aaron Willard, Jr.,
Boston, early 19th-century, 57.2.23. OSV photograph, Thomas Neill.*

Pl. 14. Brass movement, tall clock, Simon Willard, Roxbury, Mass., ca. 1800, 57.1.131. OSV photograph, Thomas Neill. (See front and back covers.)

Pl. 15. Wooden movement, tall clock, maker unknown, prob. northern Mass., ca. 1803, 57.1.147. See Pl. 6. OSV photograph, Henry E. Peach.

Pl. 16. Silvered sheet brass dial, wall clock, Simon Willard, Grafton, Mass., ca. 1770, 57.1.122. OSV photograph, Thomas Neill.

Pl. 17. Painted iron dial, patent timepiece, Simon Willard, Roxbury, Mass., ca. 1805, 57.1.8. OSV photograph, Henry E. Peach.

At left: Pl. 18.
Tall Clock,
Gardner Parker,
Westborough,
Mass., ca. 1810,
57.1.23. OSV
photograph,
Henry E. Peach.

Pl. 19.
Tall Clock,
Zacheus Gates,
Charlestown,
Mass.,
ca. 1815,
57.1.93. OSV
photograph,
Henry E. Peach.

Pl. 20.
Shelf Clock,
David Wood,
Newburyport,
Mass., ca. 1790,
57.1.58. OSV
photograph,
Henry E. Peach.

Pl. 21. Dwarf Clock, Peter Hawkes
Cushing, Braintree, Mass., ca. 1825,
57.1.25. OSV photograph, Henry E.
Peach.

*At left: Pl. 22.
Tall Clock, attr.
William
Leavenworth and
Son, Albany, N.Y.,
ca. 1815-1829,
case decorated
by Rufus Cole,
Broadalbin, NY,
ca. 1830,
57.1.130.
OSV photograph,
Henry E. Peach.*

*Pl. 23. Tall Clock,
Silas Hoadley,
Plymouth, Conn.,
ca. 1820,
57.1.195. OSV
photograph, Henry
E. Peach.*

Pl. 24. Painted birch dial, tall clock, John Edwards, Ashby, Mass., ca.1825, 57.1.225. OSV photograph, Henry E. Peach.

Pl. 25. Composite brass dial, tall clock, Jonas Fitch, Pepperell, Mass., ca. 1765, 57.1.237. OSV photograph, Henry E. Peach.

At right: Pl. 26. Composite dial on tin, tall clock, A. & C. Edwards, Ashby, Mass., ca. 1793-4, 57.1.229. OSV photograph, Henry E. Peach.

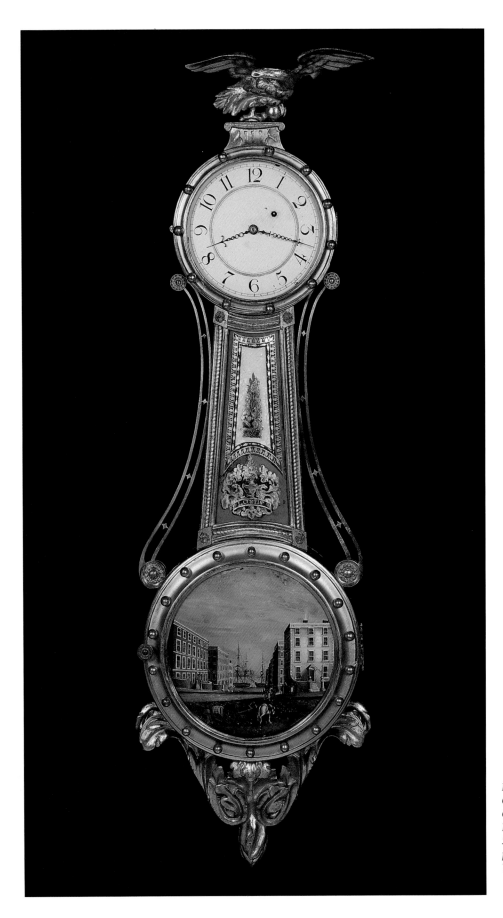

Pl. 27. Girandole Clock, Lemuel Curtis, Concord, Mass., ca. 1816, 57.1.115. OSV photograph, Thomas Neill.

Pl. 28. Shelf Clock, Lucius B. Bradley and James Bishop, Watertown, Conn., ca. 1824-1832, 57.1.47. OSV photograph, Thomas Neill.

*Pl. 29.
Gallery Clock,
attr. Simon
Willard, Roxbury,
Mass., ca.1810,
57.1.78. Shown in
the Meetinghouse,
Old Sturbridge
Village. OSV
photograph,
Robert S. Arnold.*

Pl. 30. Regulator, attr. Simon Willard, Roxbury, Mass., ca.1832, 57.1.87. Shown in the Bank, Old Sturbridge Village. OSV photograph, Robert S. Arnold.

Pl. 31. Exterior of Meetinghouse at OSV with mid 19th century tower clock, E. Howard, Boston. OSV photograph, Thomas Neill.

IT IS APPARENT from the clocks of the 1780-1820 period in the OSV collection that while their makers practiced their trade all around New England, those working outside of Boston had to face a series of economic realities. One was the pace set by the Willard family in defining desirable clocks. Another was the need for quality materials with which to make clocks. These affected the common features of the clocks being made at that time; the ways in which the different clock makers met the challenges distinguishes the clocks in this chapter.

The numerous clocks by David Wood (1766-ca.1824) of Newburyport affirm his craftsmanship, indicate the breadth of his patronage, and suggest the Willard inspiration in his designs for tall clocks, shelf clocks, and patent timepieces. (It is to some extent a bias of the collection and J. Cheney Wells's personal interests that many of the clocks of the 1780-1820 period in the Old Sturbridge Village collection have a "Willard look.") Wood's clocks suggest by their style and place of manufacture that he may have trained with Daniel Balch, Sr. towards the end of his working life. If so, it may have been in 1783, when Balch made the shelf clock dial and movement, which closely relates to Wood's work (Pl. 20).[1] (Fig. 4-1) Wood's designs for tall clocks, shelf clocks, and patent timepieces were nonetheless inspired by the Willards.[2] Three shelf clocks show Wood's gradual trend towards popular Willard prototypes and the ultimate patronage of an actual Willard supplier. The movements vary in the shape of the pillar posts and hammer, the pallets, the collets used to fix the wheels on the arbors, and the quality of the wheel cutting. Although the clocks may show Wood's personal development over time, it is just as likely that journeymen may have worked on the movements.

At the beginning of his career Wood made a clock (Pl. 20) which has an experimental two-day striking movement patterned after an eight-day mechanism and is neatly fitted into a shallow case. The skilled craftsman who made its two-tiered cabinet, applied principles of architecture in the scrolled pediment, Baroque moldings, and applied pilasters. The inner

AS NEAT
AS AT
ROXBURY
Clock Making
in Federal
New England

pair of pilasters in the base are tapered and support a segmental arch with a keystone. The entasis or slight swelling of the outer pair of pilasters eliminates the optical illusion of narrowness.[3]

A shelf clock dating from around 1800 resembles the Willards' work. The small enamel dial and pierced hands highlight the mahogany case fitted with engaged quarter columns and carrying handles. Within a decade of their introduction the decorative accents of the "Roxbury" cases of the Willards were brilliantly reduced to a hood and base with no waist by an unknown cabinetmaker for Wood. (Fig. 4-2)

At the end of the century, Wood purchased a painted dial from Spencer Nolen of Roxbury to insert in a case which conformed to the growing fashion, especially north of Boston, for furniture of highly contrasting woods.[4] (Figs. 4-3, 4-4) The stylish fretwork could be produced quickly, and the dial is decorated with less flourish than the previous example. On the back in a free-hand spiral are the words "PAINTED. BY. SPENCER. NOLEN. CLOCK. FACE. PAINTER." Nolen was Aaron Willard's son-in-law, who became the clock dial and sign painting partner of Aaron, Jr. in 1805.[5] A year later, Wood advertised Willard timepieces as well as his own for sale.[6]

As the population of the Yankee hinterland grew after the Revolution,[7] so did the number of clock makers practicing their craft along the coast and in the countryside. Informed consumers lived in population centers like state capitals, county seats, near new academies and colleges, and at the crossroads of turnpikes and river valleys. To them the clock maker offered the symbol of an age: a beautiful machine that measured productivity through passing time and whose ownership connoted prosperity and pride.

Concord, New Hampshire and Montpelier, Vermont, although small in comparison to the larger state capitals and commercial cities of southern and coastal New England each had a clock making tradition.[8] Concord was home base for several clock makers,[9] who supplied their customers with clocks and the related services that could make a business

Fig. 4-3. Shelf Clock, David Wood, Newburyport, Mass., ca. 1810. 57.1.50

neymen.[11] He was 30 years old when he advertised in 1791:

> Timothy Chandler Desires to inform the publick, that he hath for sale...warranted eight day Clocks, with enamelled, moon, or plain faces—time Pieces of various kinds—Wool cards...Clocks and Watches cleaned and repaired—and all kinds of Gold and Silver Smith work, done with regular dispatch.[12]

His offerings reflected his own training and that of his journeyman William Cummens, a former apprentice of Simon Willard. (see Fig. 3-4) The variety of their workmanship is reflected in

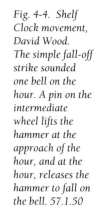

Fig. 4-4. Shelf Clock movement, David Wood. The simple fall-off strike sounded one bell on the hour. A pin on the intermediate wheel lifts the hammer at the approach of the hour, and at the hour, releases the hammer to fall on the bell. 57.1.50

successful. Timothy Chandler (1762-1848) first served an apprenticeship with the woolen-card manufacturer Jonathan Hale of Concord, who moved to Pomfret, Connecticut, in 1781, taking Chandler with him. Chandler learned clock making there, probably with Peregrin White (1747-1834) of Woodstock, since he named two of his sons after the clock maker, Peregrine White (1788-1792) and Peregrine Hale White (1793-1828).[10] Chandler returned to Concord where he built a successful business by coordinating the work of several jour-

Fig.4-5. Tall Clock seat board, Timothy Chandler. 57.1.232

Fig.4-6. Tall Clock, Timothy Chandler, Concord, N.H., circa, 1810. The yellow birch case survives with its original dark stain to simulate mahogany. 57.1.232

Fig.4-7. Detail, Tall Clock movement, Timothy Chandler. Many New Hampshire movements had cutouts on the plates to save costly brass. The clock maker saved time by finishing only the front side of the pulleys and left the back as an unfinished casting. 57.1.232

Chandler's clocks. The seat boards are sometimes stamped "T. Chandler" as if production deadlines demanded speed and inspection for quality. (Fig. 4-5) The tall clock made about 1810 (Figs. 4-6, 4-7) shows the standard Chandler product at a point when he had become a well-established businessman.[13] In 1809 his wealth was estimated at $5000 following a disastrous fire, which destroyed his house and work place. He rebuilt and confidently matched his skill against Simon Willard's in a lengthy 1815 advertisement:

> He [Chandler] has been at great pains to make a Time Piece, which he would recommend to the public: this he thinks superior to any that has been invented, not even excepting Willard's celebrated Patent: this gentleman lays the emphasis of his eulogium of his Time Piece on a long pendulum — mine is longer. It is likewise very portable — the case being less than three feet in length, and not one foot wide....Also, KITCHEN TIME PIECE which he would recommend. It may be set up by an ingenious domestic, this would save the mistres of the house from many a hearty scold to the poor maid for too long boiling the eggs.[14]

Chandler had three sons whom he trained and each joined him for a while in the family business. Timothy Jay (1798-after 1848) was briefly in part-

nership with his father until 1820 and is known to have made silver spoons marked "TJC". An 1848 inventory listed clock and watch making tools. John Bradley (1805-1864) also worked with his father and in 1830 advertised the manufacture of "Philosophical and Chemical Apparatus for Academies, lyceums and physicians."[15] Abiel (1807-1881) is best known for shelf and wall clocks. After entering into partnership with his father in 1829, Abiel went to Boston for six months to learn how to make Willard timepieces. Back in Concord, the Chandler factory produced shelf clocks with reverse-painted tablets, a few patent timepieces, and lyre clocks. (Fig. 4-8) Chandler used fashionable veneers on the lyre model instead of expensive painted glass tablets. While work in the popular and fashionable Willard tradition characterized the emphasis of this shop, Abiel also stocked and sold New Hampshire mirror clocks made with the optional "rat-trap" striking mechanism.[16]

A FEATURE OF DOING BUSINESS IN THE MORE REMOTE countryside was that the clock maker, like his agricultural neighbors, had to march to agricultural rhythms. Country pay (produce and farm work) often had to be taken in exchange. While it might have fed the craftsman's household, it did not provide cash for the clock maker to buy the costly cast metal or imported parts and may have affected the kinds of clocks that were made for sale. Even the eldest of the clock making Willard brothers, Benjamin, ended his New England career as a farming clock maker in Grafton, and he had to barter in cows and clocks with his creditors. Paying a debt in 1798, he wrote:

> Sir We are in want of the Cow....I send by my son a watch wh I expect Worth 20 dollars ... untill the matter is Settled. if the watch dont answer I have nother watch I can spare or Clock Work on hand nig[h]ly finished wh as I sale [sell] them [,] amount to 400 Dollars which I expect by the time the note must be paid.[17]

Like the Willards, the Bailey brothers of Hanover, Massachusetts, and environs had a variety of skills and expertise, extending beyond the rote production of clocks to a variety of mechanical devices, some of their own invention. Calvin (1761-1835), evidently fascinated by the celestial clock overhead, made an orrery to be used by school students. The Bailey family made sophisticated clocks in each of

Fig.4-8. Lyre Clock, attributed to Abiel Chandler, Concord, N.H., ca. 1835. Dark mahogany and carving were common features on furniture during the Empire period and clock cases followed the current taste. 57.1.91

the current popular forms. Had they taken advantage of the ways in which the Willards varied and maximized their production, they might have become as famous.

Calvin Bailey and his brothers, John (1751-1823) and Lebbeus (1763-1827), were all clock makers.[18] They followed their father John (1730-1810), who made wooden and brass clocks (see Figs. 1-15, 1-16, 1-17) in the 18th century. Calvin's account book shows how a clock maker did business in the barter economy outside of Boston. The seasonal cycle, dominated by agriculture, regulated his transactions with his neighbors. Making and selling clocks and doing other whitesmith's work which contributed to the support of his household had to fit into the farmer's year. For example, Calvin debited his neighbor Charles Turner in 1803 to silver teaspoons and mending a coffee pot, gun lock, and locket. In return, Turner bartered iron, brass, and an old silver dollar. Some of this metal ware landed in Bailey's crucible to emerge as a new product. The rest was bartered again, perhaps to someone like blacksmith Joshua Simmons, who took old iron of the sort obtained from Turner. Calvin also mowed Joshua's salt meadow. Over the years, Bailey mended Simmons's clock, as well as a teapot, pewter plates, spectacles, and gun lock for him. Simmons called on Bailey's specialized skills—although he might have done some of this work himself—and in exchange shod oxen and horses and did heavy work at the forge.[19]

When his brother John built a shop in 1786, Calvin helped, and recorded the time in his account book. John was then able to help Calvin by cleaning his watch, making eight-day clocks, silvering a dial, and providing files, oil, brass work, parts, and dozens of weights. Early in his career John also made surveying instruments. He patented Bailey's Steam Jack for roasting meat in 1792 and also invented the machinery for rotating lighthouse fixtures, later improved by Benjamin Franklin Willard (1803-1847).

Calvin's accounts reveal the names of the cabinetmakers who provided the cases for the alarm, eight-day, and moon clocks which Calvin was making between 1784 and 1814. Abial White, Ellis Dammon, Abner Harvey, and Theodore Cushing traded clock cases for lumber or an occasional clock movement to retail. Calvin boarded and later employed John's one-time journeyman, Adam Stetson. Another jour-

neyman, David Studley, (b. 1783) appears in the ledger between 1806 and 1809 and provided weight cases, sets of catguts (cords to suspend the weights), and clock bells, as well as working on clocks in the shop. Clock weights were carted from the Easton foundry. The merchant Jotham Jacobs was Calvin's link to a broader commercial world. Between 1800 and 1815, he traded clocks, watches and lumber for woodworking tools and household goods: japanned tinware, penknives, buttons, yard goods, leather, candles, chocolate, sugar, and tea.[20]

On the other side of the ledger are the names of clock customers. One was Nathaniel Howe of Abington, who paid Bailey $60 in 1805 for a clock with his name inscribed on the dial.[21] (Fig. 4-9) For that price, Howe received a well-made movement, a case of imported mahogany, and a locally painted dial showing a rocking ship flying the American flag. In sum, it looks as if it were made in Roxbury and not in a rural shop where good clocks were built during the cold months.

Other kinds of clocks made by the Baileys included shelf models which, like Willard examples, had fewer parts and materials than costly tall clocks. John made a clock cased in inexpensive native pine stained like mahogany about 1815, late in his career. (Fig. 4-10) A lunette design scratched into the base imitates inlay. The clock has a fashionable kidney-shaped enamel dial and a simple timepiece with a fall-off strike.[22]

Clocks made by Joshua Wilder of Hingham (1786-1860), not only bear some resemblance to the Baileys' work, but are of special interest because his wheel-cutting engine is also part of the OSV collection. (Pl. 12) Near the end of his life, he sold to his son, Ezra, also a clock maker, all the metal and woodworking tools in his shop, including "my time piece Regulator...and all partially manufactured clock work...and also every tool or article now [used] in making or the repairing of watches" for the nominal sum of $5.[23] Clocks by Wilder and other South Shore clock makers filled a niche undeveloped by the Willards: clocks that act bigger than they are. These clocks reveal some similarities to each other, while reflecting Willard influence on cases and movements.[24]

A shelf clock made by Wilder resembles Bailey's and suggests that he might have trained with him or his brother. (Like them, Wilder was a Quaker.)[25] Made in 1813, this clock (Figs. 4-11, 4-12, 4-13) has

Fig.4-9. Tall Clock, Calvin Bailey, Hanover, Mass., 1805. Despite the Roxbury "look" of this case, the use of a 13" dial in a short clock created heavy proportions. The low French feet are also awkward. 57.1.11

Fig.4-10. Shelf Clock, John Bailey, Jr., Hanover, Mass., ca. 1815. The loss of finial plinths, finials and fret are common damage on shelf and tall clocks. 57.1.124

the sarcophagus hood design originated by the Willards in the late 1780s, and was purchased by a shoemaker for $24.[26] Its brass hand to set the alarm suggests complexity and expense, as does the alarm mechanism powered by a separate weight. Wilder also made a Willard-like tall clock in miniature with arched hood, fretwork, waist door, quarter columns, and French feet about seven years later.[27] (Fig. 4-14)

Reuben Tower (1795-1821) probably apprenticed with Wilder. He was 21 years old when he completed and inscribed a shelf clock: "This clock was made by Reuben Tower of Hingham for Isaac

Fig.4-11. Shelf Clock, Joshua Wilder, Hingham, Mass., 1813. The original bill of sale pasted inside the hood reads: "Hingham, 12th mo, 4th, 1813/ David Sprague bought of Joshua Wilder/one eight day, brass alarm timepiece, $24./ 6th mo, 9th, 1814 received payment in full of all demands./Joshua Wilder". 57.1.45

Fig.4-12. Shelf Clock, Joshua Wilder. Back view of the dial signed in paint: "Joshua Wilder, Hingham". Names on the backs of dials were probably done by the dial painter when the job was commissioned to remind him which clock maker's signature to paint on the front. 57.1.45

Wilder in 1816."[28] A second short clock was constructed in the same year, and he inscribed the tympanum of its dial "REUBEN TOWER. HINGHAM. 1816."[29] Its movement incorporates a lunar dial, sweep second hand, and day-of-the-month and day-of-the-week hands, demonstrating his skill and versatility. Following his apprenticeship, Tower may have worked as a journeyman in Hanover between 1816 and 1818, (Figs. 4-15, 4-16 and 4-17) in Kingston and in Plymouth (1819) before returning to Hingham, where he may have been associated with Wilder, whose son Ezra married Reuben's daughter.[30]

A contemporary of Tower's, Peter Hawkes Cushing (1799-1889) of Braintree and Weymouth was probably trained by one of the same South Shore makers. A dwarf clock by Cushing offers the proportions of the tall case version and conceals a competently made eight-day movement with alarm and fall-off strike. The clock contains a second weight for the alarm which is set by the third hand on the dial. (pl. 21)

Politics, competition, and the growing demand for the luxury goods that a skilled clock maker could sell and repair were factors influencing where craftsmen would settle. Many were drawn to the market towns of rural New England in search of commissions. Thomas Harland's (1735-1807) decision to leave the unrest and tension of Boston for Norwich, Connecticut's leading port in 1773, allowed him to establish a clock making tradition separate from the Willards. Like them, he trained many of the able craftsmen who made clocks in the early republic; unlike them, he resisted the tide of change. His arrival in Norwich must have delighted area residents with the prospect of furnishing their

Fig.4-13. Shelf Clock movement, Joshua Wilder. A fall-off strike and an alarm mechanism mounted between the plates added complexity to the otherwise simple timepiece. 57.1.45

Fig.4-14. Dwarf Clock, Joshua Wilder, Hingham, Mass., ca. 1820. Dwarf clock cases came in two different hood styles: the fret top hood illustrated here and a sarcophagus top. Hoods were either removable or a full length door was hinged on the backboard to gain access to the weights and pendulum. The third hand on the dial is to set the alarm. 57.1.36

parlors with clocks that rivalled those of Boston and Newport.

Harland immediately advertised his clocks, instruments, silver, and engraving skills. Like Bagnall and Brown had done in Boston earlier in the century, this watch and clock maker capitalized on his English training.

Spring, musical and plain clocks; church clocks; regulators, &c. he also cleans and repairs watches and clocks with the greatest care....NB Clock faces engraved and finished for the trade. Watch wheels and fuzees of all sorts...cut and finished on the shortest notice, neat as in London, and at the same price.[31]

Harland was a retailer and wholesaler and by the 1790s he was employing a dozen journeymen and apprentices. They made about 25 eight-day clocks per year at approximately $60 each as well as silver flatware, surveying instruments, and watches. When the shop burned in 1795, the press reported "the loss at a low valuation is computed at 1,500 dollars!"[32] His 1807 obituary notes that he "is said to have made the first watch ever manufactured in America."[33] Although American-made watches are rare before 1840, at least two known examples are signed "T. Harland."

Although Harland did not make his clocks with

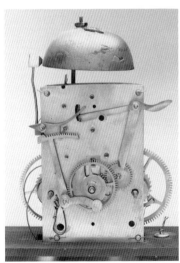

interchangeable parts, the roots of the industrialization of Connecticut clock making are found in his consistent methods. His mechanical skill and work with expensive materials brought him a wide reputation and promising apprentices. Harland taught as he must have learned—by rote rather than by theory and comparative analysis. The training was so systematic that the products of even second-generation apprentices are consistent in technique and decoration with Harland's own work.[34] His trainees practiced standardization in their own workshops and spread their master's methods through the market towns of Connecticut, western New England, and upstate New York.

The 1779 memorandum book of Daniel Burnap (1759-1838) of East Windsor, Connecticut, compiled at the end of his apprenticeship records Harland's curriculum.[35] Burnap jotted down formulas for paints, alloys, and fluxes; the numbers of teeth in the wheels and leaves in the pinions; and procedures for making, tempering, and polishing everything from clock parts to gold beads. Burnap outlined the steps for making an eight-day movement and the crucial proportioning of its parts. He detailed anchor recoil and dead-beat escapements at length; also repeating work, moon phase, calendar attachments, and musical movements, which Harland probably introduced to Connecticut. The memoranda also contain rules for making tools and silver spoons and for repairing watches. Several recipes tell how to melt, refine, solder, and plate metals. Burnap's diagram for a proper eight-day clock matches those made by Harland and his other apprentices.[36]

Despite his advanced training, it was impossible for Burnap to make clocks exclusively; he depended on the variety of skills he had learned from Harland to make his livelihood. When he bartered with cabinetmaker Eliphalet Chapin, he mended buckles, a teapot, a vice, and a watch. He cleaned a gun, made a stove pipe, cast blocks for a lathe, and made hardware for a card table and a desk.[37] Despite this, Burnap considered himself a specialist:

Brass Wheel'd Clocks. The subscriber having for a number of years applied principally to the business of Clock Making, and having met with considerable encouragement...takes this method to inform the publick that although he works in many other branches common to those in the silversmith line, as also Surveyor's

Top left:Fig.4-15. Dwarf Clock, Reuben Tower, Hanover, Mass., ca. 1816-1818. The pine case is grain painted to simulate mahogany. 57.1.29

Bottom left: Fig.4-16. Dwarf Clock movement, Reuben Tower. A compact and well made, scaled-down tall clock movement with a rack and snail strike is powered by two weights. 57.1.29

Top: Fig. 4-17. Shelf Clock, Reuben Tower, Hingham, Mass., ca. 1820. A kidney dial shelf clock with the height of a dwarf clock. Rare instances of this form by Aaron Willard have survived. 57.1.121

Compasses, Watch repairing &c., yet notwithstanding Clock Making is intended as the governing business of his shop. [38]

A few months recorded by journeyman Nichols Goddard (1773-1823) of Shrewsbury, Massachusetts, illustrate the working life of a craftsman at this level and the role that he could perform. If apprentices were a shop's agents of consistency, then journeymen were the catalysts of change as they plied their craft for their employers. Nichols Goddard worked on clocks in four shops, founding and assembling parts, which were seldom marked.[39] The skilled workmanship of individuals like him was essential to the clock maker, whose output was limited in part by the scarcity of skilled labor.

At the beginning of 1795, Nichols worked for Luther Goddard (1762-1842).[40] For him, Nichols finished a clock with an eight-day alarm movement (the twenty-third that he had made) and completed "three movements already begun," before he returned home with Luther's wheel-cutting engine, which he had rented for $2 for just under a month. Goddard next worked for Gardner Parker of Westborough (see Pl. 18) at the rate of $7 for each movement that he assembled from pre-cast stock with wheels cut by him. When not running Parker's errands in the first month, the journeyman managed to complete one movement and to charge for polishing wheels. He left for 10 days returning to "work for G. Parker by the day at 4/." [$.83] Five days later, he "Finised [sic] one 8 day Clock movement 25." This was Goddard's number 25, but for the marketplace it was Parker's clock, not his. When he "finished Work for G. Parker" in early April, he was paid in part with a waistcoat and had to return to Westborough twice for money he had loaned Parker. In April he went to Northampton to work as a brass founder. He "cast one clock" on April 24, five clocks for Isaac Gere (1771-1812), and in June finished two clocks: an eight-day movement (26) and an alarm clock (27). Two Gere movements have survived with N. Goddard's name cast on the brass pendulum cocks.[41]

In addition to his work as a shop journeyman, Nichols Goddard also performed the important function of distributing clock materials to each of the shops where he worked. His travels took him home to Shrewsbury, near Worcester, several times, partly because of his father's illness and death that year. It was more convenient for him than his employers to

Fig.4-18.Tall Clock movement, Paul Rogers and Son. Iron, rather than brass, was the raw material for the plates of many Maine clock movements. Brass bushings were inserted in the plates as suitable bearing surfaces for the pivots. 57.1.176

stop at the store of hardware merchant Daniel Waldo, Jr. In 1794 Waldo's advertisement included:

Beautiful Enamelled Clock and Watch Faces; Clock and Watch Glasses; Clock Springs; Fuzee Chains; Main Springs; Pendulum Wire; Hour and Minute Hands; Brilliant Button Stones; Emery; Crucibles and Black Lead Pots; Watch Chains; Seals and Keys; with all kinds of Watch and Clockmakers Files, Vices, Plyers, Screw Plates, Nippers, Dividers, Shears, hammers, Gravers &c.[42]

In February, Goddard bought himself "clock pliars" for 50 cents from among many imported materials sold by Waldo, who dealt with the firm of Johan and Caspar Halsbach and Sons of Cologne, Germany. In a 1789 letter Halsbach refers to Waldo's annual purchase of large amounts of German steel. Although not clock making tools *per se*, the materials are the same and suggest a possible source of supply.[43]

Finding a source for costly, and often imported, materials was part of the clock maker's job. In this regard, Paul (1752-1818) and Abner Rogers (1777-1809) of Berwick, Maine made clocks which made do. They built clocks with plates of iron, apparently reserving their costly brass. (Fig. 4-18) The case in the elegant "Roxbury" style was commissioned in

Fig.4-19. Tall Clock, Paul Rogers and Son, Berwick, Maine, ca. 1803-1809. A written label tacked inside the case reads: "For Mr. Paul Rogers, at Doutesfalls [Doughty'sFalls] for the Portsmouth Pakett". If not made in Boston or Roxbury, but in Portsmouth, this case has all the Roxbury case features: brass stop fluting, inlay, ogee feet, pierced fret, and the usual method of mounting the movement in the case. See Fig.6-8. 57.1.176

nearby Portsmouth or possibly Boston (Fig. 4-19) to house Rogers's expedient solution.

Rogers was the son of a blacksmith, who clearly had a hand in training him. (Another Paul Rogers clock in the collection (57.1.32a) has a sheet brass dial and plates of bell metal, a copper alloy, leaving little doubt that he cast most of its parts.) Abner was one of Paul's sons, who went briefly to Portland, Maine, when he came of age, married, and returned with his own young family to Berwick "together with William Purinton, apprentice boy." Back in Berwick, Abner worked with his father, whom he predeceased.[44]

The conditions of their partnership are not clear, as clocks by them either bear both their names, or just Abner's. When Paul died in 1818, the contents of his shop included

1 eight day clock $35; 1 do. 25	$60.00
1 clock case $12; 1 do. 8; 2 do. @ 10.	40.00
1 small timepiece $17; 2 do @ 10 each	37.00
1 machine	$3.00
Part set of clockmaker tools	12.00 [45]

This listing suggests a complex operation. Together Paul and Abner Rogers made at least one chime clock with a lunar dial. Abner's name also appears on a lyre-type wall clock and a mirror clock. Paul Rogers supplemented his clock making (or perhaps *vice versa*) by operating a hat factory employing 20 men. Although Abner's life was short, the Rogerses tradition of using iron plates in their clocks was perpetuated by his apprentices.[46]

Edward Sherburne Moulton (1778-1855) of nearby Rochester, New Hampshire, offered another technical option that combined quality and gadgetry. (Figs. 4-20, 4-21) His tall clock is fitted with an unusual alarm attachment driven by a third descending weight wound through the extra aperture in the dial. [47]

The customers of rural New England's clock makers were well aware of what they wanted in outward appearance and efficiency. It was the craftsman's job to comply. The threshold of making a living as a clock maker cannot be measured against the Willards' influence in post-Revolutionary America. The study of Jedidiah Baldwin's (1769-1849) account books shows the economics of doing business in a thriving country town in northern New England. Trained by Thomas Harland, Baldwin searched for a community that would support him. He tried Northampton, Massachusetts, first, but

there was already too much competition. In 1793 he moved on to Hanover, New Hampshire, a growing community that boasted Dartmouth College (founded in 1769), a printing press, and a population of about 13,000 within a 15-mile radius.[48]

For Baldwin annual earnings of $700 brought prosperity. One-half of his income came from finished products: clocks, silver, and jewelry. The other half was repair work and his income as postmaster. In 18 years in Hanover, Baldwin sold 55 eight-day clocks, an average of 3.2 per annum, at about $50 apiece. He also made "moon" and musical clocks, just as Harland had taught him. Baldwin retailed most of them during the winter months after the harvest was in and the college had settled into the academic year (December–March: 45.4%).[49]

Even in country towns a clock maker like Baldwin did little casting and could obtain parts and materials from abroad. He purchased pinions and "1 Doz. 12 [" wide] faces $47.73" (probably made in Birmingham) from John McFarland of Boston in 1806. Closer to home he traded parts with clock makers Samuel Parker and John Osgood (b. 1770) of Haverhill, New Hampshire, with Ransom Smith of nearby Lebanon, and with Phineas Bailey (wkg.

Left: Fig. 4-20 Tall Clock, Edward S. Moulton, Rochester, N.H. ca. 1810. 57.1.125

Right: Fig. 4-21 Tall clock movement, Edward S. Moulton. The alarm mechanism is mounted between the plates and is powered by a separate weight which is wound through the dial at the two o'clock position. 57.1.125

Fig.4-22. Shelf Clock, Joseph Chadwick, Boscawen, N.H., ca. 1815. This case is taller than usual to accommodate a 24" long pendulum as Chadwick was utilizing wheel work made for another clock type. 57.1.114

1810-1817) of Chelsea, Vermont.[50] He commissioned local cabinetmakers to produce cases for his clocks.[51] But once his clocks were made, he had to compete with Daniel Burnap who sold his clocks as far north as Norwich, Vermont.[52]

But by 1811, Baldwin's livelihood had evaporated, the value of his products and services rose with Embargo-driven inflation to over $700 dollars, but he sold only one clock, a few silver spoons, and a dozen Phi Beta Kappa medals. Baldwin's finished products accounted for only 16.2% of his income, far below the 50% required to make his special training worthwhile. Repair work climbed to 42.4% of his earnings, and the cash taken as postmaster, most of which was sent to Portsmouth, reached 41.4%. Money was too tight for clocks, jewelry, or silver.

Baldwin closed his business and migrated to Rochester, New York, and became a part-time tinker. In October 1827, Daniel Burnap received a letter from his nephew in Rochester: "Mr. Baldwin resides here, keeps the post office, served his time with Mr. Harland, says he knows you and desires to be remembered."[53] The phalanx of Harland apprentices, once at the forefront of metallurgy, had become a fraternity of old men. Like the other clock makers born in the third quarter of the 18th century, they had made good clocks in their time. But those times had changed and from Connecticut and New Hampshire a flood of cheaply made, easily transported clocks were transforming the way that time was kept in America's households and public places. Neither the Willard nor Harland models were the ones to emulate.

AN ECONOMICAL INNOVATION of a different sort was made in Boscawen, New Hampshire by Joseph Chadwick (1787-1868) and Benjamin Morrill (1794-1857) while Baldwin was moving across upstate New York. The cases of their clocks show Willard influence or, at least, the need to compete, but one of these men devised a movement which reduced the amount of brass used. Morrill and Chadwick were brothers-in-law, but not partners. There is no record of the details of their training, but their traditional tall and shelf clocks and innovative wall clocks assured their reputations. Morrill also constructed tower clocks and experimental models, like the so-called watchman's clock that records his rounds.[54] They may have employed some of the same workmen.

Although both men made tall clocks with traditional eight-day movements, they emphasized small clocks to meet the demand for less expensive timepieces (Fig. 4-22).[55] Chadwick followed the basic Willard lead in the design of the brass timepiece, but strove for better accuracy with a 24-inch pendulum, longer than found in most Willard kidney dial shelf clocks. To conserve brass in the well-made movement, a shallow arc was removed from the lower edge of the plates. The ribbed fretwork of the case was the innovation of a local cabinetmaker.[56]

Morrill and Chadwick's contribution to clock making was the New Hampshire mirror clock. (Fig. 4-23) More examples made by Morrill are known, probably because he continued in business longer. It is presumed that he designed the form. The concept was simple enough: take the materials of Willard's patent timepiece, especially the white dial and reverse-painted glass; put them in an economical case; add a looking glass; and frame the entire item like a mirror with split turnings all the way around.[57] The clock's appeal was based on low cost, high visual appeal, and dual use as a stylish timekeeper and looking glass.

The second innovation was its mechanism, Morrill's so-called wheelbarrow movement. It is a simple timepiece with the brass plates reduced to the shape of a wheelbarrow. While the cutouts conserved expensive brass, the layout of the clock, with the weight suspended from the left side and the pendulum from the right, assures that the two components do not interfere with one another.[58] (Fig. 4-24)

The skills of cabinetmaker, turner, and painter may have been supplied by Morrill's cousin Harrison Otis Morrill. His name is scratched on the plates of two known mirror clocks.[59] The form was later adapted to offer the option of a striking mechanism. By 1830, about 100 clocks were made annually in Boscawen: far fewer than in the Connecticut shops[60]; far more than the production of a lone craftsman awaiting commissions; but not enough to continue the business indefinitely. Chadwick left clock making in 1831, Morrill in 1840. He then made scales and keyboard instruments.[61]

In an industry that succeeded by copying the innovative work of others, particularly those named Willard, high praise is to copy. Other north-coun-

Fig.4-23. Wall Clock, Benjamin Morrill, Boscawen, N.H., ca. 1825. Morrill packaged an efficient clock which also functioned as a looking glass. 57.1.231

Fig.4-24. Wall Clock movement, Benjamin Morrill. This example of the so-called wheelbarrow movement is shown with its offset weight and pendulum removed. The paper label inside the case reads: "EIGHT DAY CLOCKS and Timepieces, MANUFACTURED BY BENJAMIN MORRILL, BOSCAWEN, N.H. (One Door South of the Academy) To make this Time Piece go faster, turn the screw up at the bottom of the pendulum, and the contrary way to make it go slower." 57.1.231

Fig.4-25.
Wall Clock,
Frederick
Wingate,
Augusta, Maine,
ca. 1825. 57.1.96

Fig.4-26. Wall Clock, Frederick
Wingate. Ample space inside the case
allowed clock makers to install striking
movements powered by two lead
weights. 57.1.96

try craftsmen followed Morrill and Chadwick's lead.[62] Both Levi Hutchins and Abiel Chandler sold mirror clocks in Concord, but not every New Hampshire mirror clock was made in the Granite State. Frederick Wingate (1782-1864), of Augusta, Maine, built them, too. [63] (Figs. 4-25, 4-26) The clocks by Morrill, Chadwick, and skilled copyists like Wingate, were clever innovations produced in rural New England's changing economy.

Most clock makers failed to develop the market just below traditional, brass, eight-day clock making. Instead, they offered an occasional non-striking timepiece or an uncased "wag-on-the-wall" to patrons who had them cased later. An eight-day movement by Asa Sibley (1764-1829) of Walpole, New Hampshire, was cased about 1820 in Meriden, New Hampshire, a generation after its construction.[64] (Fig. 4-27)

Another way to reduce the expense was to make a clock with a wooden movement. After the Revolution such clocks continued to be made in the Ashby area of Massachusetts, perhaps because Jonas Fitch taught others his method. An anonymous example from about 1803 housed in a blue-painted, pine case was made for a corner of a particular room in a now-forgotten location.[65] (Fig. 4-28) (There is no cutout for a bracket base nor hood window on the left-hand side, and both the hood and case doors are hinged at the left.) The homemade wooden dial is inscribed "No. 3." (Pl.6) The movement is powered by two field stone weights carved to receive the cord that supports them.[66] (Pl. 15)

Many of the numerous wooden-movement clocks made in the Ashby area were influenced by Jonas Fitch, who may have taught the brothers Abraham (1761-1840) and Calvin Edwards (1763-1796).[67] They numbered some 600 clocks during their six-year partnership. The clock numbered "183" was built about 1793. (Figs. 4-29, 4-30) It has a tin dial plate and its gilt-washed spandrels, chapter ring, name boss, and date ring are made of lead or pewter. (Pl. 26)

The Edwardses jointly owned their Ashby real estate and business interests.[68] How successful were they? Although their final product was cheaper than the brass counterpart, it is a mistake to think that the business was dramatically less complex because the Edwardses worked with wood. Their notes of hand totalled just below $900 and their receivables were $816. The estate inventory taken at Calvin's death shows that their tools were different from those of

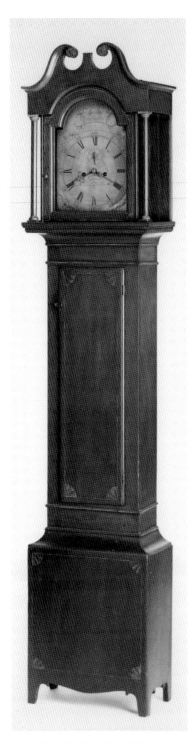

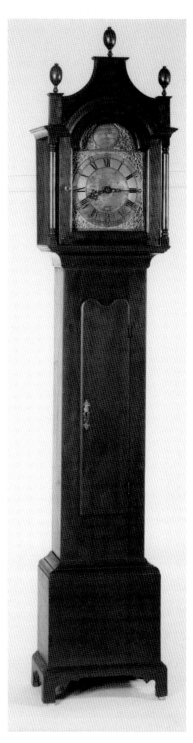

Fig.4-27. Tall Clock, Asa Sibley,
Walpole, N.H., movement and dial, ca.
1790; case, ca. 1820. Clock movements
were often cased or recased at a later
time when personal finances allowed.
The red paint and ornamental fan decoration dates from 1980 and is based on
the remains of original treatment.
57.1.118

Fig.4-28. Tall Clock, Maker Unknown, probably northern
Massachusetts, ca. 1803. See pls. 6 and 15. 57.1.147

Fig.4-29. Tall Clock, Abraham and
Calvin Edwards, Ashby, Mass., ca.
1793-1794.The pagoda top and finials
are a restoration based on evidence of
original treatment and original finials
surviving on a similar clock. See pl. 26.
57.1.229

Fig.4-31. Tall Clock, John Edwards, Ashby, Mass., ca. 1825. See pl. 24. 57.1.225

makers of brass clocks.[69] The appraisers found a newly completed clock worth $13 among the "clocks, not finished" valued at $80, and Calvin's half of the business was valued at $1942.24.

Maple boards and timber of Various kinds for Clockwork $21.87; old copper $12.25; Brass $3.55; steel $2.20; Iron .25; lead $6.72; Tin $8.17; oils, paints, and lines &c. for Clock work $16.60; Clock Glasses $2.50; wire $6.50; pot mettle and old brass $3.67; Clocks, not finished $80; stuff used $18.33; Tools, Laithe and tools for turning &c $7.41; 4 vises $5.50; a number of files and Rasps &c $2.83; Bellows, melting pots, soder &c. $3.24; Hand irons, shaves and other tools $9.25; plires [pliers], bitts, gimblets and other tools $2.23; pencils, bottles, Stone Jarrs, Boxes & kegs $3.83; Scales and weights, moulds, patterns and scives $3.32; 1 New Clock $13.00; Notes of hand $899.34; Book accompts $816.

The inventory does not suggest how the brothers divided their labor. While Abraham continued to make tall clocks after Calvin's death, he dropped the numbering system. The painted scenes on the dial may have been executed by a different hand.

Like many clock makers, Abraham Edwards sold uncased movements. A cabinetmaker named Esek Whiting (1769-1850) in neighboring Lunenburg was a regular customer. In business after 1790, he made cases and retailed the completed product. By 1820, Whiting had become a manufacturer of looking glass frames, quite possibly because Edwards had stopped making clocks in favor of scythe rifles, a sharpening tool.[70]

Edwards clock making did not end with Abraham. His son, John (b. 1787), made a movement, which

Fig.4-30. Tall Clock movement, Abraham and Calvin Edwards. Thirty-hour Ashby movements can generally be identified by their maple, birch or beech plates and arbors, cherry wheels and the long wooden lifting lever mounted in the upper left corner which extends toward the lower right, passing under the motion gearing on the front plate. See pl. 26. 57.1.229

is virtually identical to his father's work.[71] (Fig. 4-31) The dial is made of yellow birch, even less expensive than tin. Like his brother, Samuel (1788-1853), John adopted the curious manner of painting the dials in rough simulation of English enameled iron dials. The complicated layout lends a note of sophistication. (Pl. 24) John probably quit the business before the War of 1812 while Samuel left Ashby for Gorham, Maine in 1809.[72]

Alexander Tarbell Willard (1774-1850) and his brother, Philander J. (1772-1840), also made wooden tall clocks in the Ashby-Ashburnham area. A tall clock made by Alexander in the early 1820s relates to the Edwardses' work.[73] (Fig. 4-32) A native of Ashburnham, his clock making was independent of his distant cousins in Grafton and Roxbury. Willard probably trained with Abraham Edwards between 1796 and 1800 when he first lived in Ashby. His clocks have white dials with roses that may have been painted by his wife, Tila Oakes Willard.[74] (Fig. 4-33) An 1829 almanac reports that Willard made a timepiece called an "improved small clock."[75]

Urban and rural clocks made across New England in the years after the Revolution had much in common. They were, for the most part, similar and equally complex. The clocks document the skills of their makers, sometimes one craftsman, but just as likely many. Each clock represents the merger of imported concepts and materials, strengthening rather than weakening the notion of craftsmanship. In the age of Federalist prosperity and agricultural growth, the capital accrued by the elite and middle classes brought an appreciation for precise timekeeping that made life more urban in both city and country.

Fig.4-32. Tall Clock, Alexander T. Willard, Ashby, Mass., ca. 1820-1825. 57.1.138

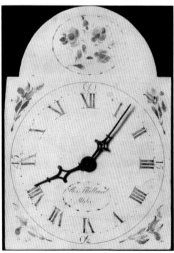

Fig. 4-33. Tall Clock, painted dial, Alexander T. Willard. 57.1.138

NOTES

[1] James E. Conlon, "The Clockmakers of Newburyport and Vicinity," Boston Clock Club, 99. Wood was only 16 when Jonathan Mulliken died, suggesting that Balch is more likely to have been his teacher. Wood's age and the characteristics of his work do not rule out a Willard apprenticeship or work in Roxbury as a journeyman during the 1780s.

[2] For examples of tall clocks and patent timepieces by David Wood, see *Sack Collection* 1:284, 2:407, 3:707, 4:948, 5:1139, 6:1484; Dean A. Fales, Jr., *Essex County Furniture: Documented Treasures from Local Collections, 1660-1860* (Salem: Essex Institute, 1965) figs. 69-70. A tall clock and a shelf clock are in the collection of the Yale University Art Gallery.

[3] Parsons, 182, 311; Morrison H. Heckscher, *American Furniture in the Metropolitan Museum of Art, Vol. II, Late Colonial Period: The Queen Anne and Chippendale Styles* (New York: Random House, 1985) 310-311; Distin and Bishop, 94-95; Anita Schorsch, *The Warner Collector's Guide to American Clocks* (New York: The Main Street Press, 1981), 117. The Newburyport cabinetmaker is unidentified. A similar case houses a timepiece by Wood, another by Daniel Balch, Jr., (1761-1835) of Newburyport, and two others contain movements by William Fitz of Portsmouth, N.H., who was born in Newburyport. Thanks to Douglas R. Currie for emphasizing the sophistication of the case. The neo-classical eagle finial is original.

[4] Similar shelf clocks by David Wood are owned by the Baltimore Museum of Art, the Chipstone Foundation, Winterthur Museum, and Yale University Art Gallery.

[5] J.W. Willard, 94-5.

[6] *Newburyport Herald*, July 25, 1806.

[7] Boston's population was about 16,000 on the eve of the Revolution, Newport's was 9,209 and Portsmouth had 4,596 residents. There were about 7,000 inhabitants in Norwich, Conn. in 1770.

[8] Levi Pitkin (1774-1854) of Montpelier, Vt. trained with Daniel Burnap in East Windsor, Conn., (see below) and moved to Montpelier in 1796. The regulator used by Pitkin is in a private collection. The circular, brass dial has three hands: two small and one large. The upper small hand measures the minutes. The lower one tracks the hours, one through twelve. The large hand sweeps the entire dial and measures the seconds around the perimeter. After 15 years, he left for New York state. See *Antiques* 127, no. 2 (February 1985): 356.

[9] Parsons, 302-305. In addition to the Hutchins and Chandler families, Concord clock and watch makers included Thomas Baker (1793-1820), Robert Davis (1790-1861), Abiel B. Eastman (1788-1822), Seth Eastman (1801-1855), Isaac A. Hall (1812-1834), Ivory Hall (1795-1880), Joseph Giles (wkg. 1804), Elijah Knight (1813-1886), Ephraim Potter (wkg. after 1771), John Robie (wkg. 1804-1811), William Virgin (1796-1861), and Jonathan Ward (1744-1822). Philip Brown (1789-1854) and Edmund Currier (1793-1853) worked in nearby Hopkinton.

[10] George Chandler, *The Chandler Family: The Descendants of William and Annis Chandler Who Settled in Roxbury, Massachusetts, 1637* (Worcester, Mass.: Press of Charles Hamilton, 1883), 592-593.

[11] Parsons, 303.

[12] *Concord Herald*, June 1, 1791.

[13] Parsons, 80-81, 96-97; *Plain & Elegant, Rich & Common: Documented New Hampshire Furniture, 1750-1850* (Concord: N.H. Historical Society, 1978), 52-53, 56-57, 84-88; Donna-Belle Garvin, "Concord, New Hampshire: A Furniture-Making Capital," *Historical New Hampshire* 45, no. 1 (Spring 1990): 8-87; Boutin, 286, 683-685. The backboard of this clock case is inscribed "D. Potter." Daniel Potter (b. 1782) was the son of Ephraim, who moved to Concord from Ipswich, Mass., in 1771 with his brother Richard. Ephraim was a joiner who made wooden clock movements. The brass tag on the dial with Chandler's name appears to be old, but its origins are unclear. The maker of the case is also unknown, but both the Hutchinses and Chandler used local cabinetmakers.

[14] *Concord Gazette*, n.d. 1815 (?) in Parsons, 277.

[15] Chandler, 995-996; Parsons, 304-305; *New Hampshire Patriot*, (Concord), May 18, 1830. The property of Timothy, Jr. was inventoried when he was declared insane in 1848.

[16] Parsons, 26, 184, 188-189, 199-200, 215-216, 218-223, 226-233, 240, 242, 304-305; Distin and Bishop, 229, 236; Charles S. Crossman, "A Complete History of Watch and Clock Making in America," *Jewellers Circular, Horological Review* (March 1890). Chandler, 996-997; Abiel Chandler, Journal, 1848-1851. N.H. Historical Society. Abiel ended his career as a florist.

[17] Letter, Benjamin Willard to Luke Drury, Grafton, Mass., May 29, 1789. Winterthur Museum.

[18] Donald K. Packard, "The Baileys of Hanover, Massachusetts," Boston Clock Club, 189-96; *Bailey Genealogy, James, John, and Thomas and Their Descendants*, ed. Hollis R. Bailey (Somerville, Mass.: The Citizen Company, 1899), 322-4; Bailey, *Two Hundred Years*, 48, 50-2, 94, 96.

Eventually John (1751-1823) moved to Lynn Mass. and Calvin to Bath, Me.

[19] Account Book, Calvin Bailey, Hanover, Mass., 1784-1824, 2, 8, 23. NAWCC Library, Columbia, Penn.

[20] Ibid., 3, 14, 33, 22.

[21] Bailey recorded the sale of a clock for $60 to Nathaniel Howe in 1805. Ibid., 39.

[22] The fall-off strike on this clock is incomplete. A shelf clock by John Bailey is owned by the Western Reserve Historical Society, Cleveland, Ohio. A shelf clock is pictured in *Sack Collection* 3:645.

[23] Deposition, Joshua Wilder, South Hingham, Mass., September 18 1860, Boston Clock Club, 66. James Conlon owned the document in 1936.

[24] *History of Hingham, Massachusetts*, 3 vols (1893) 3:321.

[25] Chris H. Bailey, *Two Hundred Years*, 52.

[26] *History of Hingham* 3:176. David Sprague (1780 -1849) was a shoemaker. He married Mary Gardner in 1809.

[27] A clock in a private collection was made for Martin Fearing in 1821. Wilder also made tall clocks and patent timepieces. Distin and Bishop, 50,77,232.

[28] *Sack Collection* 2:836.

[29] Christie's Auction Catalogue, sale 6622, June 4, 1988, lot 226.

[30] Distin and Bishop, 81-2; a patent timepiece by Reuben Tower is owned by the Hood Museum, Dartmouth College, Hanover, N.H. For a shelf clock with reverse-painted tablets, see Sotheby's Auction Catalogue, sale 6201, June 27, 1991, Lot 352.; *Early American Clocks*, ed. Don Maust, 3 vols (Uniontown, Penn.: E.G. Warnan Publishing Co., 1971) 1:24-6. 38-9,46.

[31] *Norwich (Conn.) Packet*, December 9, 1773.

[32] *Connecticut Gazette* (New London), December 11, 1795.

[33] *Norwich Courier*, April 8, 1807. In 1806, when Thomas, Jr., predeceased his father, the shop also contained 117 gold and silver watches of English, Irish, and French manufacture. Estate Inventory of Thomas Harland, Jr., Norwich, Conn., 1806, as quoted by Chris H. Bailey, *Two Hundred Years*, 66. See also, Bailey, "Thomas Harland of Norwich: Forerunner of the Clock Manufacturing Industry," *The Connecticut Historical Society Bulletin* 51, no. 4 (Fall 1986): 226-249. Bailey demonstrates that while Harland's craftsmanship did not equal the finest London work, competition in Norwich was meager. His real skill was an engraver. Hoopes, *Connecticut Clockmakers of the Eighteenth Century* illustrates several examples.

[34] Hoopes, *Shop Records of Daniel Burnap*, passim.

[35] Zea, "Clockmaking and Society at the

River and the Bay, Jedidiah and Jabez Baldwin, 1790-1820," Dublin Seminar for New England Folklife, *Annual Proceedings, 1981*, (Boston: Boston University Press, 1982): 44-45. For example, Harland apprentices usually mounted the dial on the movement with four visible screws rather than the more prevalent method of using dial feet riveted to the back of the dial. Among Harland's apprentices were Daniel Burnap (1750-1838), East Windsor and Coventry, Conn.; Seril Dodge (1759-1838), Providence, R.I.; Nathaniel Shipman (1764-1853), Norwich, Conn.; David Greenleaf, Jr. (1765-1835), Hartford, Conn.; Ezra Dodge (1766-1798), New London, Conn.; Jedidiah Baldwin (1769-1849), Norwich, Northampton, Mass., Hanover, N.H., and upstate New York; William Cleveland (1770-1837), Norwich and New London; Thomas Harland, Jr. (1781-1806), Norwich; Richard Huntington of Norwich; possibly Benjamin Hanks (1755-1824), Mansfield, Windham, and Litchfield, Conn.; possibly David Haynes (1756-1837), Brookfield, Mass.; and possibly Gurdon Tracy (1767-1792), New London, Conn.

[36] The Burnap papers and tools are in the collection of The Connecticut Historical Society.

[37] Daniel Burnap, Ledger Entries with Eliphalet Chapin, as quoted in Hoopes, 78-80.

[38] *Connecticut Courant* (Hartford), March 14, 1791.

[39] Diary, Nichols Goddard, Shrewsbury, Westborough, and Northampton, Mass., 1795, Winterthur Museum.

[40] The Goddards were second cousins and Luther may have trained Nichols. The authors thank Chris H. Bailey for sharing his genealogical research, also Bailey, 191-193; Small, "Luther Goddard and His Watches," *NAWCC Bulletin*, 6 (February and April 1954).

[41] A clock with an unsigned dial stamped "N. GODDARD," was owned by C.L. Prickett Antiques, Yardley, Penn., in 1990. Another, signed by Gere on the dial, was formerly owned by Robert C. Cheney.

[42] *Massachusetts Spy* (Worcester), May 27, 1794.

[43] Letter, Johan and Caspar Halsbach, and Sons, Cologne, Germany, to Daniel Waldo, March 10, 1789, Waldo Family Papers, Box 2, Folder 2, American Antiquarian Society, Worcester, Mass.

[44] Estate Inventory, Abner Rogers, May 13, 1809, York County Registry of Probate, York, Maine. Abner Rogers clocks signed "Berwick" were manufactured between 1803 and 1809, and possibly in the late 1790s before he moved to Portland. Abner apparently lived with his parents.

After he died on January 25, 1809, the appraisers of his estate found some household effects, but no real estate, tools, or work in progress.

[45] Estate Inventory, Paul Rogers, September 26, 1818, York County Registry of Probate.

[46] When Paul died in 1818, Oliver Brackett (1800-1869) of Limington, Maine, was probably serving his apprenticeship. His older brother Rueben (1791-1867) had finished his training. John Taber (1796-1859), Rogers's grandson, was a fourth apprentice. The Tabers were also Quakers, and John was the second cousin of the clock maker Elnathan Taber (1768-1854). Samuel Buffum, *Historical Sketch of North Berwick* (n.p. 1931); Herbert I. Brackett, *Brackett Genealogy* (Washington, D.C.: Herbert I. Brackett, 1907), 298-299; Katra 57-59, 67-76; George L. Randall, *Taber Genealogy: Descendants of Thomas, Son of Philip Taber* (New Bedford, Mass.: Vining Press, 1924), 35,83; Bernard and S. Dean Levy Catalogue 6 (1988):183; Distin and Bishop, 250,258,261. (The photographs on pp. 258 and 262 are of the same clock.) A non-striking dwarf clock by Nathaniel Rogers of Berwick is also known.

[47] Thomas Moulton, *A Genealogical Register of Some of the Descendants of John Moulton of Hampton and of Joseph Moulton of Portsmouth* (Portland, Me.: B. Thurston and Co., 1873), 36-38; Parsons, 324; Katra, 20-24,36.

[48] Zea, 45-53; roughly one-fourth of Baldwin's patrons were Hanover residents and teachers at Dartmouth College, the new medical school, or Moors' Indian Charity School; one-fourth were students; another fourth lived in Lebanon or across the Connecticut River in Norwich, Vermont; the final quarter inhabited surrounding towns.

[49] Zea, 47. The next most productive period for clock making was between April and July (34.5%). The least productive period was in the autumn (20%). This analysis is based on Baldwin's ledgers and papers on deposit at the Dartmouth College Archives, Baker Library, Hanover, N.H.: Account Book, 1799-1807; Account Book 1806-1811; Daybook 1797-1802; Daybook 1802-1805; Daybook 1806-1809; Daybook 1809-1811; Watch Book 1793-1804; and Watch Book 1804-1810.

[50] Zea, 47,50. Some parts for Baldwin's clocks may also have come from Conn. and New York City. He distributed pills and sold wallpaper for New York and London merchants.

[51] See Zea, 48, for a complete listing with references.

[52] Hoopes, 48, 55, 58; *Highlights from the Bennington Museum*, ed. Laura C. Luckey

(Bennington: The Bennington Museum, ca. 1989), 5, 15-16.

[53] Letter, Ela Burnap to Daniel Burnap, Rochester, N.Y., October 10, 1827. Burnap Papers, The Connecticut Historical Society.

[54] Parsons, 148-152; George Wadleigh, *Notable Events in the History of Dover, New Hampshire* (Dover: G.H. Wadleigh, 1913), 236,68. Charles C. Coffin, The History of Boscawen and Webster (Concord: Republican Press, 1878), 485.

[55] Parsons, 104-107. For a tall clock by Morrill, see Skinner's Auction Catalogue, Sale 1446, May 30, 1992, lot 191.

[56] Parsons, 175-181; *Antiques* 137 (January 1990):238; One example is labeled by Asa Kimball (probably Jr., 1767-1815) of Concord and made about 1810 near the beginning of Chadwick's career. The variation among these small clock cases suggests that several cabinetmakers made them. For more information about Asa Kimball, see *Plain & Elegant*, 56-57. OSV's Chadwick shelf clock is illustrated with detailed specifications in Parsons, 181.

[57] Morrill secured the movements to the backboard with either two long bolts that pass through both plates, as in Willard's patent timepiece, or two wood screws that passed through the rear plate alone and into the backboard of the case.

[58] Morrill also made a few Willard-style patent timepieces. See Parsons, 153, 195; Morrill's wheel-cutting and pinion cutting engines survive at the American Clock and Watch Museum, and may have been used to make these clocks, Parsons 47-48.

[59] Parsons, 197, 324.

[60] 1830 Census of Manufactures, as quoted in Parsons.

[61] Parsons, 599-589, 643.

[62] For craftsmen who made New Hampshire style mirror clocks, see Parsons, 199-213. 215-223, 226-228, 230-234, 259.

[63] Charles E.L. Wingate, *History of the Wingate Family* (Exeter: James D.P. Wingate, 1886) 158-160. Frederick, the younger brother of clock maker Paine Wingate (1767-1833), was born in Haverhill, Mass., and moved to Augusta in 1804, where he made fine clocks with mixed success. A tall clock made by him is owned by the Yale University Art Gallery, See also Skinner's Auction Catalogue, Sale 1446, May 30, 1992, lot 199.

[64] Hoopes, 111-112; Martha M. Frizzell, *A History of Walpole, New Hampshire*, 2 vols. (Walpole: Town of Walpole, 1963), 151-152, 301, 304, 306, 313, 373, 385, 387; Chris H. Bailey, *Two Hundred Years*, 22, 61, 63-64, 87. Parsons, pp. 55, 100-101, 318-319, 330. Asa Sibley was born on March 29, 1764, in Sutton, Mass. He apparently was apprenticed to Peregrin White (1747-

1834) in Woodstock, Conn. He married and remained there until at least 1795, returned to Sutton, then moved to Walpole, N.H., in 1797. He eventually moved to Rochester, N.Y., where he died in 1829. Although antiquarians have cited the absence of surviving work by Sibley during his 13 years in Walpole, three clocks are known: at OSV, Historic Deerfield, Inc., and in a private collection in Walpole. OSV's Sibley clock was owned by Mrs. John Cann (1865-1937) of Meriden, N.H. 30 miles north of Walpole. The movement was apparently purchased uncased from the maker. The case is very similar to one that descended in the Westgate family of nearby Plainfield; its painted surface has been restored.

[65] Robert C. Cheney, "Bluebird," *Cog Counters Journal*, no. 21 (July 1985). The attribution to the Ashby area is based on wheel counts, the long lifting lever transversing the front plate for the strike release, and the return wind system on the strike train. The strike train is a rope pull up system like that found on the OSV tall clock by Benjamin Cheney of East Hartford (57.1.117).

[66] Another instance of these rare field stone weights is found in an advertisement for clocks from Goshen in the western part of Mass. Zelotes Reed began to make wooden clocks about 1796 and even to cast his own bells. His advertisement in the *Hampshire Gazette* (Northampton), March 13, 1799, confirms that he "carries on the CLOCKMAKING BUSINESS" and also "Japanns Clock Faces and Executes Painting in its Various Branches." Hiram Barrus, *History of the Town of Goshen, Hampshire County, Massachusetts* (Boston: for the author, 1881), 91-92.

[67] A profile portrait of Abraham Edwards by Ruth Henshaw Bascom is in the collections of the Concord Museum, Concord, Mass. Chris H. Bailey, *Two Hundred Years*, 52; Ward Francillon, *Cog Counters Journal* (1980); Ward Francillon to Robert Cheney, January 1980. Wheel counts of clocks by Jonas Fitch, Abraham and Calvin Edwards, John Edwards, and Alexander T. Willard show only minor variations in the number of teeth in the time second wheel, the strike great wheel, and the warning wheel. Other teeth counts are identical. So are the strike warning levers, hoop and count-wheel detents, strike lifting levers, winding system—a pull cord and barrel, and method of attaching the dial to the extension of the four posts.

[68] Deed, Joseph Davis to A. & C. Edwards, April 24, 1789, Book 100:401; Reuben Brown to A. & C. Edwards, April 22, 1791, Book 104:490; Jonathan Stickney to A. & C. Edwards, April 29, 1793, Book 112:426.

Middlesex County Deeds, East Cambridge, Mass.; John Ware Willard, 121-122; Laurence Luther Barber, "The Clockmakers of Ashby, Massachusetts," *Antiques* 23, no. 5 (May 1933): 178-180. Barber stated that he owned numbers 14 and 385. See also his principal source, Ezra Stearns, who notes the existence of clocks 199, 363, 396, and 532. Clock 505 is described in Parsons, 71. Clock 183 is illustrated here.

[69] Docket 6885, First Series, Registry of Probate, Middlesex County Courthouse, East Cambridge.

[70] Stearns, 121, 123. He describes his research on Whiting and hoped "to speak at greater length concerning the good service of Mr. Whiting in the world of clocks." He also attributed Edwards's withdrawal from making tall clocks to the popularity of shelf clocks. See also, Nelde K. Drumm and Margaret P. Harley, *Lunenburg: The Heritage of Turkey Hills, 1718-1978* (Lunenburg: ca. 1977), p. 167; Lunenburg, ms 70, U.S. Census of Manufactures, 1820; Bigelow, *Statistical View of Massachusetts* (Boston: 1837). The entry for Ashby lists the manufacture of 3,000 scythe rifles, valued at $1,125, employing two hands; Docket 31231, Probate Court, Middlesex County, East Cambridge.

[71] The standard Ashby movement is modified slightly by mounting the minute, hour, and corresponding intermediate wheel one-inch lower on the front plate of the movement, extending the front plate strike lifting lever about an inch for the lower placement of the minute wheel, and extending the escape wheel arbor to receive a second hand.

[72] A 30-hour tall clock by Samuel Robert Edwards is described by Katra, 10-12. It also has a painted wooden dial with the chapter ring and hands in a small circle on the lower part intersected by a similar circle containing the large seconds hand and markings at each quarter minute. Samuel manufactured tall clocks in Gorham, Me., until about 1823 when he moved to Portland and he engaged in brass casting until purchasing an iron foundry. Back in Ashby, his brother, John, also made cases, according to Ezra Stearns, 124, and Barber, 178.

[73] The clock by A.T. Willard was constructed with a count-wheel striking mechanism. The parts of the 30-hour wooden movement are made of cherry wheels, maple arbors and pinions, and maple or beech plates. The painted wooden dial has a red wash on the back and a chamfered edge. The winding barrels have a divided drum. The minute hand is brass while the hour hand is lead.

[74] According to John Ware Willard, A.T. Willard was self-taught, 121-122, 127. Pl. 37 shows a dial hung beside the door of A.T. Willard's clock shop as a sign.

[75] Stearns, 124-125; Willard, 127-128. A.T. Willard also reportedly built musical and turret, or public, clocks. Willard's estate inventory lists three wooden clocks and cases, one brass clock, and one marble clock. His tools included watch lathes and "forge bellows and tools for casting," which, although appraised at only two dollars, indicate that he may have made the compasses, gunter's chains, scales, and other items attributed to him. Docket 37384, Middlesex County Courthouse, E. Cambridge.

CLOCKS WITH WOODEN MOVEMENTS made in Connecticut revolutionized the way clocks were built and sold between 1800 and 1830. Connecticut became the center of the industrialized production of clocks and consumers looked to them as an affordable way of keeping time at home. Clocks from this period by Eli Terry (1772-1852) and his sons Eli, Jr. (1799-1841), Henry (1801-1877), and Silas (1807-1876), Seth Thomas (1785-1859), Silas Hoadley (1786-1870), Riley Whiting (1785-1835), William Leavenworth (1759-1836), Ira (1775-1848) and Joseph Ives (1782-1862), and Ephraim Downs (1787-1860) are part of the OSV collection, as is a contemporary clock with a brass movement by Heman Clark (1783-1838). Each of these clocks illustrates one or more important aspects of the industry which transformed Plymouth, Bristol, and Waterbury, and, indeed, the Farmington and Naugatuck valleys in the first quarter of the 19th century.

Cheney Wells, like many collectors of his generation, found these clocks and their story much less appealing than the glamorous 18th- and early 19th-century urban tall clocks and other forms made by the Willards, their apprentices, and competitors. However, Wells collected several of the highlights in Connecticut clocks, among them a Terry Patent Box Clock made by Seth Thomas, pillar and scroll cased clocks with wooden movements, and several mechanical curiosities.[1] The Bishop and Bradley clock with a brass movement by Heman Clark (Pl.28) brings the story of New England clocks made between 1725 and 1825 to a full circle. Its movement was made by Clark, a former apprentice of Eli Terry, and yet it alludes to the Willards and their influence on the clock-making trade.

Heman Clark trained with Terry from about 1797 until 1804 and was an active clock maker until 1825. He developed the patented movements for Eli Terry's 30-hour shelf clock into an eight-day brass movement like the one in the Bishop and Bradley clock.(Fig.5-1) The brass version of the 30-hour movement may have been ignored by other makers for good reason. For a relatively inconvenient clock,

A CLOCK FOR EVERY HOME
Connecticut's Clock Makers Show the Way

Fig. 5-1. Shelf Clock movement, James Bishop and Lucius B. Bradley, Watertown, Conn., ca.1824-32. Their eight-day movements were the finest manufactured brass shelf clocks in Connecticut in the early 19th century. See pl.28. 57.1.47

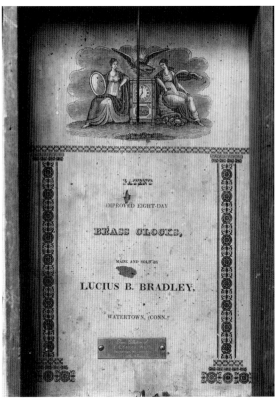

Fig. 5-2. Shelf Clock dial, James Bishop and Lucius B. Bradley. The painted iron dial was probably the work of the Boston dial painter, Samuel Curtis. 57.1.47

Fig. 5-3. Shelf Clock label, James Bishop and Lucius B. Bradley. The pendulum bob is removed to show the label on the backboard of the clock. 57.1.47

its expense was a strong drawback. The extra cost of the brass, when reflected in the final price of the clock, would not have outweighed its advantages over wood for a 30-hour movement. To the redesigned movement Clark added painted iron dials purchased from the Willards' suppliers—Spencer Nolen and Samuel Curtis of Boston.(Fig. 5-2) The clocks were housed in pillar and scroll cases, often with elaborate reverse-painted glass tablets. Among Clark's customers for eight-day timepiece and eight-day striking movements were James Bishop and Lucius B. Bradley of Watertown, Connecticut, as well as merchants in Salisbury.[2] (Fig. 5-3) Bradley, whose father was a Watertown goldsmith, jeweler and repairer of clocks and watches, advertised in 1823 that he was "manufacturing the lately improved Eight-day brass clocks, which are warranted to be equal to any clock ever offered to the public, either for time or durability." The next year he associated with James Bishop and together, they operated a retail store and manufactured and sold clocks with both brass and wooden movements from 1824 to 1832.[3] Like their contemporaries, Lemuel Curtis, Joseph Nye Dunning, and other clock makers in the flourishing towns of the New England countryside, Bishop and Bradley planned to make, sell, and quite possibly repair a line of luxury consumer goods.

The reverse-painted glass tablet in the Bishop and Bradley clock is one of the finest of its kind and has survived in excellent condition.(Fig. 5-4) The subject, commemorating General Lafayette's acclaimed tour of the United States in celebration of the 50th anniversary of the Revolution, suggests that it was painted in, or after 1825. The painting features Liberty holding a wreath over Lafayette's head, with the flags of the United States and France, a drum, a cannon, and cannon balls arranged in a pyramid.

Clark, his family, and associates were remembered for having "started the business of making *Brass* clocks, a new thing in those days."[4] The irony of this reminiscence is that it shows the distinction between clock making in Connecticut and most of the rest of New England. Wood was the commonplace material for clock makers in Connecticut, while elsewhere clocks with brass movements were being made. But as Clark's misfortune showed, his was neither the time nor place for brass clocks made on a small scale, with "no power except foot power." The era of the Connecticut brass clock awaited the application of mass production in the 1840s.

For Old Sturbridge Village, showing the story of the development of wooden movement clocks in the gallery, complements important themes emphasized in the museum's living history interpretation and demonstrations. The manufacture and

Fig. 5-4. Shelf Clock reverse-painted tablet, James Bishop and Lucius B. Bradley. The painter of this glass is unknown. 57.1.47

advertised in 1800 that he "had invented an improvement in clocks and Timekeepers. One... is available for sale [and] other clocks made and watches repaired as usual," he was still making brass clocks and training his apprentice, Heman Clark.[10] Sometime during the first years of the new century, Terry began to make some changes. Having received instruction "in East Hartford by a Mr. Cheeney,"[11] he would have known that wooden movements were less costly and lent themselves readily to rapid production using waterpower and piecework.[12] The price of clocks had to be reduced from the $25 to $60 or more that they customarily cost. Their marketing had to be extended from the few clocks that a single man could carry on a horse. Their movements had to be simplified, so that they could be quickly produced, assembled, and set up without requiring a skilled clock maker.

There are glimpses of the level of clock-making activity in the Waterbury-Plymouth-Bristol areas between 1804 and 1806 in the diary kept by Candace Roberts (1785-1806) of Bristol.[13] This young woman, whose father was Gideon Roberts (1749-1813), a clock maker and tinner, was a skillful ornamental painter on tin and recorded many days on which she "flowered tin" or "drawed flowers." She soon began to paint clock dials as well. Late in 1804 she received a visit from "Mr. [James] Harrison (1766-1845) of Waterbury, [who] wanted me to go and paint clock faces for him." She "consented to go, but with some reluctance," not realizing, at the time, that she was about to develop a new and useful skill. Her informal circuit included Colonel (William) Leavenworth, her brother Elias, Mr. E. Porter[14], and on February 26, 1806, Roberts "went to live with Mr. Terry in Plymouth." She stayed with the clock maker until early March and often she "worked very diligently all day" painting dials for him. Ten weeks later, she again "heard the unpleasant news that Mr. Terry was coming after me" for a stint of work which she completed by July 4 and returned home with obvious relief.[15] One wishes that she had noted how many clock dials she painted or whether any of the people who hired her were working on a plan for a wooden movement. She may well have been part of Terry's plan in 1806, when he prepared to sign a contract for 4,000 clocks to be produced and delivered to the partners Levi Porter and Edward Porter of Waterbury within three years.[16] (Fig. 5-5)

With the contract, Terry established the pattern

distribution of consumer goods like clocks are an important aspect of the growth of the New England economy and its effect on everyday life.[5] Studies of New England probate inventories by the museum's research staff for furnishing Village exhibits indicate that by 1850 one in three households in central New England owned a clock. Many of these were Connecticut shelf clocks with wooden movements.

In the transformation of life at home and in the workplace, Eli Terry, Sr. was a key player. Through his innovations in manufacturing and marketing, the production of clocks changed from a craft to an industry. The prices of clocks were reduced and the number that could be made and sold increased each year. Terry entered the trade in the traditional late 18th century way, as an apprentice with one of the best trained clock makers in Connecticut, Daniel Burnap. Terry spent a year in East Windsor, making clocks with both brass and wooden movements and in 1793 settled in the Naugatuck Valley, where there was already a cluster of clock makers.[6] He began modestly in Plymouth. "After finishing three or four [clock movements]," his son reminisced, "he was obliged to go out with them on horse back and put them up where they had been previously engaged or sold."[7] When he approached a potential customer about the purchase of a clock with a brass movement, he must have frequently heard that they were too expensive. He made sales by accepting "various kinds of farmer's produce, which made the terms of payment so easy as to conclude the bargain."[8] Terry learned first-hand that more people wanted to buy clocks, but he needed time to marshal his resources.

Terry received his first patent in 1797 for a clock which confirmed his mechanical ingenuity,[9] but would not transform the marketplace. When he

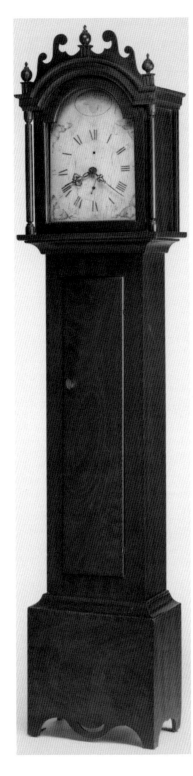

that he would follow throughout his career. This time, as he would many times in the future, Terry purchased property and equipped a shop to carry out his new manufacturing idea. To make the 4,000 clocks, he turned his back on "the then ordinary way" of making movements by "having a hand engine for cutting the teeth or cogs of the wheels and pinions and using a foot lathe for doing the turning."[17] He purchased a grist mill to introduce the novelty of "manufacturing clocks by the thousand."[18] The stream, which had already been harnessed, provided "the benefit of water power and additional machinery in doing some portion of the work." Thus prepared, Terry "began turning and doing mechanical business." With the purchase of so many clocks guaranteed, they could be produced as efficiently as current technology would permit.

Terry hired young men trained in carpentry, not the clock business, to run the factory. Silas Hoadley supervised "apprentices and several workmen to convert the grist mill into a clock factory."[19] The later-to-be famous, Seth Thomas came to work when Terry began production in the following year. Since the label used in these clocks is dated August 1, 1808, it confirms that clocks were in production by that date, if not sooner. The clocks made for the Porter contract have 30-hour, weight-powered wooden movements with count-wheel strike systems.(Figs.5-6, 5-7) The hands are pewter.

Terry had to prepare instructions for setting up the clocks, since they would be sold wherever the Porters—or their peddlers—could find buyers.[20] The label states that the clocks were "made by Eli Terry" for the Porters "and warranted, if cased and well used."

Let the Clock be set in a perpendicular position. This is necessary, in order to its having an equal beat; and if it fails to beat equally, it may be put in beat, by raising one or the other side of the Clock. And having found the right position, there let it be fastened. If the Clock goes too fast, lengthen the pendulum; but if too slow, shorten it, by means of the screw, at the bottom. If the hands want moving, do it by means of the longest, or by turning the face-wheel on the time side of the Clock: turning at any time, forwards, but never backwards, when the clock is within 15 minutes of striking; nor father [sic] than to carry the longest hand, if it varies from the truth, may be put forward with

Fig. 5-6. Tall Clock movement, Eli Terry, Plymouth, Conn. Front view with the dial removed. Terry movements have oak plates, cherry wheels and maple arbors and pinions. Wheel teeth were sawn with water-powered equipment. 57.1.221

Fig. 5-7. Tall Clock movement, Eli Terry, Plymouth, Conn. Connecticut wooden tall clocks utilize the count wheel which is mounted off center on the back plate of the movement. The bell is mounted above. 57.1.221

Fig. 5-5 Tall Clock, Eli Terry, Plymouth, Conn., ca. 1807-09. Sold uncased, "Porter Contract" Terry tall clock movements were cased by the purchaser's cabinetmaker. This pine case retains its original painted finish. 57.1.221

the finger. And if the Clock fails to strike the proper hour, press downward, with your finger, the small wire on the striking side of the Clock, and it will strike as often as you repeat the pressure. Keep the clock as much as possible from dust and apply no oil, at any time, to it, unless it be a very small quantity of sweet oil, or the oil of almonds.[21]

Proof that Terry and his associates delivered the clocks by 1810, as contracted, is found in the record of land deeded by the Porters to Eli Terry in Plymouth, Waterbury, and Watertown. It was not equivalent to the full $16,000 for the delivery of 4,000 clocks at $4.00 each that Terry should have received, but he was able to resell the real estate worth $7,000 transferred by the Porters for $9,496. Terry also divested himself of the clock factory by selling it to Thomas and Hoadley for $6,000. In all, the completion of the contract made Terry a wealthy man[22] and the era of the wooden tall clock movement had begun.[23]

Other producers then entered the market rapidly. Terry had apparently retired and the Porters never attempted to buy and sell so many clocks again. They left a legacy of clocks that were cheap to manufacture and apparently easy to sell. The three years that Terry had spent producing the wooden movements were ample time for his improvements to be incorporated by other established wooden clock makers into their own designs. Clocks by Thomas and Hoadley, Ephraim Downs, Riley Whiting, William Leavenworth, and the Ives family, illustrate the work of several others, who were soon engaged in this business.

As early as 1809, certainly before the Porters could have sold all their clocks, Lemuel Harrison and Company also entered the business of having clocks made in quantity by contracting with others for parts and assembly. Heman Clark, who had left Terry's employ before the Porter contract, was commissioned to make "Wheel Stuff for 1000 Clocks"[24] and wrote in December 1811, Ephraim Downs "began my job for Lemuel Harrison & Co." He and his helpers produced 9,162 tall clock movements in the next three years: just under 1,000 were "plain clocks" and the majority were called "day of month" clocks. Downs mastered the technique of large-scale production, and also learned its risk, when Harrison's warehouse, which was filled with his clocks, burned to the ground in 1814 with

$600 still owed to him. (He had to wait four years for payment.) He spent a few months after leaving Harrison, "in cutting all the parts for 500 clocks," for Clark, Cook, and Company of Waterbury, and then headed for Ohio. There he did similar work for another Connecticut emigrant, Luman Watson (1790-1834), and his partner, Amasa Read (wkg. 1809), who were making clocks in Cincinnati. For Downs this six-year period provided a useful understanding of the western market. He maintained contact with several peddlers or merchants in Ohio to whom he continued to supply wooden movement clocks on terms for resale for the rest of his 33-year career.[25]

Back in Plymouth "Thomas and Hoadley Mechanics in Company" continued to manufacture tall clocks with wooden movements from 1810 until late in 1813. The final job of their partnership indicates that, like others who made wooden clock movements, they worked on contracts which specified delivery and payment schedules. They should have completed a contract for 500 clocks at $7.00 each to be made between April and November 1813, when Thomas left to go out on his own in December. It was claimed that only 150 clocks had actually been made and delivered and the stalemate over payment and delivery schedules continued until 1820.[26] Nonetheless, both Thomas and Hoadley continued to make clocks. Thomas purchased Heman Clark's property in Plymouth "with a clock factory standing thereon, together with all the machinery and tools belonging to said Factory."[27]

Hoadley made tall clocks long after most other Connecticut makers had ceased. Part of the reason for his conservatism was that he had found distant markets, which he served by sending peddlers out to them. One was William Alcott, later a schoolteacher and writer, who was one of Hoadley's employees in 1814. Living about a mile from the factory, he had been hired at the age of 15 for "fitting and putting together clocks." As he did not find mechanical work to his liking, he peddled Hoadley clocks in the South instead.[28] When Ephraim Downs returned to Connecticut from Ohio in 1821, he helped make sales in that state. He married Hoadley's sister-in-law, and then worked for him between September 1823 and March 1824. Downs was one of ten men and three women working for Hoadley in that year, who produced some 1,400 clocks with 30-hour wooden movements worth $4.50 each.[29] (Pl. 23, Figs.

5-8, 5-9, 5-10) These clocks were sent south to Georgia and west to Cincinnati to be sold by Luman Watson.[30] While he might have had to content himself with "less business," by continuing to produce tall clocks, Hoadley and Riley Whiting, among others, were "successful and more so, than many who subsequently engaged in this occupation."[31] Hoadley was remembered as an active Mason and faithful member of St. Peter's Episcopal Church in Plymouth for many years. The Masonic eye and other symbols and the crossed keys of St. Peter, reflecting those interests, are painted in the tympanum of the tall clock's dial.[32] (See Pl. 23.)

Several clocks in the collection were originally sold as uncased wooden movements. The stories of clocks by the Ives family, William Leavenworth, and Riley Whiting illustrate several facets of how these clocks might find an owner. Clocks with wooden movements were sometimes sold to case makers and sometimes directly to consumers to be "hung up without a case."[33]

The Ives brothers were born into a clock making and woodworking tradition. Gideon, Elias, and Candace Roberts were cousins and Joseph Ives married Almenia Rich.[34] Ira and Joseph Ives, and their brothers Amasa and Philo, were active manufacturers and merchants in Bristol between 1803 and 1815.[35] Joseph made wooden tall clock movements until it became apparent that they had very

Fig. 5-9. Tall Clock dial, Silas Hoadley, Plymouth, Conn., ca. 1820. Painted poplar dials were fitted with seconds and day of the month hands. The hour and minute hands are pewter. 57.1.183

Fig. 5-8. Tall Clock movement, Silas Hoadley, Plymouth, Conn., ca. 1820. Shown from the time train side, cherry wheels, maple arbors and solid pinions cut from the arbor stock are suspended between oak plates. See pl. 23. 57.1.195

Fig. 5-10. Tall Clock movement, Silas Hoadley. The hours are struck on the bell mounted above the movement and controlled by a count wheel. 57.1.183

Fig. 5-11. Tall Clock movement, Joseph Ives, ca. 1815. The rolling pinions are mounted on the maple arbors opposite the wheels. Each wooden pinion "leaf" rolls on a steel wire. See fig. 5-8 for a comparison of the pinions. 57.1.188

Fig. 5-12. Tall Clock, Joseph Ives, Bristol, Connecticut, ca. 1815. The pine case retains the original painted decoration. The reverse-painted dial is a restoration. 57.1.188

little future when sold uncased by peddlers, but he continued to play a role in the industry for many years. Early in the 19th century Joseph and Ira both patented their improvements in clock making, specifically the distinctive feature of a rolling pinion in the wooden time and strike trains. A patent was issued to Ira Ives for a rolling pinion on February 12, 1812, but its description was lost in the Patent Office fire.[36] The rolling pinion is used in place of the more common cut wooden pinions to reduce friction in the operation of the clock. Unlike stationary pinion leaves, there was no likelihood that the rolling pinions would fracture. (Fig. 5-11)

Without the leveling provided by installation in a case, movements were frequently provided with directions on printed labels. Such a label for a Joseph Ives clock sold in 1814, provides "Directions for setting up and regulating said clocks," in a "perpendicular position ... necessary in order to its having an equal beat."[37] The movement may have been transported to northwestern Massachusetts and then housed in a case which has painted decoration that bears some similarity to the work broadly attributed to Thomas Matteson of Shaftsbury, Vermont.[38] (Fig. 5-12) The label inside the OSV clock states: "This clock cleaned & warranted if well-used, Arad Dennison, Leyden, Mass. Aug. 1850." Dennison was a miller, but he evidently did enough trade in cleaning clocks to print up a label.

William Leavenworth was no longer making clocks in Connecticut when he made the movement now housed in a case decorated by Rufus Cole of Broadalbin, New York. Leavenworth was a carpenter who made tall clocks with wooden movements. He established a sawmill and gristmill on the Mad River in Waterbury about 1800 and later, a turning shop through which he became successful enough to establish himself as a leading citizen of Waterbury, its first postmaster, a merchant and distiller. But after his business failed, he and William, Jr., (1786-1829) moved to Albany, New York, where Leavenworth and Son made clocks from 1815 until 1829 or later.[39] (Mark Leavenworth [1774-1842], who began to make clocks in 1810, was his nephew.) A clock, attributed to William, is in a stenciled case dating from circa 1830 signed by R. [Rufus] Cole (1804-1874).[40](Pl. 22,Figs. 5-13, 5-14) More than a dozen clocks housed in Cole cases have been identified, several with movements by Riley Whiting. The star and cornucopia decoration in the arch

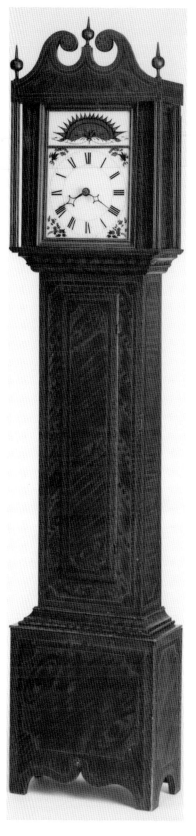

Fig. 5-14. Tall Clock attributed to William Leavenworth and Son.The count wheel is mounted in the approximate center of the back plate of the movement. See fig. 5-7 for comparison. 57.1.130

Fig. 5-13. Detail, Tall Clock attributed to William Leavenworth and Son, Albany, N.Y., ca. 1815-1829. Case decoration by Rufus Cole, Broadalbin, N.Y., ca.1830. The original painted decoration on the pine case is signed: "R. Cole, Painter", on the bottom center of the base. Note the stenciled shadow of a running deer along the lower right and left front edges of the base. See pl. 22. 57.1.130

of the Leavenworth-Cole dial resembles the Whiting clock face. (See Fig. 5-15) The families' connection is documented by a letter from Riley Whiting to Mark Leavenworth about agreeing to lay aside a patent obtained by William Leavenworth, "as he made no improvement."[41]

Whiting was another who "engaged in the manufacture of the old fashioned hang-up clock."[42] He entered the clock business in 1807 and continued until his death in 1835. He joined his brothers-in-law, Samuel and Luther Hoadley, in Winchester, Connecticut, where they, like other hopeful novices, were adapting their water-powered manufacturing facility by adding a small factory for producing tall clocks to the sawmill and gristmill on the site. These partners developed a procedure for casting clock bells in about 1810, which they shrouded in secrecy, making them in a separate building and excluding visitors. In 1812, the partners erected a wire factory to meet the need for wrought iron wire in wooden

Fig. 5-15. Tall Clock dial, Riley Whiting, Winchester, Conn., ca. 1820. The painted winding holes on the dial give the false impression that this is an eight-day, brass clock, wound through the dial. Thirty-hour, wooden tall clocks are wound by pulling the cords inside the case. 57.1.63

movement clocks.[43] When wartime military service beckoned Samuel and Luther Hoadley shortly afterwards, they left the business to Whiting, who was generally able to find "a ready market for all clocks manufactured at his establishment."[44] (Figs. 5-15, 5-16)

ELI TERRY WHO HAD SET THE CLOCK INDUSTRY on its ear once, did so a second time with his patent for "improvements in mechanism and layout" for a clock to fit on a shelf or mantelpiece.[45] Coincidentally this was also in 1816, the year in which Simon Willard's patent on his timepiece expired. For Terry it was the result of several years of work, much of it between 1814 and 1816. The patent was for a "new and useful improvement on the thirty-hour brass and wooden clocks," claiming aesthetic and technological distinctions. Terry substituted a half-seconds pendulum for a seconds pendulum, and reduced its length to 9.8 inches. He used wheel counts which were designed for a shorter weight fall and he neatly mortised a frame of cherry together to form plates.

The discovery of a new way to fix the pallet and hang the pendulum insured that the critical parts could be removed for cleaning with the minimum of disturbance. The clock would, therefore, run more accurately with less friction than the older style movement. Nor should it be overlooked that the number of wooden wheels—nine and a count wheel—and the resultant number of teeth that had to be cut to make a functioning clock—367—for each wood movement—made Terry's recent manufacturing improvement for cutting the cogs or teeth on wooden wheels a key to this clock's successful production.[46]

The movement is mounted directly in a case resembling a cupboard with a glass door, "about twenty inches long, fourteen wide and three in depth or thickness." The clock's size ("smaller, handsomer, [and] less cumbersome") and its 'packaging' in a case that was integral to its design, resulted in a selling price that was "cheaper including the case." Other conveniences noted were that it was "easier moved from one room to another, and having the weights in sight," the owner was more likely to remember to wind it."

The surviving clock considered closest to Terry's patent description was made by Seth Thomas. His clock-in-a-box (Fig. 5-17) has no attached dial or face, just as the patent states; instead, the upper part

Fig. 5 16. Tall Clock movement, Riley Whiting, Winchester. Whiting eliminated the decorative turning found on pillar posts, arbors and strike levers of other Connecticut makers. Pewter hands of this type are commonly found on Whiting tall clocks. 57.1.63

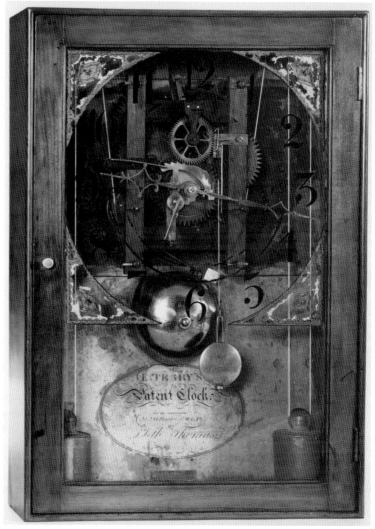

Fig. 5-17. Box Clock, Seth Thomas, Plymouth, Conn., ca. 1816-18. 57.1.116

Fig. 5-18. Pillar and Scroll Shelf Clock, Seth Thomas, Plymouth, Conn., ca. 1818-1822. Note the off-center aperture in the lower glass to view the pendulum swing. 57.1.236

of the glass door is a reverse-painted dial and spandrels as stated in the patent description. The entire movement is visible through the glass: the hands mark time on the glass dial, the wooden strap movement, the off-center pendulum, the rack and snail strike, and cords suspending the weights threaded through a pulley in each of the two top corners. But the clock was labelled "E. Terry's Patent Clock. Made and Sold by Seth Thomas: Plymouth, Con." When Thomas made his clock in 1816, he made one change in the box clock which distinguished it from Terry's patent description. Its off-center pendulum differs significantly from the patent, which states clearly that "the pendulum is hung under the center socket."[47] Thomas continued to use the off-center pendulum in his later pillar and scroll top cases.(Fig. 5-18)

Meanwhile Chauncey Jerome, who "accidentally heard that Mr. Eli Terry was about to fit up his factory [which was built the year before] for making his new Patent Shelf Clock" got himself a job. That winter, Jerome recalled, Terry "drew another plan of the Pillar Scroll Top Case with great improvement over the one which Thomas was then making." In Jerome's view Terry was

> a great mechanic [who] had made many improvements in the way of making the cases, ...which completely revolutionized the whole business.... The pillars were about twenty-one inches long, three-quarters of an inch at the base, and three-eights at the top—resting on a square base, and the top finished by a handsome cap. It had a large dial eleven inches square, and tablet below the dial seven by eleven inches. This style of clock was liked very much and was made in large quantities and for several years. [48]

Jerome, who had expected to be put to work on case production—"nearly all" of which Thomas had been doing by hand—was busied "setting up machinery and benches."

Terry soon encountered the problem of controlling his patented technology. When Jerome left, he took his pay in clock movements, which he cased and sold. As Terry's sons were still too young to enter the business, he had to continue to employ others to make clocks for him. Whoever worked for him between Jerome's departure in 1817 and September 1818 is not known, but that month Terry signed two different kinds of agreements to spur production within a few days. He hired his brother Samuel to come to Plymouth from East Windsor "to put together and set up clocks" for three shillings and nine pence, or approximately 60 cents apiece. In the other, he licensed Seth Thomas, despite his departure with knowledge of the patent and his own improvements in mind.[49]

Samuel Terry made clocks for Eli which followed the patent, noting in his invoice that clocks "with the swing wheel [escape wheel] under the face...[were] extra work than to put in so many of the other kind." Terry paid more for each clock than their original agreement,[50] while Thomas was permitted to "make, sell or other wise dispose of wooden clocks made on the plan and with the improvements mentioned in said Patent and the schedule thereto annexed, at one factory only and without a partner." He was to pay a royalty, but was not required to acknowledge Terry's patent. His label states: "Clocks made and sold by Seth Thomas, Plymouth, Con. ...The public may rest assured that clocks made at this Factory are equal if not superior to any made in this country." Seth Thomas worked with his adapted design, which allowed him to manufacture clocks profitably.[51] (Figs. 5-19, Fig. 5-20) When his sons were old enough in 1823, Terry formed Eli Terry and Sons, with Eli, Jr., and Henry as his partners to

Fig. 5-19. Pillar and Scroll Shelf Clock, Seth Thomas, ca. 1825. 57.1.62

Fig. 5-20. Pillar and Scroll Shelf Clock movement, Seth Thomas. The count-wheel strike is mounted on the upper left of the front plate in this 30-hour wooden movement. The escape wheel (center) is the only brass wheel in these clocks. 57.1.62

produce pillar and scroll cased clocks. This company was in business for a decade. (Fig. 5-21)

The process of making the patent clock was described as one requiring considerable precision in the selection of the wood, its levelling, marking, sawing, drilling, sanding and finishing. Another observer recalled the wonder of a childhood visit to a wooden clock factory:

> I watched the piles of thin boards of cherry, touched by swift saws, falling as clock wheels into boxes below. Then I found that the clocks were not made by one man, but by as many sets of men and women as there were pieces; and then they were assembled.[52]

Terry was unable to retain strict control of production and profits. He paid his employees with movements, sold uncased movements, and granted manufacturing rights to others. Terry patent movements were used—and adapted—by at least 22 other clock makers from 1818 through the 1820s.[53]

> The public mind in a Yankee country was not content that Eli Terry should make his thousands of dollars a year, while they only got an old-fashioned living at one dollar a day or so; and one after another in the contiguous towns...they found their way into the same business.[54]

Even after the formation of Eli Terry and Sons,

Fig. 5-21. Pillar and Scroll Shelf Clock, Eli Terry and Sons, Plymouth, Conn., ca. 1823-33. 57.1.28

Fig. 5-22. Detail, Pillar and Scroll clock case and movement, Ephraim Downs. Shown with the dial removed, the wooden movement was mounted between two vertical supports which separates it from the two weight channels. 57.1.94

Samuel Terry still continued to make clocks on contract. Silas Hoadley created an inverted train or "upside-down" version without paying royalties. Ephraim Downs began to make shelf clocks after he left Hoadley's employment to go into business in his own shop. He made and labelled shelf clocks for Bristol merchant George Mitchell from November 1825 until March 1828.[55] (Fig. 5-22) Downs's clocks had a 30-hour, weight-driven, wooden movement, with count-wheel strike, painted wood dial, and were housed in pillar and scroll cases with reverse-painted tablets.(Fig. 5-23)

Mitchell was a second-generation storekeeper, who inherited a peddling business, adding clocks to the stock of traditional Yankee notions, by commissioning clock and case makers. To meet the growing demand for shelf clocks, Mitchell had first enticed Chauncey Jerome to move to Bristol in 1821, accepting his note for Terry Patent clocks in payment for a house.[56] Four years later, Mitchell assembled a water-powered mill site, which included a turning shop, which he sold to Downs. After making 3,036 clocks in this shop for Mitchell in three years,[57] Downs began to work independently making and selling movements to others, including Eli Terry and Son. His agreement with Terry signed on November 1, 1830 granted the full use of his patents, with payment in clock movements.[58] Perhaps this was a graceful way of avoiding a protracted and costly suit with Terry whose design he had been using and would continue to produce.

Terry's son recalled that his father's patent became "a source of no little trouble, strife and litigation."[59] From 1822 until 1827, Terry pressed Thomas to abide by their agreement made in 1818. About to return to the Patent Office with a revised description of his patent clock, Terry and Thomas signed a new agreement in which Thomas paid $1000 to balance accounts and moving forward, pledged that he would:

> continue to make the movements of his clocks as he does now nor ...make use of any of the improvements made by the said Terry since the date of the within agreement nor make any alterations in his clocks similar to those now made by said Terry.[60]

Terry's initial attempts to press his patent rights by going to court seem to have been most successful in pointing out his need to clarify the patent claim. He filed a new description in 1826, stating explic-

Fig. 5-23. Pillar and Scroll Shelf Clock, Ephraim Downs, Bristol, Conn., ca. 1825-1828. 57.1.94

itly: "I do not claim any one of the parts of the above described clock separately as my invention, but I do claim the above arrangement and conformation of the whole as a new and useful invention."[61] He sued Thomas the following year claiming to have urged him to desist from adopting unlicensed improvements several times, but always without success. Thomas countered that he was satisfied with the clock he was making and as he "doubted the utility" of the new patents, was "unwilling to change his tools and machinery to enter upon said new manufacture."[62]

In 1847 when Mrs. Elizabeth A. Howland and her husband published *The American Economical Housekeeper*, there was one illustration in the book. (fig. 5-24) It is of the preparations for a hearth-cooked meal: the tin kitchen (reflector oven) was heating before the fire, and on the mantelpiece, a Connecticut shelf clock was ticking away. This meal would be ready on time. Workers and housewives had learned the importance of the designated times for working and taking breaks, and clock makers reponded with timekeepers in many shapes and sizes. But this clock in the kitchen was not a stylish model in 1847. By then it was probably considered old-fashioned and out of date and was relegated to the kitchen mantel.

As the market grew, the dominance of the Terry family was superceded as new manufacturers entered the marketplace and new case styles were introduced. Downs, for example, whose modest shop produced 7,000 clocks in the decade of the 1830s, purchased frames, faces, bells and weights from local suppliers and shipped clocks in looking glass, fancy, "short brunze with carved feet," square top, and "scrowl" cases to be sold primarily in Ohio and western New York.[63] After Jerome introduced the one-day brass clock in 1838,[64] Eli Terry and his companies found themselves left with an increasingly limited market. They sold most of their clocks in the South and to do business there, "operated large two horse covered wagons." Reluctantly even Seth Thomas "finally gave up making the Scroll Top" substituting Jerome's bronze looking-glass case and eventually introducing other current movements and case styles. When Thomas stopped making clocks with wooden movements, old clocks which needed repair were sent to one retired worker, who had been given a quantity of unused wooden parts.[65]

Eight-day movements, one-day brass movements, new case designs,[66] (Fig. 5-25) and new manufacturers contributed to the diversity and competitiveness in the marketplace in the 1830s. In 1836 Eli Terry, Jr., responded to a potential customer in Ohio: "Your letter to father has been handed over to me (he does not make clocks)." The firm was then able to supply seven different kinds of clocks, but three years later he wrote to a customer that he was:

> unable to furnish you [with] any more 30-hour wood clocks beside this lot for some months if indeed ever. Our arrangements have been such of late but we have but very few of that kind to sell. The fact is that they afford us so little profit that almost all the Manufacturers have turned their attention to other businesses and we have in a measure followed suit. ...We deemed it our duty to state frankly the difficulty you will have in obtaining 30-hour wood clocks in this section of the country as above. ...Please let us know whether the brass and eight day wood will answer your purpose."[67]

IN THE CENTURY SINCE GAWEN BROWN and William Claggett had come to Boston to make and repair clocks for the wealthy, the whole notion of timekeeping had changed. Along with it the craft, once guarded as a mystery and handed down to selected apprentices, had been transformed. While there was still a market for handcrafted clocks in 1825, there were more customers for manufactured clocks priced well below the former threshold of clock ownership.

Fig. 5-25. Wall Clock, Eli Terry, Jr., ca. 1832-1835. This Connecticut adaptation of the Willard patent timepiece was an attempt at developing a new case style. Wall clocks with wooden movements are rare. 57.1.238

Driven by the market, clock makers responded to the possibilities of transforming their product. Clock movements, as the 18th-century examples in the OSV collection show, were adapted and made with materials other than brass. While the Blaisdels and Rogerses proved that they could substitute iron for brass in clock movements, this material was not generally adopted as the alternative for the costly alloy. Smaller movements, imported movements, and wooden movements offered better solutions.

The renowned Willard family of clock makers in Grafton and Roxbury, Massachusetts, were aggressive businessmen who introduced innovative designs for wall and shelf clocks and the widespread use of pre-cast parts. However, their response to the challenge of making clocks in the post-Revolutionary era was to continue to fabricate (or assemble, depending on the model) expensive clocks on a piecemeal basis. It was Eli Terry who saw the market for 4,000 inexpensive 30-hour wooden tall clock movements in the first decade of the 19th century, and then patented a shelf clock in 1816 that was less costly than the Massachusetts version. Both the wooden movement and most elements of the stylish case were made of local materials and were designed for efficient production in a factory setting. Here the individualized concepts taught by a master to his apprentice were muffled by the drone of machinery.

The Claggetts and Gawen Brown would have been surprised to see the clocks of 1825, which were pouring out the Connecticut shops with oak plates, cherry wheels, and maple pinions and arbors. Nor would they have recognized the western destinations of many of these clocks. They would have been equally surprised to see that clocks had become affordable items of household furniture enabling their owners to be punctual in the conduct of their daily lives. At last there were so many clocks available that their owners could be prompt for their appointments. For two centuries New England's clock makers had been responding to the 1633 charge of the General Court of Massachusetts that "No person, householder or other, shall spend his time idly or unprofitably." By the 19th-century, enough clock mechanisms were on hand for most Americans to accurately monitor the passage of time.

NOTES

[1] These include two balance wheel skeleton clocks (57.1.89, 57.1.106), a sharp Gothic clock with a spring powered fusee balance wheel (57.1.182), and an eight-day weight powered balance wheel clock with wooden wheels and brass plates, by Eli Terry and Sons (57.1.145). Experimental time pieces by Silas B. Terry were evidently of particular interest to J.Cheney Wells, who authored "Silas Burnham Terry, Experimental Balance Wheel Clocks, Pioneering Work in Development of Marine-Type Movement," *NAWCC Bulletin*, 1949, IV: 14-15, 31-36.

[2] Heman Clark made no movements after 1823, but his brother, Sylvester, continued to make them. Whether made by Heman or Sylvester Clark, this movement dates between 1823 and 1827. While the names of Bishop and Bradley are found in clocks with both brass and wooden movements, the OSV clock has a rack-and-snail eight-day brass movement.

[3] See Chris H. Bailey and Dana J. Blackwell, "Heman Clark and the 'Salem Bridge' Shelf Clocks, *NAWCC Bulletin*, Supplement 13, 1980, 1-36.

[4] Recollection of P. Sanford, December 9, 1886 in Bailey and Blackwell, 19.

[5] Jack Larkin, *The Reshaping of Everyday Life, 1790-1840*, (New York: Harper and Row, c. 1988), 105-148, 320-324.

[6] Virginia and Howard Sloane, "4,000 Clocks: The Story of Eli Terry and His Mysterious Financiers," *NAWCC Bulletin*, 204 XXII:5-14.

[7] Henry Terry, "A Review of Dr. Alcott's History of Clockmaking," *Waterbury American*, June 10, 1853, in Kenneth D. Roberts, *Eli Terry and the Connecticut Shelf Clock* (Bristol, Conn.: Ken Roberts Publishing Co., 1973), 35-38; *History of the American Clock Business, for the past sixty years and a Life of Chauncey Jerome, written by himself*, (New Haven Conn.: F.C. Dayton, Jr., 1860),36.

[8] Joel Blakeslee, *Historical Address*, (Bridgeport, 1877), 14, quoted in Roberts, 23; Chauncey Jerome tells a similar story, which he attributes to Riley Blakeslee, 36.

[9] His clock which showed the equation of time had two minute hands to show mean time and solar time. Charles S. Parsons, "Eli Terry's Equation Clock," *NAWCC Bulletin*, 202, October 1979, XXI: 522-35; Michael O'Malley, *Keeping Watch: A History of American Time* (New York: Viking Penguin, 1990), 1-8.

[10] Although trained in brass movement making, Terry apparently—and wisely—ignored this part of the business after 1800, while Clark would struggle, but never find long term financial success. V. and H. Sloane, 6,13,15; Bailey, Blackwell, "Heman Clark and the 'Salem Bridge' Shelf Clocks."

[11] Henry Terry does not specify whether Benjamin or Timothy Cheney., Roberts,36.

[12] Elsewhere guns and textiles were taking the lead in transforming the definition of manufacturing. See Merritt Roe Smith, *Harper's Ferry Armory and the New Technology: The Challenge of Change* (Ithaca: Cornell University Press, 1977, esp. chapters 7 and 8.

[13] Diary of Candace Roberts, Bristol, Conn., 1801-1806, Typescript. OSV photocopy.

[14] Harrison's clock factory in Waterbury was purchased by Edward Porter on July 26, 1806, and Harrison moved to Boston. V. and H. Sloane, 18.

[15] Diary of Candace Roberts, Bristol, Conn.

[16] It has long been assumed that with the same surname, Levi Porter and Edward Porter were brothers. They were unrelated business partners. V. and H. Sloane, 22-33; Jerome states that "a number of men in Waterbury associated themselves together and made a large contract with [Terry], they furnishing the stock and he making the movements." 36.

[17] For example Gideon Roberts's shop was on the corner of his property, not near water. His clock tools included three lathes, four vices, a wheel cutting machine, a screw plate, and other hand tools including four saws, a hatchet, three hammers and 2 pairs of cutting pliers for a total value of about $25. Inventory, Estate of Gideon Roberts, January 5, 1815, Bristol (Farmington District), Docket 2313, Connecticut State Library.

[18] Chauncey Jerome, who was 14 years old in 1807 and infatuated with the clock business, begged his guardian to "get me a place" with Eli Terry. He "was at that time making more clocks than any other man in the country, about two hundred in a year, which was thought to be a great number." His guardian tried to discourage him by saying that "there were so many clocks then making the country would soon be filled with them and the business would be good for nothing in two or three years." Jerome, 17.

[19] Silas Hoadley's father, Ammi, owned a gristmill where he manufactured wooden wheels and parts for clocks. Albert L. Partridge, "Silas Hoadley, Clockmaker," Boston Clock Club, November 1940, 203.

[20] Thomas Chandler Haliburton, *The Clockmaker, or the Sayings and Doings of Sam Slick, of Slickville* (Philadelphia: Carey, Lea and Blanchard, 1838), 15-18.

[21] The OSV clock has no label. An example is reproduced in Roberts, 29.

[22] John Joseph Murphy, "The Establishment of the American Clock Industry: A Study in Entrepreneurial History," Ph.D. diss. Yale University, 1961; see also, Rob-

erts, 32, 41.

[23] See Shepard Roberts, "Identification and History of Wood Movements in Tall Clocks," *NAWCC Bulletin* (April, 1970) XIV:

[24] Bailey and Blackwell, 6; Lemuel was James Harrison's brother.

[25] Ephraim Downs Account Book, American Clock and Watch Museum, Bristol, Conn.; John A. Diehl, "Luman Watson: Cincinnati Clockmaker," *Antiques*, (June 1968) 93:796-799.

[26] "Yet although the plaintiffs have at all times been ready to deliver said clocks and did in fact deliver 150, they have not kept and performed their sd agreement...nor has Warner since the death of Comstock paid $3500 or for such clocks so delivered." Warner and Comstock vs. Thomas and Hoadley, September 27, 1820, ms. 72596, Papers mostly legal relating to clock makers of Plymouth 1807-1886, The Connecticut Historical Society, Hartford, Connecticut.

[27] Bailey and Blackwell, 7.

[28] Alcott left the industry to become a schoolteacher and writer. *History of the Town of Plymouth, Connecticut, with an account of the Centennial Celebration, May 14 and 15, 1895*, comp., Francis Atwater (Meriden, 1895), 305.

[29] Plymouth, Litchfield County, Census of Manufactures, 1820, 176.

[30] A 'Cincinnati' clock with a painted dial signed Read and Watson and a 30-hour wood movement presumably made by Downs, not surprisingly, resembles Hoadley's work. Marius Peladeau, "Silas Hoadley, Connecticut clockmaker," *Antiques* (July 1972) 101:90-95; L. Watson, Cincinnati to Silas Hoadley, March 4, 1819, The Connecticut Historical Society.

[31] Henry Terry in Roberts, 36.

[32] Atwater, 237; He had left the clock business long before his death and his probate inventory includes neither a clock among his household effects or any items that show his former occupation. Estate of Silas Hoadley, 1870, Probate Files, Plymouth District, Connecticut State Library.

[33] Jerome, 36.

[34] It is not known who trained the clock makers, but since at the age of 23, Joseph Ives married the Almenia Rich, he may have followed the tradition of the able apprentice marrying into a clock making family.

[35] Although most of these eight-day wooden movement rolling pinion clocks have been dubbed "Joseph Ives" as the maker, the truth is that they were manufactured by "A. Ives, Jr., & Co.", by Amasa and Chauncey Ives" and by "Joseph Ives" and very probably all by the same shop,

the firm names changing rather than the operation. Joseph Ives was probably involved in all three firms and being the best known and longest involved, he has been most commonly considered the maker. Chris Bailey to Caroline Sloat, December 24, 1990.

[36] Ira Ives's 1812 patent is known only by its title, as the specifications were lost in the 1836 Patent Office fire, and having been superseded for so long, its reconstruction was considered unnecessary. Chris Bailey considers that the rolling pinion feature of this clock was the subject of this patent. Letter to Caroline Sloat, December 24, 1990.

[37] Kenneth D. Roberts, The Contributions of Joseph Ives to Connecticut Clock Technology, 1810-1862, (Bristol, Conn.: American Clock and Watch Museum, 1970), Pl. V, 28.

[38] Stylistic similarity between the decorated case of the Ives clock bequeathed to OSV by Clarke Maynard, whose family originated in western Massachusetts and signed items in the OSV and Henry Ford Museum collections has led to this attribution. See Caroline Hebb, "A Distinctive Group of Early Vermont Painted Furniture," Antiques (September 1973) 104:458-461.

[39] Leavenworth and Son, clockmakers are listed from 1815-1821, 1824-6, The William Leavenworth listed between 1831 and 1839 is probably not William Sr, who died in Bridgeport, Conn. in 1836. See Chris H. Bailey "Mr. Terry's Waterbury Competitors—The Leavenworths and Associates," NAWCC Bulletin, Whole No 200, June 1979, Albany, Childs Directories.

[40] Cole appears in the censuses of 1840 and 1850 in Broadalbin, New York and is listed in the Broadalbin Business Directory as a "Painter, House and Sign." "Rufus Cole: A Mohawk Valley decorator," The Decorator (1981), 4-11.

[41] Whiting to Mark Leavenworth, May 7, 1823, in Bailey, Two Hundred Years, 113.

[42] Jerome names both Chauncey Boardman of Bristol and Asa Hopkins of Northford, History, 38; during his 28 years in the industry, Whiting also manufactured 30-hour and eight-day shelf clocks.

[43] The use of wrought iron wire and other raw materials in wooden movement clocks is discussed by Donald Hoke, Ingenious Yankees: The Rise of the American System of Manufactures in the Private Sector (New York, 1990), 92.

[44] "Riley Whiting's Wood Clock Manufactory," Winchester, Litchfield County, Conn., 1820 Census of Manufactures. In 1820 the shop profitably produced 3000 wood clocks valued at $4.25

each. However, he also had to weather difficult economic times, twice managing to save his business from bankruptcy. Bailey, Two Hundred Years, 113.

[45] Specifications of Eli Terry's letters patent, dated June 12, 1816, Roberts, 44.

[46] Henry Terry notes that his father improved the cutting machine patented by Asa Hopkins in 1813 or 1814, both of which were still in use in 1853. Henry Terry in Roberts, 36; Hoopes, Early Clockmaking in Connecticut (New Haven: 1934), 15-17 faults Terry's contemporaries for not recognizing that Terry's inventiveness extended to the machinery for the implementation of his ideas.

[47] How this clock with the Seth Thomas label fits into the chronology and Terry's lengthy dispute with him has long been a puzzle. It has been concluded that only Thomas actually produced the labelled Terry-patent clock because of two features exclusive to Terry-made patent clocks of later design and two differences exclusive to Thomas-made patent clocks. Terry followed the patent in regard to the removable bridge and the pendulum hung from the center of the movement. W.F. Pritchett, "The Terry Patent Clock Pre-Standard Production," NAWCC Bulletin, 1971 XIV:1367-1391.

[48] Jerome 33, 39, 41-49.

[49] Petition of Eli Terry to the Superior Court at Litchfield, August 1827, in Roberts, 48.

[50] Lockwood Barr, "Samuel Terry, Clockmaker's Clockmaker," Antiques, (January 1955) 67:62.

[51] Terry-Thomas agreement, October 2, 1818, Roberts, 95.

[52] Joseph Hawley, "Centennial Address," in Roberts, 185.

[53] Snowden Taylor, "Characteristics of Standard Terry-Type 30-Hour Wooden Movements as a Guide to Identifying Movement Makers," NAWCC Bulletin 208 (October 1980) XXII:450-462; also Hoke, Ingenious Yankees, 61.

[54] William A. Alcott, The History of Yankee clocks and Clockmaking, Daily Evening Traveller (Boston), April 13, 1853.

[55] Account Book and Ephraim Downs' Book for Notes, Bristol, Conn., American Clock and Watch Museum. Downs signed his name without an e before the final s, which appears in the printed label.

[56] Jerome purchased 13 1/2 acres for $2500 from Mitchell on July 21, 1821, giving him three notes for Eli Terry Patent Clocks, 100 by September 15, 50 by February 1, 1822, and 157 by June 1, 1822. (Deeds 13:227, Town Clerk's Office, City Hall, Bristol Conn.) Roberts asserts that Downs clocks for Mitchell were cased by Jerome, based on his

analysis of a simplifying feature within the clock, 160-161. If so, this was done on Mitchell's account, as no mention appears in the Downs account books.

[57] The property is described in a quitclaim deed from Elias Foot to John Swathell, 11 April 1823, 13:538 Bristol Deeds. Downs' purchase is recorded at 15:137. Mitchell's purchase price was $983.33; Downs paid him $1000. Downs names seven individuals who worked with him between 1825 and 1828, although generally he worked with three others, one a "mettle worker," in the shop. Downs ceased to be Mitchell's exclusive supplier of movements in 1828, although between January and June of 1829 he made 1213 movements for the "new style of clock case" developed by Elias Ingraham a Hartford cabinetmaker, who had moved to Bristol.

[58] Agreement signed by Eli Terry and Ephraim Downs, Bristol, November 1, 1830, copy of ms at American Clock and Watch Museum.

[59] Henry Terry in Roberts, 36.

[60] Agreement and receipt, February 23, 1822, Roberts, 95.

[61] Patent, March 4, 1826, Roberts, 304-7.

[62] Eli Terry vs. Seth Thomas, docket entries, U.S.Circuit Court, New Haven, last Wednesday of April, 1829, cited in Roberts, 92.

[63] Accounts with James Smith, Clear Crick Twp., Warrent Co., Ohio, August 23, 1830 and others, Ephraim Downs Account Book, American Clock and Watch Museum.

[64] The Memorial History of Hartford County, Connecticut 1633-1883, J. Hammond Trumbull, 2 vols (Boston: Edward L. Osgood, 1886) I:53.

[65] The remaining wooden parts were given to a worker named Morse and were ultimately purchased from his family and given to The Connecticut Historical Society as the Lewis B. Winton collection, Hoke, 281, note 88.

[66] Other examples of the 'Connecticut banjo' form are at Bayou Bend, Houston, Tex., Connecticut State Library, Hartford, Conn. and the Time Museum, Rockford, Ill.

[67] Eli Terry Jr., Terrysville, Conn., August 1836 to Messrs Robert Felson and William Ensign East Fairfield, Ohio; Eli Terry Jr., 22 March 1839 to Mr. I.L. Langston, Wheeling [W.]Virginia in Roberts, 278, 280.

I believe the public are not generally aware, that my former Patent Right expired 6 years ago [1816]; which induces me to caution them against the frequent impositions practiced, in vending spurious Timepieces. It is true, they have "Patent" printed on them, and some with my name, and their outward appearance resembles those formerly made by me: Thus they are palm'd upon the public. Several of them have lately been brought to me for repairs, that would certainly put the greatest bungler to the blush. Such is the country inundated with, and such, I consider prejudicial to my reputation; it therefore disclaim being the manufacturer of such vile performances.

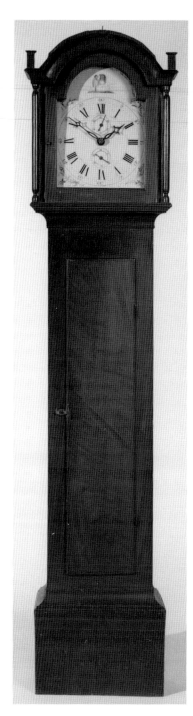

Fig 6-1. Shortening a tall clock is a common alteration. This pine-cased clock has had its fret, finials, and feet removed. 57.1.197

CLOCKS HAVE LONG BEEN REGARDED as a complicated realm that only a collector with an esoteric comprehension of mechanical contrivances can understand. While it cannot be denied that clocks are mechanical devices, a complete understanding of them requires an extensive background in the decorative arts as well as an appreciation of the craft. The collector well versed in furniture, glass, painting (on metal, wood and the reverse side of glass), iron, pewter and brass will be ahead of the collector with a degree in mechanical engineering. A review of some of the common problem areas found in early clocks shows that through careful analysis of key components, the collector can determine the authenticity of the clock. This may be done in part by an informed analysis of materials and construction, rather than by delving into all of the technical horological details.[1]

SPURIOUS TIMEPIECES
Alarming signs and how to recognize them

CLOCK CASES

THE CASES OF HANDCRAFTED CLOCKS are like any other wooden object, so the collector should apply previously published evaluation procedures for handcrafted furniture.[2] Knowledge of furniture styles and craftsmanship is essential to developing an understanding of early clocks: study of primary and secondary woods, appropriate tool marks, construction techniques, glue, natural oxidation of unfinished surfaces, finish, fastening devices, and hardware are all key components. The astute collector should develop a hardened suspicion toward a number of areas on clock cases and should study each with care to determine authenticity.

Tall clock cases are most likely to have evidence of change at top and bottom. Look for signs of having been shortened to fit in a room by the removal of feet on the base and ornamentation above the dial door. (Fig. 6-1) (While shelf clocks may also have lost these components, it is largely due to their delicacy rather than a need to modify the height of the object.) Always check the top and bottom of the clock to prove that these two areas of

early clock cases are original.

The form and age of the case are the most common clues to determine if elements are either missing or restored. The cases of clocks dating from the early to mid-18th century sit on a molded bottom or flat on the floor; generally there were no feet. Similarly, clocks of this period may or may not have additional ornamentation, such as a scroll, pagoda, or sarcophagus top. By the late 18th and early 19th centuries, clocks often had ogee or bracket feet in conjunction with a pierced fret design placed between three finial plinths.(Fig. 6-2) The absence of these features in a clock of this period may be troublesome. Clock case construction was rather standardized by this time and only a few rural craftsmen varied from the norm. Look for unused nail holes, traces of old glue, evidence of missing glue blocks or other signs of recent workmanship to establish the original intent of the maker.

Careful scrutiny of the type and texture of both primary and secondary woods is often the only test required to determine authenticity. The wood should relate to the wood used in other areas of the case. Look for evidence of the work of the home handyman or amateur cabinetmaker who has made replacement feet in cherry for a mahogany-cased clock or used oak glue blocks where pine is the only other secondary wood on the case. The pattern of the

replaced element may also demonstrate the amateur restorer's limited background in style and design.

The knowledgeable furniture restorer, well versed in the styles, designs, and species of wood used in clock cases, can work with little fear of detection. To find evidence of restoration, the collector should examine several key areas. Look at the bottom of feet for signs of wear (Fig. 6-3); check the glue blocks for natural oxidation or artificial age; scrutinize glue, nails, and other fasteners to be sure that style and construction techniques synchronize. Do not be fooled by what appears to be 200 years of dust on glue blocks and on the top of hoods. Vacuum cleaner bags have often been emptied over newly stained areas to add artificial age and color to the restored elements. Obviously, signs of recent workmanship, modern tool marks (such as a circular saw), modern white glue, wire nails, unoxidized new surfaces, or conversely, stained or artificially aged surfaces are cause for suspicion. The evaluator must determine whether these are warnings of outright replacement or the honest repair of original elements.

The alteration of a tall clock case to fit low-studded rooms may also be detected in its structural members. The evidence is most often found at the point where the waist of the clock meets with the lower, base section. The case may have been disassembled, the waist section cut down or dropped lower into the base and finally reassembled. When this has happened, the backboard of the case is also shortened to fit the new dimensions of the clock. The backboard is often the most visible sign of the alteration.(Fig. 6-4) Clock cases with odd proportions are candidates for a thorough examination. A mirror and a strong light source are often helpful to examine the inside of the case for signs of recent workmanship. Fortunately, this is not a common alteration on New England clocks, but is seen with regularity on our taller neighbors from the mid-

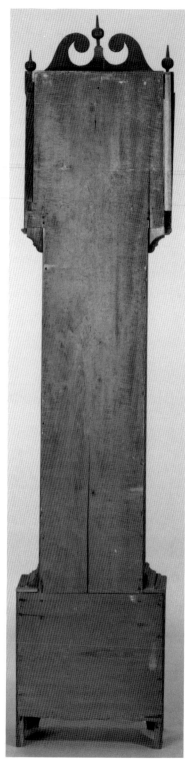

Fig. 6-4. The backboard of a tall clock may have evidence of being cut down. A typical method was to cut it at the top of the base, drop the waist into the base, and reglue the case in its shortened condition. In this instance the construction is original. 57.1.188

Atlantic states.

Waist doors on clock cases provide access to the weights and pendulum for winding, regulating, or starting the clock. Through the middle of the 19th century, these doors were generally solid or veneered and intended to protect the moving parts, while hiding the crude lead or cast-iron weights. An exception worth noting are the doors of some early clocks which were originally fitted with a bull's eye or other small aperture to view the swing of the pendulum. (See fig. 1-6 Isaac Blaisdel Tall Clock) In the late-19th and early 20th centuries, however, tall clocks began to be manufactured with full-length glass doors to reveal highly polished brass weights, fancy pendulum rods and bobs and even tubular bells hung from the backboard to sound Westminster chimes on the quarter hour. (Fig. 6-5) This fashion of revealing the components of the clock prompted many owners to "update" their antique clocks by cutting a full-length opening in the waist door and installing a glass to reveal the weights and pendulum. As the lead, sand-filled tin, or cast-iron weights of antique domestic clocks were considered less decorative than their Victorian counterparts, the "update" often included a fresh coat of gold paint for the weights and pendulums or their replacement with highly polished, brass components. As tastes changed and a desire for authenticity emerged, waist doors on clocks with Victorian-era alterations have been restored with new, solid replacements in the original style.

To determine whether the waist door has been altered and/or replaced requires a thorough examination of each of the components individually and in relation to the rest of the clock case. Look closely at the wood, the coloration of primary and secondary surfaces, the hardware (hinges, door locks), the fasteners (nails and screws), and the stylistic features such as inlay and molding details around the edge of the door. (Fig. 6-6) Original doors are often covered with information written in pencil or chalk, noting repair dates, family history, or other "facts" about the clock. The skillful faker often adds these details to the new replacement door as well!

The final group of problems associated with tall-clock cases focuses on confirming the originality of the movement and dial to the case. All early clocks are technically "marriages"; the movements made by the clock maker were united with the dial from the dial maker (sometimes the clock maker also

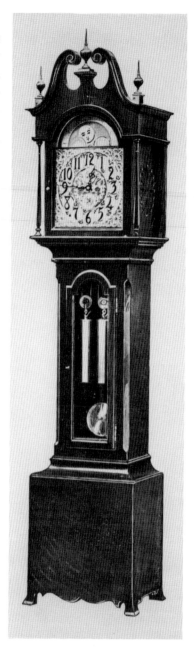

Fig. 6-5. Victorian tall clock with full-length glass door in the waist to view the brass-cased weights and pendulum. This fashion led many owners of early clocks to "update" their clocks in a similar manner. Photograph reprinted from "Herschede Clocks, A Selection from Four Catalogues, c. 1904-1927". Courtesy, American Clock and Watch Museum.

Fig. 6-6. The authenticity of the waist door is confirmed by the hinges, proper natural coloration, and exterior stylistic details such as molding profiles and inlay. 57.1.144

missing, ruined or inferior. A certain maker naively informed me he was making a dozen old sets of works. He charged several dollars extra for each clock to 'age' the works....An old case and an old works may be put together, thus multiplying the value."[5]

While there are some marriages "made in heaven", the marriage of a movement, dial and case usually involves the alteration of at least one or more of the following elements:

1. seat board for the movement;

2. case stiles—the structural supports for the seat board, movement and dial;

3. dial mat—the thin wooden frame enclosing the dial, which provides a background for the dial inside the hood. Not all clocks of this period had dial mats; 18th-century rural clocks often did not have this added cosmetic element;

4. hood door (Fig. 6-7, 6-8).

The movements of most early tall and shelf clocks are attached to a seat board often made of pine. In tall clocks, the dial is attached to the movement, and the movement and seat board are attached to, or sometimes simply sit on, the case stiles or the extensions of the sides of the case. The seat board, movement, and dial of a shelf clock are generally supported by projections attached to the backboard with nails or screws. (Fig. 6-9) The position or height of the movement and dial in the case is therefore determined by the thickness of the seat board and either the height of the stiles in tall clocks or the position of the seat-board supports in shelf clocks.

The appropriate dimensions of the dial opening in the hood door and the dial mat are also important elements to consider in the fit of a movement and dial to the case. In the late 18th and early 19th centuries, a remarkable standardization of dial sizes both in tall and shelf clocks made the cabinetmaker's job routine. He simply fit up a seat board to the movement, "adjusted" the height of the stiles of the case as needed, and thus completed the final stages of the clock manufacture. The dial mat and dial door were made to the standard dimensions of dials preferred at the time, and the final fit-up was simply adjusting the height and centering the dial in the opening. Since clock manufacture was not greatly standardized before about 1775, the modern marriage of component parts made during this period relies on a great deal of luck in acquiring dials with dimensions that match door openings and dial

made the dial) and finally fit to the case, which was made by the cabinetmaker. This process of original manufacture is not the concern of the collector. It is rather, the recent "marriage" or combination of components from various sources which seriously detracts from the monetary and historical value of the clock. While suitable "marriages" often make a clock useable again after a fire,[3] theft,[4] or other damage, most "marriages" are performed to enhance financial gain by combining movements, dials, and cases into a more salable whole. Wallace Nutting's description of this practice earlier in the present century is, regrettably, just as true today.

"In the buying of clocks the works are sometimes

mats. This, of course, assumes that the marriage is all the more successful if the original dial mat and hood door remain intact, and the movement and dial are stylistically correct for the case.

It follows that the originality of the seat board is an important factor in identifying a marriage of movement and dial to the case. The seat board on most New England tall clocks is generally unfinished pine, which oxidizes naturally on the underside and is usually a darker color on the upper side due to dust accumulation and clock oil stains. Some Rhode Island clocks have chestnut seat boards and on later Willard shelf clocks, mahogany and cherry

were used. The seat board should have a hand-planed surface, generally top and bottom, and should show no signs of recent workmanship other than explainable repairs. If there are nail or screw holes at each end, they should align well with the holes through the case stiles or backboard projections indicating that the two elements were mated originally and have "aged" together.

Extra holes in the seat board or the stiles without corresponding holes in the mating component are always a cause for concern. To complicate matters, seat boards were often nailed to a repairman's test stand or bench while the clock was in the workshop, creating extra holes in the seat board and undue concern about the authenticity of the movement and dial with the case. Generally, a faker marrying a movement and dial with a case will make a seat board of suitable thickness using old wood with undisturbed major surfaces. Attention is devoted to the proper "look" of all surfaces, but evidence of stained age or artificial coloration is most likely

Fig. 6-7, 6-8 (left). The back of a dial mat, seat-board supports, and seat board showing that they are undisturbed, oxidation is natural, and nails are original. There should be no alteration in these areas. 57.1.144

Fig. 6-9. The movement of a shelf clock is attached to a seat board which rests on projections nailed or screwed to the backboard of the clock. These components are original if the movement/dial is original to the case. 57.1.66

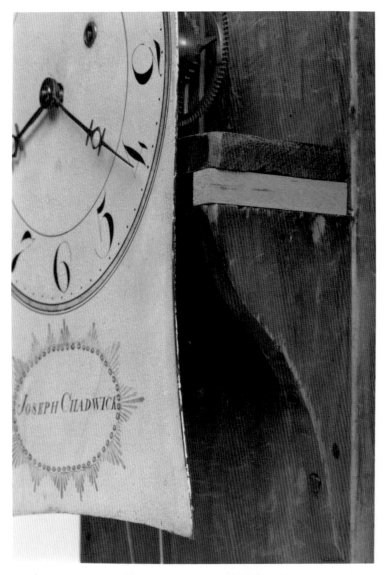

Fig. 6-10. Many rural clocks have period shims under the seat board, but an obviously new shim under the seating board, apparently a well-meaning attempt to restore a period shim, raises doubt about the originality of the movement/dial to the case. There should be no need for a new shim under the seating board to raise the movement/dial in the hood opening. 57.1.114

Fig. 6-11. Horizontal framing of tall clock cases often obstruct the weight travel. Carved recesses in the case provide a clear path for the weights. This example shows original recesses in correct alignment with present weight travel. Weights suspended from movements/dials married to a different case do not always travel in the same path as the originals and this serves as another point of examination. 57.1.2

found in the holes where the weight cords pass, and the pendulum swings, as these must be newly cut to suit the movement. There are additional subtle points related to seat board authenticity which have been purposely omitted. It is not the authors' intent to create a "faker's handbook."

A common source of period wood for replacement seat boards is interior house lumber. Fortunately, wood from this source is planed on one surface only and has a rough-sawn appearance on the other surface. Cabinetmakers generally finish-planed both surfaces on furniture wood and, thus, interior house lumber may be quickly identified.

The case stiles, or backboard projections should also pass the test of proper age, materials, workmanship, and fastening devices. New shims under the seat board or new additions to the stiles indicate a possible attempt to marry the movement and dial to the case.(Fig. 6-10) It is not uncommon on rural work to see period shims used to elevate the movement and dial properly in the case. If shims are present, examine them carefully to determine if this work was done at the time of manufacture or in the faker's workshop.

The dial mat and hood door restrict the size of the dial that will fit in the case. A standard, painted 12" tall clock dial looks odd in an opening intended for a 13" dial and a successful marriage would, therefore, require a new mat and hood door. An undisturbed dial mat (best examined from inside the hood) and dial door made with the correct type and texture of wood, joinery, fasteners and stylistic details such as inlay and molding profiles is always a welcome sight. Inside surfaces, stained to give the appearance of age on any of these elements is usually a sign of recent changes, as these surfaces were generally left unfinished. Also, the proportion of the dial and hood often look unusually cramped or spacious if a different dial size is mated to a case designed for another dial dimension.

Handcrafted clocks often provide other hints of a marriage. Weight-powered clocks, regulated by a pendulum, often show signs of wear where the weights have rubbed on the inside of the case or waist door. On tall clocks, this evidence is often visible on the waist door and the adjoining areas, displaying itself as a rubbing or scarring of these unfinished areas caused during the winding process or the natural descent of the weights during operation. Often cabinetmakers carved out recesses in the structural members of the case to further ease the weight descent. (Fig. 6-11) On shelf clocks, such wear is usually apparent along the backboard or weight-support boards mounted to the backboard. While this evidence is not always conclusive, it is worth consideration. Weight scarring should coincide with present weight travel in the clock. Do not overlook the possibility that, if the weights were changed in the past, the dimensions of replacement weights may not match the scarring or recesses caused by the original weights.

The pendulum bob also provides another hint of the originality of movement and case. If the clock is leaning backward when set going, the pendulum bob can rub slightly on the backboard and can make a slight scar or rub mark along its path. (Fig. 6-12) If the scarring is not consistent with the present pendulum path, it is a possible sign that another movement with a pendulum of different length was once mounted in the case.[6]

Due to the constantly escalating values of antique clocks and buyers' insistence on authenticity, furniture restoration and faking have reached new and extremely sophisticated levels. Talented craftsmen with a keen eye for details of design and construction produce restoration work which is virtually undetectable. By carefully selecting old wood of quality, salvaged from discarded period furniture, and reusing old glue blocks and fasteners, their restoration work has the look and feel of an undisturbed antique. It is, therefore, imperative when examining clocks from a furniture perspective to assume all the afore-mentioned danger areas GUILTY of malfeasance until proven innocent.

DIALS OR FACES

JOHN WELSH OF BOSTON advertised imported "dial plates" in 1774; Osborne and Wilson of Birmingham, England, describe their product as "White Clock Dials". In contrast, the Connecticut clock maker Daniel Burnap provides "directions for the face" in his memorandum book of 1779. Abel Hutchins of Concord, New Hampshire, advertises English manufactured "clock faces" among other imported supplies. Spencer Nolen considered himself a "clock face painter."[7]

The styles of clock dials or faces used in America closely parallels fashion in Britain. Imported clocks defined taste, which was interpreted in New En-

Fig. 6-12. The horizontal scar on the backboard of a tall clock is caused by the thickest profile of the pendulum bob rubbing along the path of swing. These marks can be made by the regulating nut at the bottom of the pendulum rod and can also be used as a confirmation of the originality of the movement/dial with the case. Unexplained rub marks at odd locations for the present pendulum rod can be an indication of a marriage between movement/dial and case. 57.1.7

gland by local clock makers and dial or face painters. The earliest dials on tall clocks, and bracket or table clocks in Britain, are compositions of brass elements on a square or arched brass plate. These are the "clock dial plates, ornaments, etc." that John Welsh advertised in 1774.

Brass dials are composed of a number of separate elements and, as Welsh called them, ornaments, which are applied to the dial plate:
—engraved chapter ring (the ring with the numerals);
—second's bit (to register the seconds beat of the pendulum);
—recessed date ring to show the day of the month;
—maker's name boss (usually applied to the arch of the plate);
—spandrels (cast brass or gilded-lead corner "ornaments"). (Fig. 6-13)

The cast-brass chapter ring, second's bit, date dial and name boss were hammered flat, polished, and engraved. A silver salt solution was then used to deposit a thin layer of silver on the polished brass surface.[8] The engraving was filled with black shellac or a mixture of beeswax and lampblack to make it more legible. The "zone" or surface inside the chapter ring on many tall clocks made prior to about 1770 was matted, either by a punch and hammer or a roller.[9] This treatment provided a "flat" or unpolished background for the hands and the

Fig. 6-13. A composite brass dial by William Claggett with applied components removed from the polished dial plate. The cast-brass spandrels are attached to the dial plate with square-headed screws, while the chapter ring, name boss and second's dial are pinned in place. The date ring is positioned behind the dial on rollers and shows the date through the square opening in the dial plate just above the six o'clock position. 57.1.99

engraved components.

Brass spandrels were cast in sand molds, removed, then "cleaned-up", a process of removing the excess brass from the casting. Later the spandrel was burnished (decorative details highlighted) and sometimes gilded by one of three methods. Fire gilding is a dangerous process in which gold leaf and mercury are applied to the object. When the mercury is burned off, it leaves a beautifully gilded surface on the metal and violently toxic fumes in the air. New England brass dials do not generally have evidence of fire gilding. Instead either the water gilding method was used or a gilding agent in a varnish medium was applied over the metal parts. Rural brass dials often have pewter or lead spandrels, chapter ring, date ring and maker's boss. These economical raw materials often resembled the more expensive brass composite dial when the manufacture and gilding was finished. The pewter chapter ring, name boss and date ring were polished to look silvered and the spandrels gilded to resemble the cast-brass decorative elements of the most fashionable dials. The spandrels were attached to the polished background in the corners of the dial and encircled the name boss in the arch. Steel hands were polished and finished in a bluish tone by heating to "blue" heat and quenching in oil or water. The combination of a polished brass plate, with silvered-brass or polished pewter components, matted center, gilded spandrels, and blued hands created a dial that was attractive and readable.

The components of brass dials must be carefully examined for assurance of their age and authenticity. Each element should be cast and display some evidence of hammering, hand filing, or finish work. The screws used to attach the spandrels should be hand cut, slotted or square-headed screws. The backs of the spandrels should bear evidence of casting marks or rough filing rather than efforts to smooth the unseen surface. The chapter and seconds rings should have projecting studs passing through the brass dial plate and pinned at the back. The reverse sides of both rings should present evidence of sand-casting marks and/or hammering or filing.

The authenticity of the name boss is of utmost concern because it is the "signature" of the maker. Expect to find evidence of sand casting, hammering, filing, or lathe turning marks on the back. Mounted on the reverse of the boss is a stud to attach the boss to the dial by inserting it through a hole in the brass plate and pinning it securely. A clean fit without any extra holes through the dial plate is important. Question the authenticity of the name boss when it has extra holes through the dial plate, signs of recent workmanship, or if the back appears relatively smooth or made of modern rolled brass. Instances are known in which old name bosses, resurfaced on the front and re-engraved with more salable names have been "transferred" to other dials. This tedious method of deception preserved the old appearance of the back of the boss. Clock makers' supply houses in England continue to advertise newly made "domed bosses with any name engraved". Of course, the historical and monetary value of a clock with an altered or new name boss is compromised. Especially, for instance, if the name boss from a London brass dial clock were resurfaced and engraved with the name of Gawen Brown of Boston: if the monetary value of the clock has been dramatically increased in America, the history of the clock and its original maker is lost forever.[10]

By the mid-1770's, the composite brass dial began to go out of fashion, but its influence is readily apparent in the two alternative styles gaining popularity. The silvered, sheet-brass dial eliminated the applied components and ornaments and accomplished the same end with engraving on the single sheet. (See Pl. 7) The brass dial plate was prepared by hammering to increase hardness, filing or scraping it flat, then polishing and engraving the surface.[11] The engraving was then filled with black shellac or wax to provide needed contrast. The combination of the polished dial sheet, black numerals and decorative engraving, and blued hands created legible and pleasing dials. Fortunately, alterations by fakers to the engraved maker's name on this type of dial was difficult to accomplish without destroying the original decorative engraving on the dial sheet.

In the last quarter of the 18th century, a second alternative to the composite brass dial was introduced. The innovation of the white, painted dial would set the pace in taste and manufacture for the coming century. (see Covers, Pl. 11) Although this dial is most commonly found on New England clocks, scholars and collectors may have overlooked its importance.[12] Painted dials were first advertised in England in 1772 and soon eclipsed brass dials. T. Hadley Osborne and James Wilson of Birmingham, England entered into partnership to manufacture and sell "White Clock Dials in imitation of enamel, in a manner entirely new" in l772. [13] Their partnership ended before any white dials were imported into America, but they are the first known manufacturers of painted dials for the American market. The names "Wilson" or "Osborne" are cast or stamped on the painted dials of many New England clocks made in the final decade of the 18th and into the early 19th century. In 1785 Paul Revere was the first to advertise these imported, white dials in New England[14] and American clock makers soon began to make their movements to fit the imported, Birmingham dial.

The positions of the center or hand arbor, winding arbors, seconds dial and date apertures were predetermined by the imported dials. The dial maker's name may be found on the back of the dial plate, stamped on the moon's age or date dial, or cast onto the false plate.[15] (Fig. 6-14) As Wilson and Osborne supplied only the dials (not movements) to the trade, finding their signatures on the back of a dial is not an indication that they made the clock.

Iron, rather than brass, was the basic material for the painted dial. The dial was generally treated with a red lead primer coat before the background and decorative paint was applied. Brightly colored floral decorations replaced cast-brass spandrels or engraved decoration in the corners of the dial. The arch was often embellished with a mythological scene or an attached moon's age dial. The numerals and clock maker's name were applied in an oil base paint and then the entire dial, or at least the deco-

Fig. 6-14. The back of an imported, painted dial showning the attached iron false plate inscribed: "OSBORNE'S MANUFACTORY, BIRMINGHAM". American clock makers drilled holes in the false plate and attached dial posts to mount the English dial to their movement, while not disturbing the pre-painted finish on the front of the dial. The large toothed wheel in the arch of the dial is the moon's-age indicator. The brass wheels in the center of the photograph trip the day of the month hand. 57.1.131

ration, was varnished to prevent deterioration. Often the back of the dial was painted black. Because the final fit up of the dial to the movement was left to the American clock maker, the English dial manufacturers noted that "dial feet will be rivetted in the dials and such methods used as will enable the clock makers to fix them to the movements."[16] Dial makers provided an iron "false plate" behind the painted dial because riveting dial feet on a prepainted dial would instantly destroy the finish. The posts connecting the false plate to the back of the dial were attached prior to painting and the riveted areas were covered by the succeeding paint layers.

The dials on both tall and shelf clocks are generally attached directly to the movement. Composite brass, engraved sheet brass and New England-made, painted-iron dials were generally fit up to the movement at the time of the clock's manufacture. Thus the clock maker laid out the dial positions of the center arbor (the attachment point for the hands), winding arbors, seconds arbor and date indicators to match the relative positions of the movement's mechanical components. The dial was attached to the movement by three or four posts, called dial feet.(See Fig. 6-16) Their positions were laid out

Fig. 6-15. Dial feet or posts are projections to attach the dial to the movement. They are pinned securely to the inside of the front plate as shown. The extra hole in this front plate is probably an error made by the clock maker who laid out the position of the dial post. Extra holes may indicate that the movement and dial did not start life together. 57.1.107

with care that they not interfere with any of the movement's mechanical functions. The dial feet were riveted to the dial plate or the false plate and the locations drilled through the front plate of the movement. Pins through the dial feet, wedged to the inside of the front plate of the movement, held the dial firmly in place.(See Fig. 6-15) On brass dials, the rivet placements on the dial plate were either hidden under the chapter ring, matted along with the rest of the "zone", or filed, polished and engraved. After the introduction of painted dials, the rivet locations were painted along with the rest of the dial plate.

Marriages between movements and dials are not uncommon. A tall clock first photographed in 1893 was examined by the author more than a half century later and was found to have an Eli Terry dial wed to an unknown maker's movement and housed in a very questionable case. Obviously fakers have been uniting dials and movements from different sources in America since the late 19th-century. Owners of early clocks probably updated their brass dials with the more stylish, white painted dial. If damaged by fire or harsh cleaning, white dials were often replaced with clean, newly painted ones, much to the pleasure of the owner. A simple test of the marriage of a face and a movement is a comparison of the face to the case. A composite brass dial in an early 19th-century Roxbury case or an early 18th-century case with a white, painted dial should immediately appear incongruous. Of course, the incongruity could also signal a marriage of movement and dial to the case.

It is also helpful to observe the position of the center arbor, winding arbors, the second hand arbor, and the respective holes through the dial to determine the originality of the movement and dial. If they were fit at the time of manufacture these arbors should be perfectly centered in the dial holes; indications of a later fit up would include dial holes that have been elongated or enlarged, fitting poorly with the arbors of the movement.

Other less obvious factors in identifying a marriage between a movement and a dial involve the position of the dial feet which hold the dial to the movement. Relocated dial feet on the false dial plate, extra and unused holes through the front plate of the movement or the false plate should always be noted. (Fig. 6-15) It is highly unlikely that the clock maker had a bad day in the workshop and placed dial feet in the wrong locations at the time of manufacture, only to redrill the holes in the proper place after the mistake was apparent! Clock maker error of this type is not unheard of, but most unlikely. In short, question authenticity when extra holes are present.

A common tell-tale sign of a marriage between a movement and dial may be discovered when the clock is in the workshop for repair. Evidence on the movement of wheelwork or studs which formerly supported wheelwork to trip moon's age, date dials, or "Strike/Silent" attachments are cause for concern if these functions are not represented on the dial. Clock makers were economical and would not make the gearing to support these functions if the dial did not require these extra mechanical features. (Fig. 3-5)

A further word of warning relates to New England tall clock dials with a rocking ship in the arch. The concave background for the rocking ship in the arch is generally pinned to the back of the dial plate and painted with a decorative seascape. The rocking ship is attached to the pallet arbor on the movement, which transfers the back-and-forth motion of the pendulum to the ship in the arch. (See Fig. 2-34.) With readily available square-painted dials of English manufacture, fakers added rocking ship arches to square dials to improve the saleability of the clock and to marry the movement and dial to an arch dial case. Examine the reverse of these concave, background arches to confirm similar paint history or evidence of recent workmanship. (Fig. 6-16)

The dial of the patent-timepiece (commonly called the "banjo" clock) is attached to the case rather than the movement. The dial is confirmed as original to the clock when the holes or notches through it align precisely with the holes through the wooden head of the case. Extra holes in the dial or on the case without corresponding holes through the case component indicate that the dial and case did not begin life together. Examine both elements for evidence of holes plugged when they no longer served a useful purpose.

Many white dials were signed with the clock maker's name and place of manufacture. A surprising number of dials, however, remain unsigned and provide no assistance in identifying the maker or origin. The signature is the sole, unquestionable factor in determining the maker of the clock and its probable history. The importance of the originality of the signature is of utmost historical and monetary concern. In other instances, authentic name bosses on composite brass dial clocks have been moved to other dials, resurfaced and re-engraved with a more prominent clock maker's name, or made up new with just the right name for a quick sale. Previously unsigned brass dials now glimmer with a recently engraved and very plausible signature and origin. (Fig. 6-17) A comparison of engraving styles with other work on the dial or perhaps a slight trace of an element of original engraving not completely removed will reveal the deception. The collector of brass dial clocks should become thoroughly familiar with 18th-century engraving styles and techniques to judge each dial on its own merits.

Forgery on painted dials is even more prevalent than on brass dial work. Many painted dials, both locally made and English imports, were left unsigned. Logic suggests that a rural clock maker working alone in a remote location would have little reason to have his name on the dial; the local buyers all knew the resident clock maker and that he had made the clock. Further, as urban clock makers in the early 19th-century often served as retail agents for clocks made elsewhere, adding their names as makers on the dials would have been an unnecessary deception. Given the abundance of unsigned painted

Fig. 6-16. The back of a painted iron dial with attached rocking ship background in the arch. Since the back is also painted, look for a consistent paint history between the square lower section and the attached arch. Rocking ship arches are frequently "added" to square English dials to marry the dial and movement to an arched dial case. Note the three dial feet to secure the movement to the dial. 57.1.70

dials, the would-be faker has a wealth of material waiting to be "improved" with the addition of a prominent maker's name.

Signatures were typically applied to a painted dial along with the numerals during production. Thinly-based oil paint or asphaltum[17] was generally the medium used over the base paint. The delicacy of the numerals and the signatures combined with the thinned nature of the paint, created the most fragile aspect of the painted dial. Years of handling by winding and setting the clock and attempts by ambitious owners to clean up the tired face, has worn out numerals and signatures on many painted dials. Use a raking light (a bright light aimed at an angle on the dial), or an ultra-violet lamp (also called a "black light") and magnification to aid in detecting the remains of signatures and dial lining. (Fig. 6-18) Under proper lighting conditions and with a little experience, the remaining evidence is often visible to the naked eye.

Original numerals and signatures applied over the base paint of the dial tend to discolor the base paint below. Often this discoloration or imprint

Fig. 6-17. Originally unsigned, this dial has been "improved" in the faker's workshop by adding the inscription: "Simon Willard, Grafton, No. 2". It is without doubt a genuine Willard clock. Note the inconsistency between the light touch on the engraving of the numerals and lining and the heavy hand on the signature. 57.1.103

thorough evaluation requires a familiarity with authentic examples, an understanding of the original techniques, a keen eye for recent workmanship, and a lot of luck.

PATENT TIMEPIECES

A PATENT TIMEPIECE in original condition is, perhaps, the most difficult New England clock to acquire today.[19] Two major contributing factors for this are the clock's inherent vulnerability to damage and the ease with which the form can be reproduced.[20] Weight-powered clocks with delicate cases and fragile reverse-paintings on glass—all suspended by a wall fastener—offer potential risks of damage. Weight-cord breakage, wall hook failure and general carelessness in handling these clocks during winding and transporting have severely diminished the survival rate of this form. These problem situations, combined with the popularity of "banjo" clocks, have prompted the appearance of many reproductions, fakes, and heavily restored clocks.

Simon Willard first warned of the difficulties in acquiring an original patent timepiece as early as August 10, 1822.[21] The great popularity of the patent timepiece prompted Willard apprentices and others to continue production of this type of clock almost continuously from about 1800 to the present day.[22]

Over 50 years ago Wallace Nutting noted that "banjo and other clocks in very elegant forms are

may be barely visible around the edges of an original signature or numeral, as these applied graphics have actually shrunk with age. This "shadow" around a signature is always worth a sigh of relief! Further, the discoloration or imprint will be visible if all of the original signature or numerals are worn away, giving the dial restorer a clear pattern to renew the missing elements. This process of renewing the missing graphics is known as "relining" the dial.[18]

Evaluation of a painted dial signature requires a close comparison of the graphic work of the numerals and signature. Look at the paint carefully to insure that its intensity and texture are the same in these two areas. The paint of the signature should not flow into shrinkage cracks in the base paint, but rather display the same separation as the paint below. It should be stylistically consistent and show evidence of normal abrasion through handling. If the entire dial has been relined, then some of these important check points will be missing. Be suspicious if only the signature area appears abraded or the general "gloss" of the dial is inconsistent. The faker can attempt to age the signature by rubbing fine steel wool over it, but this tends to dull the gloss of the signature and not the remainder of the dial.

The fine art of forging signatures on painted dials is well practiced and skillfully accomplished. A

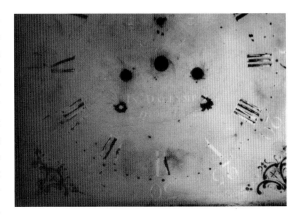

Fig. 6-18. Photograph taken under ultra-violet light showing the remains of the numerals and signature which have been worn off a painted dial. The missing elements fluoresce white and give a clear indication of the original layout and signature. UV light is not always helpful in this evaluation, but it is a useful tool. Courtesy, The Dial House, Dallas, Georgia.

now reproduced...the banjo clock, being small and popular, is especially liable to forgeries."[23] Other contemporary writers warn of the many pitfalls awaiting the buyer of "banjo" clocks.

> New dials, painted with antique finish...bearing the name of Aaron Willard may be had in quantity...Advertisements in the magazines offer for sale "Willard movements" made exactly like the originals...There are many artists who can make excellent reproductions of original painted panels...and an antique appearance may be easily obtained.[24]

Despite warnings like these, decorative arts collectors continue to be fooled by heavily restored, fraudulent and outright fakes of this popular clock. During a recent visit to a nationally known and widely respected New York City antiques shop, the author noted a "Willard" patent timepiece offered for sale at $85,000. The dealer was not the least bit interested to hear that the maker of the clock is still alive!

During the first half of the 19th-century, the patent timepiece moved from the front parlor of the home to the bank, office, railroad station, and finally, the schoolroom. Along the way it lost its highly decorative gilded frames, hand-painted scenic glasses, and fancy brass hardware. Simple black and gold glasses or mahogany veneered panels were substituted, while the basic form remained the same. Ambitious antiques dealers of the early 20th century, eager to fill requests for Willard patent timepieces, sought clock makers to alter austere, factory-made clocks to resemble those of a half century earlier.(Fig. 6-19)

Factory-made after the mid-19th century, the patent timepiece became known as a "regulator." From the mid-19th to early 20th century, their cases were made of seasoned cherry, poplar, or basswood, often stained or grain-painted to resemble rosewood or mahogany. The backboards and glue blocks were generally pine or basswood. The frames of the clock in the throat and box section were half-round in profile or a flat bevel towards the glass or panel. The bezel surrounding the dial was generally the same primary wood as the case, half round in shape. If used, wooden side pieces or sidearms, mounted on the sides of the throat section replaced the earlier, cast-brass elements. Generally the finial was a simple, turned wooden acorn or eliminated from the design. Presentation brackets or pedestals were rarely found

on the bottom of regulator cases.

The glass on a regulator was generally a transfer-printed gold oval in the box section with a simple perimeter outline in the throat. All background areas were painted black. Towards the beginning of the 20th century, red was added as a third color. In many mid 19th-century clocks, mahogany and mahogany-veneered panels were used instead of painted glasses. Regulator dials were painted on zinc and had a much lighter "feel" than the earlier painted-iron dials. The hands were typically a pressed out, simple "moon" hand with a pointer.

The movement was generally attached to the case with one screw through the backboard of the clock and into the back plate of the movement. Recoil escapements, an "alternate" train layout,[25] and a brass

Fig. 6-19. Despite their apparent differences, the decorative clock on the left was like the clock on the right, a mid-19th century regulator. Ambitious antiques dealers hired clock makers to convert these inexpensive regulators to the more decorative and saleable "patent-timepieces" of 50 years earlier. Private Collection

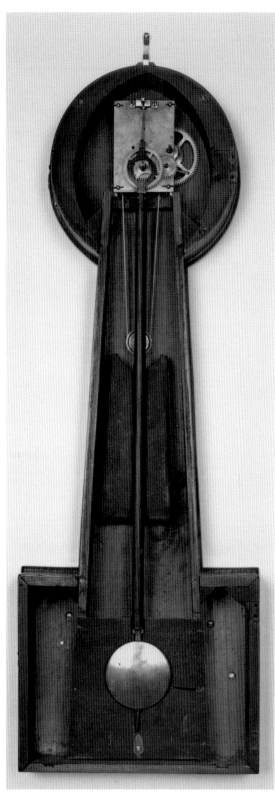

crutch wire were normally found on regulators of this type. The wooden pendulum rod was generally painted black and the pendulum bob motion was protected from the weight by a wooden weight baffle. The keystone, or portion of the pendulum which circumvents the hand arbor, was made of sheet brass and circular in shape.

The factory-made regulator had the basic form, some appearance of age and a good eight-day, weight-powered movement. This provided the foundation for a major reconstruction and transformation to resemble the patent timepiece produced by Simon Willard. Cosmetic "improvements" were relatively simple. The frames for the glasses were often replaced with gilded rope moldings and a gilded pedestal added below the clock. Glasses could be added, or replaced with naval ship battles, mythological scenes and the traditional geometric style signed, "S. Willard's Patent". A cast-brass bezel could replace the wooden surround for the dial. Side pieces, cast in brass might be added to ornament the sides of the case. With a decorative eagle or other typical finial perched on the top, the plain, factory-made regulator had apparently become a patent timepiece from an earlier era.

Several other steps would make a more complete transformation. The zinc dial might be replaced by iron, usually signed with the most marketable name. Willard-style, barbed arrow hands could be substituted for the "moon" hands. An iron baffle could replace the wooden weight baffle. The cast-iron weight could be replaced by a sand-cast lead weight, and finally, the wooden rod and circular keystone replaced by an iron rod and cast-brass keystone in a trapezoidal shape. (Fig. 6-20)

With these relatively simple alterations the most sophisticated early collectors of the patent timepiece were misled. The potential buyer with sufficient knowledge to look under the dial, would find that the "restorer" had fit up a cast-brass, T-bridge and steel filister head bolts to mount the movement in the case in the Willard tradition. The rolled-brass plates, shallow cut teeth and small size of the factory-made movement went largely unnoticed.

In evaluating a patent timepiece, today's collector should have a good understanding of the points which might be transformed. In addition, the collector should become familiar with legitimate, factory-made regulators, to be able to understand the hand-crafted clock more clearly. And finally, an apprecia-

Fig. 6-20. Mid-19th century regulator by George Hatch, Attleboro, Mass. Features of these later clocks include a two-piece wooden pendulum rod with detachable bob, round keystone (the portion of the pendulum rod which circumvents the hand arbor), iron weight, and a wooden weight baffle. Compare with Fig. 2-41. Private Collection

tion of the proper proportions is essential to correct identification. The patent timepiece of the first quarter of the 19th century had a large head (approximately 9" across the bezel) and slender waist (approximately 3" across the top and 4 1/2" across the bottom, where the waist meets the box). The factory-made regulators had smaller heads (approximately 8") and wider waists (approximately 3 1/2" across the top of the waist and 5" across the lower section of the waist).[26] The box sections varied only slightly. While identification is not made on the basis of dimensions alone, a keen eye for proportion can quickly separate a hand-crafted patent timepiece from a factory-made regulator and thus start the evaluation process with an advanced warning. As with the other danger areas already noted, assume the worst and have the clock prove itself.

REVERSE PAINTINGS ON GLASS

THE EMBELLISHMENTS OF THE PATENT TIME-PIECE and "dish dial" or concave-dial shelf clock are essentially reverse painting on glass or eglomisé. As very legitimate clocks with restored reverse paintings are available at a fraction of the price of similar clocks with original glass, the authenticity of the glass is worthy of careful evaluation. Much of the clock's importance is based on the authenticity of the glass and its painting.

Ornamental painting was a widely accepted decoration for the inside of the glass surface of the patent timepieces, shelf clocks, and looking glasses of the early 19th century. Much has been written on the process[27] and the history[28] of this decoration. The advantage of this technique is that the painting was protected from fireplace soot, dust and fly specks, while the front was easily cleaned without damage to the painting.

The authentication of the reverse-painted glass on patent timepieces and shelf clocks remains an inexact science. The subject matter of the painting is an aspect to consider. Look for simple, yet elegant, geometrical designs in pastel colors on the box glasses made in the first decade of the 19th century.(See fig.2-36.) Gilded borders defined the perimeter of the glass, and the opening to view pendulum motion. The decoration of throat glasses includes delicate gilt cross-hatching or a series of oak leaves backed with a subtle color. This treat-

ment, or a variation on a theme was the traditional, Willard design.

By 1812, the popularity of the patent timepiece had soared and so had patriotic fervor. Clock glasses with commemorative scenes based on American subjects captured this spirit. Battle scenes from the War of 1812, such as the "Constitution and the Guerriere" and "Perry's Victory on Lake Erie" were embellished with the Stars and Stripes, eagles, and war banners.(See Fig. 3-12.) Always popular with collectors, naval glasses have been widely reproduced for this eager market.

Later in the decade, mythological or allegorical scenes were introduced, including "Aurora" perched on her chariot, "Truth and Justice," and "Liberty". (See Fig. 3-18.) By the mid 1820's romantic scenes of rural life, farms, or children with animals, enclosed in stenciled borders, had become popular subjects for the decorative glasses on shelf and patent timepieces.(See Fig. 2-64.) Knowledge of the decorative motifs and their historical sequence is essential to evaluate the appropriateness of the subject to the date of the clock. A battle scene from the War of 1812 is obviously out of place on a Simon Willard patent timepiece from 1805. Similarly, Willard-style geometric glasses on a later clock with half-round mahogany, factory-type frames are equally inconsistent.

Evaluation should also be based on several technical considerations. Become familiar with modern mirrors and glass to be able to recognize the thinner glass seen on shelf and wall clocks in the early 19th century. Because old glass is much thinner than modern plate glass, there are a couple of simple distinguishing tests. Take pieces of old and new glass and hold them separately between the thumb and forefinger to develop a feel for the difference in thickness. To determine thickness (and therefore, possibly the age) of looking glasses, place the point of a pencil against the glass to reflect from the silvered surface at the back of the glass. Make similar tests on modern plate mirrors, and note the difference. In addition, old glass generally has imperfections. Striations or streaks in the glass, small bubbles, or dimples may also be visible. The 19th-century craftsmen who selected and painted the glass often chose the best glass available, so an over-abundance of imperfections is cause for suspicion. Also observe the flatness of the glass. Modern plate glass is perfectly flat, but old glass generally has a bowed or convex appearance so that the edges may be as much a 1/16" from a flush fit with the frames in some areas of the glass.

Once the originality of the glass is confirmed, inspect the inside of the frame closely for evidence of the possible removal of the glass from the frame. (Fig. 6-21) Triangular wooden wedges or wooden strips were generally used to keep the glass in place. Both the wedges and the square-cut nails holding the wedges should be old. If not, there may be extra holes from wedges no longer in use and, of course, signs of recent workmanship. Repair of frames and attempts to relieve stress on original glass are logical reasons to remove glasses from the frames, but a more common reason is to install a newly re-painted one.

Examination of the painting from the front should reveal an element of skill in the draftsmanship and the layout of borders and other "technical" areas. The free-hand decoration, particularly in the mythological, allegorical and rural scenes, can vary dramatically from very skilled to amateurish, and does not provide a satisfactory guide. When both glasses are original, the paint and gesso layers on the back of both glasses should be identical. If the top layer of paint or gesso on one glass differs from the other, it may be a replacement glass. (Fig. 6-22)

Do not be misled by an appearance of age resulting from the application of a layer of paint or stain to "muddy" the back of the painting. This attempt to give credibility to the glass can be quickly recognized as "applied age" and should never be convincing. Look for and be skeptical of, repair dates and history written in pencil on the back side of the glass. Fakers commonly penciled in dates, falsifying the age of the glass and possibly the clock, in an attempt to convince collectors of authenticity. If

you assume that all painted glasses are replacements, you will be right more often than wrong and probably save yourself a costly mistake.

REPRODUCTIONS

THE POPULARITY OF NEW ENGLAND hand-crafted clocks of the 18th and 19th centuries coupled with the high prices paid for original examples continues to prompt many craftsmen to produce the more desirable forms right to the present day.[29]

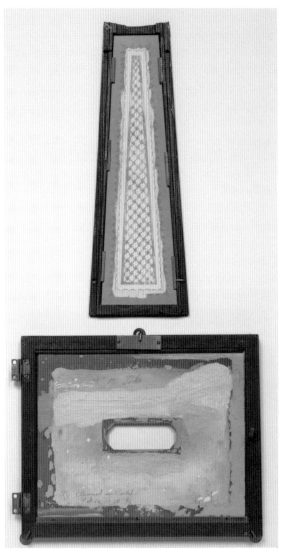

Fig. 6-22. Back view of reverse-paintings on glass from a Simon Willard patent-timepiece. The upper glass is a replacement and color and paint texture varies slightly from the original lower glass, which also shows areas of later inpainting to fill in missing areas. Examination of the back side of glasses is often very helpful in determining authenticity. 57.l.77

Fig. 6-21. Back of a reverse-painting on glass from a Simon Willard patent-timepiece. Wooden strips of various lengths are nailed into the frame to secure the glass in place. Courtesy, The Willard House and Clock Museum.

Many of these modern reproductions are clearly marked, make no pretension of being old, and are marketed legitimately.

Since the beginning of the 20th century, however, "basement tinkers" and professional clock makers have been making reproductions using old wood, old components, and all the elements of hand craftsmanship found on antique examples. It can be observed that "Simon Willard is alive and well, and still making clocks today!" Legitimate, clearly marked reproductions, pose no threat to the serious collector. However, old reproductions often made with old components, appear on the market today as "fakes," which may not have been the intent of the clock maker who made it.

One of the leading clock maker-restorers of the early 20th century was James E. Conlon of Boston (October 14, 1880-December 31, 1948). Conlon apprenticed with George Greer of Dorchester and was a journeyman with John R. Knight and the Wilson Brothers of Boston, before opening his first shop in 1918.[30] Later he moved to a large shop at 38 Province Street, where he restored, maintained, and sold some of the finest hand-crafted clocks in the Boston area. He sold many clocks to J. Cheney Wells during the 1920s and 1930s and cataloged the collection as it was being acquired.

Conlon made thorough searches of town histories for information on clock makers. He also took exhaustive notes of measurements, wheel counts, stylistic details, movement layouts, and construction details of period clocks to aid him in restoration work and the manufacture of his reproductions.[31] Membership in the Boston Clock Club, which according to the bylaws, excluded dealers was extended to him. He was a frequent contributor to the club's proceedings during the 1930's, which led to their departure from tradition and in making him an honorary member in recognition of his knowledge and contributions to New England horology. Conlon reproduced, but did not sign with his own name, Simon Willard thirty-hour wall clocks and patent timepieces, Curtis girandole clocks, Willard patent-alarm timepieces ("lighthouse" clocks), and Massachusetts shelf clocks. It is not known whether he made tall clocks. James E. Conlon made superb reproductions.(Fig. 6-23) Quality movements, dials, case hardware, and glasses are his trademark. Now that they are at least 60 years old, Conlon reproductions are difficult to distinguish from antique prototypes.

The reproduction made today—or earlier—however, is simply too crisp, edges of case work too sharp and lacking the signs of age and abuse which characterize period clocks. The collector should always be sensitive to the existence of early reproductions when evaluating the widely reproduced forms enumerated above.

"Basement clock makers" were not always so straightforward in their workmanship. Scavengers for old components, they often built an entire clock around an old dial, movement or even a finial. These fakes are often such careful blends of old and new workmanship that they are very confusing to evaluate accurately. The only saving grace in examining these pieces is to detect inconsistencies in the appearance of age. The fakers often took great time and care to produce the "right" effect; the collector must take equal time and care to classify these difficult clocks.

The most widely faked New England clocks during the early 20th century have been the Willard thirty-hour wall clock, the patent-timepiece, patent-alarm timepiece, the Massachusetts shelf clock, girandole,(Fig. 6-24) and the so-called "diamond-head banjo".[32] The relatively small size of these clocks made it easy to acquire sufficient wood from old, discarded or damaged furniture dating from the early 19th century. Collectors eagerly sought these forms, providing a ready market for the faker's time and talents. A Boston area collection with many of these forms represented, was recently evaluated to settle an estate. With the exception of one period tall clock, all of the remaining fourteen clocks were fakes! The entire collection was acquired in the 1920's and had numerous examples of the types listed above. It is unclear if the deceased owner knew what he was buying or was the faker's dream-come-true customer. As this experience indicates, any of these forms should always be deemed "guilty until proven innocent".

Hand-crafted clocks represent a unique mixture of the decorative arts: cabinetmaking, painting, glassmaking, metal-work, and the mechanical arts. The accomplished student must have a basic understanding of each of the components of a clock to evaluate it properly. Viewing the clock as a whole and then "dismembering" it into the component specialties provides a picture of authenticity. The seasoned collector is a student who learns to trust

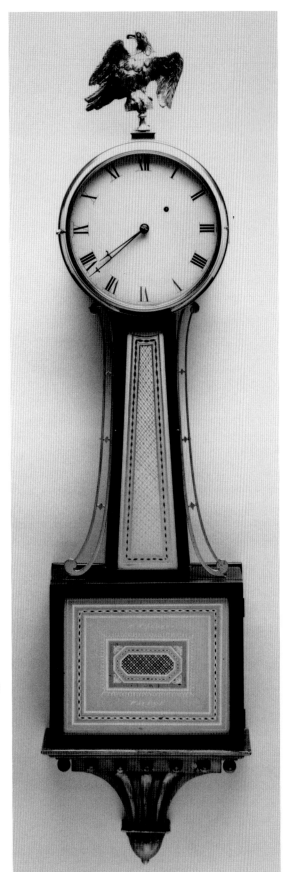

Fig. 6-23.
Reproduction
patent timepiece
probably made by
James E. Conlon,
Boston, Mass., ca.
1930. Superb
reproductions
such as this are
often mistakenly
identified as
period clocks.
57.1.104

Fig. 6-24. A faker
might modify a
patent timepiece
by adding a round
base, gilded
carving, fancy
hardware, and
decorative eagle
to create a
girandole clock.
These clocks
represent a clever
mixture of old
and new
components and
are difficult to
evaluate. 57.1.41

instinct very quickly; failing to develop this sixth sense can often be costly.

In a lecture for collectors held at Old Sturbridge Village, the late Harold Peterson stated that the "purchase price of a fake was the collector's tuition to study the subject." Ownership becomes the often-costly process to develop the sixth sense, the gut reaction, the suspicious nature and the sharp eye which are the characteristics of the seasoned collector. To keep the tuition bill in check, one should remember the old adage: "The buyer needs a thousand eyes, the seller, but one."[33]

[1] For the serious student of the connoisseurship of handcrafted clocks, the following books provide chapters which address fakes, forgeries and other pitfalls: Tom Robinson, *The Longcase Clock* (Suffolk, England: The Antique Collectors Club, Ltd., 1981); Brian Loomes, *Country Clocks and Their London Origins,* (North Pomfret, Vt.: David and Charles, 1976); Richard C.R. Barder, *English Country Grandfather Clocks-The Brass Dial Longcase,* (North Pomfret Vt.: David and Charles, 1983); George White, *English Lantern Clocks* (Suffolk, England: Antique Collectors Club Ltd., 1989); Brian Loomes, *Grandfather Clocks and Their Cases* (New York: Arco Publishing, Inc.,1985).

[2] Myrna Kaye, *Fake, Fraud of Genuine?—Identifying Authentic American Antique Furniture* (Boston: Little, Brown, 1987); Nancy A. Smith, *Old Furniture, or Understanding the Craftsman's Art* (Boston: Little, Brown, 1975); John T. Kirk, *Early American Furniture* (New York: Alfred A. Knopf, 1974); Harold Peterson, *How Do You Know It's Old?* (New York: Scribners, 1975).

[3] A recent fire in a collector's home destroyed eight tall clock cases, while the movements and brass dials remained damaged but intact. These movements and dials will soon be housed in new cases, made to look old, or housed in suitable old cases if available.

[4] 57.1.15 and 57.1.16; see entries in Appendix I.

[5] Wallace Nutting, *The Furniture Treasury,* 3 vols (New York: Macmillan, 1933, repr. 1949), 3:264.

[6] Brian Loomes correctly points out in *Grandfather Clocks,* 334, that rub marks which have no relationship to the present pendulum may appear on the backboard of an otherwise legitimate clock. This could be explained by a replaced escapement, escape wheel, or third wheel.

[7] *The Boston Gazette and Country Journal,* January 3, 1774, in Francis G. Walett, *The Boston Gazette, 1774,* (Barre, Mass.: Imprint Society, 1972), 1; Brian Loomes, *The White Dial Clock* (New York: Drake Publishers, 1975), 28; Hoopes, Penrose, *Shop Records of Daniel Burnap, Clockmaker* (Hartford, Conn.: The Connecticut Historical Society, 1958), 113; Parsons, *New Hampshire Clocks and Clockmakers,* 276; OSV 57.1.50, see Fig.4-3.

[8] Hoopes recounts Daniel Burnap's process of silvering dials, as noted in his memorandum book, 114.

[9] Percy G. Dawson, C.B. Drover, and D.W. Parkes, *Early English Clocks* (Suffolk, England: Antique Collectors Club, Ltd., 1982), 94.

[10] Robert C. Cheney has examined many clocks which have been "improved" in

this manner, a practice which continues to the present.

[11] Avery, Amos, *Clock makers and Craftsmen of the Avery Family in Connecticut* discusses many aspects of the work of specialist artisans. Plates 71-73 show a sheet-brass dial from a clock by Reuben Ingraham also signed by the engraver, "JN. Avery".

[12] When Loomes suggested that scholars and collectors have neglected white dial clocks by collecting and studying earlier brass dial examples instead, he had overlooked Hoopes's September, 1931, article in *Antiques*, *White Dial Clock*, 13, 32.

[13] *Ibid*, 28.

[14] Carter J.Harris, The Clock and Watch Maker's American Advertiser, Vol.3, entry #2166, (undated compilation) cites *The American Herald*, May 23, 1785. The authors are indebted to the American Clock and Watch Museum for the use of this unpublished material.

[15] Brian Loomes offers a full discussion of how clock makers obtained white dials and lists 69 Birmingham dial makers, 16 of whom stamped or cast their names on dial plates. Most of these dials were sold in Britain. *White Dial Clock*, 33-51, 45-48.

[16] *Ibid*, 28.

[17] Asphaltum is a brownish-black substance found as a residue from coal tar and according to the late Edwin Burt, was "purchased in a ball, ground on a glass and thinned with fresh thyme and fatted oil". For more information on these materials see: Gibbs, James W., "American Clock Glass, Its Origins, Manufacture and Decoration", *NAWCC Bulletin*, XXI, no. 4, Whole No. 201, August, 1979, 387-398.

[18] Accomplished dial restorers reline dials slightly shy of the original shadow lines so that this important evidence remains.

[19] The combined experience of three generations of Cheney clock makers indicates that 80-90% of patent timepieces examined have undergone significant restoration or alteration.

[20] The important features of original Willard timepieces are detailed in Chapter 2.

[21] The advertisement is illustrated in Brooks Palmer, *A Treasury of American Clocks* (New York: Macmillan, 1974), 54.

[22] The patent timepiece was widely copied by the Willard apprentices. Adapted by Aaron Willard, Jr.'s apprentice, Edward Howard, the form was produced well into the 20th-century. Such Connecticut firms as Seth Thomas, Elias Ingraham, and Sessions manufactured spring-powered versions of this clock until World War II. Several makers still produce good copies

of the original Willard patent timepiece.

[23] Wallace Nutting, *The Clock Book* (Framingham, Mass.: Old America Company Publishers, 1924), 21.

[24] Edgar Miller, Jr., *American Antique Furniture* (New York: M. Barrows & Co., Inc., 1937) 2:992-993.

[25] Robert C. Cheney uses the term "alternate" train layout for a time train which mounts the third wheel of the train towards the front plate. In earlier Willard timepieces the third wheel is mounted towards the rear plate, a layout known as a "step" train.

[26] It is always risky to evaluate a period clock by measurements alone. These measurements are only for discussion and should not be used to confirm the maker or origin.

[27] In the *NAWCC Bulletin*, see: G.E. Vandervort, "How To Do It—Reverse Painting on Glass," X, no. 12, Whole No. 106: October, 1963, 977; Lee H. Davis, "Some Notes Concerning Reverse Painting on Glass," XIV, no. 5, Whole No. 147, August, 1970, 386; Francis D. Burleigh, "Reverse Painting Techniques," XXI, No. 4, Whole No. 201, August, 1979, 399.

[28] In the *NAWCC Bulletin*, see: G.E. Vandervort, "A History of Reverse Painting on Glass," XV, no. 7, Whole No. 161, December, 1972, 843; Lillian Baker Carlisle, "Curtis and Dunning Clock Glasses and the Men Who Painted Them," XX, no. 1, Whole No. 192, February, 1978, 21; James W.Gibbs, "American Clock Glass—Its Origins, Manufacture and Decoration," XXI, no. 4, Whole No. 201, August, 1979, 387.

[29] Joseph E. Martines, "Contemporary Clockmaking: An Overview," NAWCC Bulletin, XIX, no. 6, Whole No. 191, December, 1977, 571.

[30] Obituary of James E. Conlon, *NAWCC Bulletin*, III, no. 10, Whole No. 30 October, 1949, 707.

[31] Robert C. Cheney is indebted to the late Charles S. Parsons of Goffstown, N.H., for photographs of Conlon's detailed notes originally written on 3x5 index cards. Herschel Burt, Curator of the Willard House and Clock Museum, has also been most generous in sharing his information.

[32] From 1970 to 1992 Robert C. Cheney has examined only one complete fake tall clock. This clock, probably made in the first quarter of the 20th century, contains period wood and some period components such as the movement and dial with a forged signature. A fake Willard label printed on old paper was pasted inside the waist door. A fabricated family "history" pasted to the inside of the backboard was based on clever genealogical research and was placed to hide modern tool marks on the backboard. It is not clear who pro-

duced this clock, but evidence points to the Boston area.

[33] Cescinsky, Herbert, *The Gentle Art of Faking Furniture* (London: Chapman and Hall, 1931), frontispiece.

The initials JCW refer to all clocks acquired by J. Cheney Wells and given by him to the museum to form the Old Sturbridge Village collection.

57.1.2
Tall Clock
Elnathan Taber (1768-1854)
Roxbury, Mass.
ca. 1800
Movement: weight powered
Duration: eight day
Materials: brass and steel
Strike: rack and snail
Escapement: recoil
Dial: painted iron; no false plate
Case: Primary wood: mahogany and mahogany veneer; Secondary wood: white pine
Inscriptions: "WARRANTED BY/E. TABER" on dial; hand-written label of instructions tacked inside door. "C.W. Wordin, 1888, 84", repairer's mark, stamped on back plate. "FT" , probably dial painter's mark, painted on reverse top of dial.
Dimensions: OH: 89 5/8" (229.8cm); OW: 19 5/8" (20.5cm); OD: 10 7/16" (26.8cm)
Provenance: JCW purchase 1933

57.1.3
Patent Timepiece
Simon Willard (1753-1848)
Roxbury, Mass.
ca. 1810
Movement: weight powered
Duration: eight day
Materials: brass and steel
Strike: timepiece
Escapement: dead beat
Dial: painted iron
Case: Primary wood: mahogany and mahogany veneer
Inscriptions: "S. Willard's Patent" painted on lower glass tablet.
Dimensions: OH: 34 3/8" (87.3cm); OW: 10" (25.4cm); OD 3 3/8" (8.6cm)
Provenance: JCW purchase 1931.

57.1.4
Patent Timepiece
Simon Willard (1753-1848)
Roxbury, Mass,
ca. 1810
Movement: weight powered
Duration: eight day
Materials: brass and steel
Strike: timepiece

Escapement: recoil
Dial: painted iron
Case: Primary wood: mahogany
Inscriptions: "S. Willard's Patent" on lower glass,"Patent" on throat glass
Dimensions: OH 32 7/8" (83.5 cm); OW 10" (25.4 cm); OD 3 1/2" (8.9 cm)
Provenance: JCW purchase 1931

57.1.5
Shelf Clock
Aaron Willard (1757-1844)
Roxbury or Boston, Mass.
ca. 1790
Movement: weight powered
Duration: eight day
Materials: brass and steel
Strike: fall off
Escapement: recoil
Dial: painted iron
Case: Primary wood: mahogany; Secondary wood: white pine
Inscriptions: "A. Willard" on dial
Dimensions: OH 31 7/8" (79 cm); OW 12 3/4" (32.4 cm); OD 5 1/2" (14 cm)
Provenance: JCW purchase 1933

57.1.6
Tall Clock
Simon Willard
Roxbury, Mass.
ca. 1800
Movement: weight powered
Duration: eight day
Materials: brass and steel
Strike: rack and snail
Escapement: recoil
Dial: painted iron; false plate
Case: Primary wood: mahogany, mahogany veneer; Secondary wood: white pine, cherry
Inscriptions: "Simon Willard" painted on dial; date dial stamped: "OSBORNE'S MFG., Birmingham"; Willard's paper label printed by Isaiah Thomas, Jr., of Worcester, Mass., pasted inside waist door.
Dimensions: OH: 101 3/8" (257.5cm); OW: 19 1/4" (48.9cm); OD: 10 1/8" (25.7cm)
Provenance: JCW purchase 1931

57.1.7
Tall Clock
Aaron Willard (1757-1844)
Boston, Mass.
ca. 1800
Movement: weight powered
Duration: eight day

APPENDIX I
Technical Data on the Old Sturbridge Village Collection

Materials: brass and steel
Strike: rack and snail
Escapement: recoil
Dial: painted iron, no false plate
Case: Primary wood: mahogany, mahogany veneer; Secondary wood: white pine
Inscriptions: "Aaron Willard, Boston" painted on dial, "Roskell Liverpool" stamped on back plate of movement, Aaron Willard label engraved by Paul Revere pasted inside waist door.
Dimensions: OH: 97" (246.4cm); OW: 20 1/2" (52.1cm); OD: 10 1/2" (26.7cm)
Provenance: JCW purchase before 1937

57.1.8
Patent Timepiece
Simon Willard (1753-1848)
Roxbury, Mass.
ca. 1805
Movement: weight powered
Duration: eight day
Materials: brass and steel
Strike: timepiece
Escapement: recoil
Dial: painted iron
Case: Primary wood: mahogany
Inscriptions: "S. Willard's/PATENT" painted on lower glass.
Dimensions: OH: 33 3/8" (84.8cm); OW: 9 3/4" (28.6cm); OD: 3 3/8" (8.6cm)
Provenance: JCW purchase 1929

57.1.9
Patent Timepiece
Simon Willard (1753-1848)
Roxbury, Mass.
ca. 1805-1810
Movement: weight powered
Duration: eight day
Materials: brass and steel
Strike: timepiece
Escapement: dead beat
Dial: painted iron
Case: Primary wood: probably birch; Secondary wood: white pine
Dimensions: OH: 42 1/2" (109cm);OW: 10 1/2" (26.4cm); OD: 3 7/8" (9.9cm)
Provenance: Sylvester (1785-1863) and Abby Taylor Brownell of Providence, R.I, to Sophie (Brownell) Mitchell to Cora Mitchell; JCW purchase 1931

57.1.10
Wall Clock
Elnathan Taber (1768-1854)
Roxbury, Mass.
ca. 1820
Movement: weight powered, alarm attachment
Duration: eight day
Materials: brass and steel
Strike: timepiece
Escapement: recoil
Dial: painted iron

Case: Primary wood: mahogany; Secondary wood: white pine (weight guides)
Inscriptions: "Made by E. Taber, August 16, 1820", "Cleaned by J. Beals, Feb. 16, 1829—J. Hardy" scratched on front plate; "Made by Elnathan Taber, Roxbury" scratched on iron weight baffle
Dimensions: OH: 35 1/2" (90.2cm); OW: 8 3/4" (22.2 cm); OD: 3 3/4" (9.5 cm)
Provenance: JCW purchase 1934

57.1.11
Tall Clock
Calvin Bailey (1761-1835)
Hanover, Mass.
1805
Movement: weight powered
Duration: eight day
Materials: brass and steel
Strike: rack and snail
Escapement: recoil
Dial: painted iron; no false plate
Case: Primary wood: mahogany, mahogany veneer; Secondary wood: white pine, chestnut (sides of hood)
Inscriptions: "Made for Nathl Howe./ CALVIN BAILEY." on dial; "Calvin Bailey" on back of dial.
Dimensions: OH: 86 3/4" (220.3 cm); OW: 20 1/4" (51.4 cm); OD: 9 1/2" (24.1 cm)
Provenance: JCW purchase, date unknown

57.1.14
Tall Clock
Aaron Willard (1757-1844)
Roxbury, Mass.
ca. 1785
Movement: weight powered
Duration: eight day
Materials: brass and steel
Strike: rack and snail
Escapement: recoil
Dial: painted iron; no false plate
Case: Primary wood: mahogany; Secondary wood: white pine
Inscriptions: "Aaron Willard" on dial; Aaron Willard label engraved by Paul Revere inside waist door.
Dimensions: OH 92 1/2" (235 cm); OW: 20 7/8" (53 cm); OD: 10 1/4" (26 cm)
Provenance: JCW purchase before 1937

57.1.15
Patent Alarm Timepiece
Simon Willard (1753-1848)
Roxbury Mass.
1833; case 1982
Movement: weight powered, alarm attachment, 10-inch pendulum
Duration: eight day
Materials: brass and steel
Strike: timepiece
Escapement: dead-beat
Dial: silvered brass with painted numerals
Case: OSV reproduction; Primary wood:

mahogany; Secondary wood: white pine
Inscriptions: "Made by Simon Willard in 1833/—in his 80th year" engraved on brass disk supporting movement in case
Dimensions: OH: 27 5/8" (70.2cm); OW: 8 7/8" (22.5cm); OD: 8 7/8" (22.5cm)
Provenance: JCW purchase 1937

57.1.16
Patent Alarm Timepiece
Simon Willard (1753-1848)
Roxbury, Mass.
ca. 1825; case 1981
Movement: weight powered, alarm attachment, 16 1/2" pendulum
Duration: eight day
Materials: brass and steel
Strike: timepiece
Escapement: dead beat
Dial: porcelain
Case: OSV reproduction; Primary wood: mahogany; Secondary wood: pine
Inscriptions:"SIMON/WILLARD" painted on dial
Dimensions: OH: 27 5/8" (70.2cm); OW: 8 7/8" (22.5cm); OD: 8 7/8" (22.5cm)
Provenance: JCW purchase 1929.

57.1.17
Shelf Clock
Aaron Willard (1757-1844)
Boston, Mass.
ca. 1810
Movement: weight powered, 10" pendulum
Duration: eight day
Materials: brass and steel
Strike: timepiece
Escapement: recoil
Dial: painted iron
Case: Primary wood: mahogany, mahogany veneer; Secondary wood: white pine
Inscriptions: "Aaron Willard Boston" on dial
Dimensions: OH 36 7/8 (93.7 cm); OW 14 3/16" (36 cm); OD 6 3/8" (16.9 cm)
Provenance: JCW purchase before 1937

57.1.18
Shelf Clock
Aaron Willard, Jr. (1783-1864)
Boston, Mass.
ca. 1810
Movement: weight powered, 10" pendulum
Duration: eight day
Materials: brass and steel
Strike: timepiece
Escapement: recoil
Dial: painted iron
Case:Primary wood: mahogany, mahogany veneer; Secondary wood: white pine
Inscriptions: "Aaron Willard Junr/Boston" painted on dial; "AW Jr" painted on reverse of dial.
Dimensions: OH: 32 1/2" (83.3cm); OW: 13 7/8" (33.3cm); OD: 6 1/8" (20.5cm)
Provenance: JCW purchase before 1937

57.1.20
Shelf Clock
Aaron Willard Jr. (1783-1864)
Boston, Mass.
ca. 1820
Movement: weight powered, 10" pendulum
Duration: eight day
Materials: brass and steel
Strike: rack and snail
Escapement: recoil
Dial: painted iron
Case:Primary wood: mahogany, mahogany veneer; Secondary wood: white pine
Inscriptions: "Aaron Willard" ["Jr." missing] upper glass tablet
Dimensions: OH 35 1/4" (89.5 cm); OW 13" (33.2 cm); OD 6" (15.2 cm)
Provenance: JCW purchase before 1937

57.1.23
Tall Clock
Gardner Parker (1772-1816)
Westborough, Mass.
ca. 1810
Movement: weight powered
Duration: eight day
Materials: brass and steel
Strike: rack and snail
Escapement: recoil
Dial: painted iron; no false plate
Case:Primary wood: cherry, mahogany banding, maple string inlay; Secondary wood: white pine
Inscriptions: "WARRANTED FOR Mr SOLOMON ESTE./G Parker" on dial.
Dimensions: OH: 86 3/8" (219.5cm); OW: 19 1/2" (49.5cm); OD: 9 3/8" (23.3cm)
Provenance: JCW purchase ca. 1930

57.1.25
Dwarf Clock
Peter Hawkes Cushing (1799-1889)
Braintree, Mass.
ca. 1825
Movement: weight powered, alarm attachment, 20" pendulum
Duration: eight day
Materials: brass and steel
Strike: fall off
Escapement: recoil
Dial: painted iron; no false plate
Case:Primary wood: mahogany, mahogany veneer; Secondary wood: white pine
Inscriptions: "Peter H. Cushing/Braintree" painted on dial
Dimensions: OH: 51 3/4" (131.5cm); OW: 11 1/4" (28.6cm); OD: 5 1/2" (14cm)
Provenance: JCW purchase 1931

57.1.26
Shelf Clock
Aaron Willard (1757-1844)
Boston, Mass
ca. 1825
Movement: weight powered, 10" pendulum

Duration: eight day
Materials: brass and steel
Strike: timepiece
Escapement: recoil
Dial: painted iron
Case:Primary wood: mahogany, mahogany veneer; Secondary wood: white pine
Inscriptions: "81" on frames and weight baffle
Dimensions: OH: 34 1/2" (87.6cm); OW: 12 3/4" (32.3 cm); OD:6 1/4" (15.8 cm)
Provenance: gift to JCW 1945

57.1.28
Shelf Clock
Eli Terry and Sons,
Plymouth, Conn.
ca. 1823-1833
Movement: weight powered
Duration: thirty hour
Materials: oak plates, cherry wheels, maple arbors
Strike: count wheel
Escapement: recoil
Dial: painted pine
Case:Primary wood: mahogany, mahogany veneer; Secondary wood: white pine
Inscriptions: paper label – "Eli Terry and Sons, Plymouth, Conn."
Dimensions: OH: 31 1/4" (79.4cm) OW: 17 3/8" OD:4 1/2"
Provenance: gift to JCW 1945

57.1.29
Dwarf Clock
Reuben Tower (1795-1881)
Hanover, Mass.
1816-1818
Movement: weight powered, 20" pendulum
Duration: eight day
Materials: brass and steel
Strike: rack and snail
Escapement: recoil
Dial: painted iron; no false plate
Case: Primary wood: white pine
Inscriptions: "Reuben Tower/HANOVER" on dial
Dimensions: OH: 47 5/16" (120.2cm); OW: 11 9/16" (29.6cm); OD: 5 3/4" (4.7cm)
Provenance: JCW purchase 1931

57.1.32A
Tall Clock
Paul Rogers (1752-1818)
Berwick, Me.
ca. 1785
Movement: weight powered
Duration: eight day
Materials: brass and steel (plates appear to be bell metal and pillar posts are steel)
Strike: rack and snail
Escapement: recoil
Dial: silvered brass
Case:Primary wood: maple and birch; Secondary wood: white pine

Inscriptions: "Paul Rogers Berwick" engraved on dial
Dimensions: OH: 80 7/8" (207.4cm); OW: 17 1/4" (44.2cm); OD: 10 1/8" (26.0cm)
Provenance: Museum purchase 1938

57.1.35
Shelf Clock
Daniel Balch (1735-1789)
Newburyport, Mass.
1783
Movement: weight powered, 16" pendulum
Duration: two day
Materials: brass and steel
Strike: rack and snail
Escapement: recoil
Dial: silvered brass
Case:Primary wood: mahogany; Secondary wood: white pine
Inscriptions: "1783/D.BALCH/NEWBURY-PORT" on dial
Dimensions: OH: 25 1/4" (64.8cm); OW: 10 1/16" (25.0cm); OD: 6 1/16" (15.54cm).
Provenance: JCW purchase 1928

57.1.36
Dwarf Clock
Joshua Wilder (1786-1860)
Hingham, Mass.
ca. 1820
Movement: weight powered, alarm attachment, 20" pendulum
Duration: eight day
Materials: brass and steel
Strike: fall off
Escapement: recoil
Dial: painted iron
Case:Primary wood: mahogany, mahogany veneer; Secondary wood: white pine
Inscriptions: "Warranted by J. Wilder/Hingham" on painted dial;
Dimensions: OH 50 1/2" (128.3cm); OW 11 1/2" (29.2cm) OD 5 3/4" (14.6cm)
Provenance: JCW purchase 1931

57.1.36A
Wall Clock
John Sawin (1801-1863)
Boston, Mass.
ca. 1835
Movement: weight powered, 18" pendulum
Duration: eight day
Materials: brass and steel
Strike: timepiece
Escapement: recoil
Dial: painted zinc
Case: Primary wood: mahogany; Secondary wood: white pine
Inscriptions: "JOHN SAWIN./BOSTON." painted on dial.
Dimensions: OH: 38 1/8" (97.8cm); OW: 11 1/4" (28.9cm); OD: 4 5/16" (11.1cm).
Provenance: Museum purchase 1940

57.1.41
Girandole Clock
maker unknown
Boston area
early 20th century, made up of old components
Movement: weight powered
Duration: eight day
Materials: brass and steel
Strike: timepiece
Escapement: recoil
Dial: painted iron
Case:Primary wood: mahogany; Secondary wood: white pine
Inscriptions: "L. Curtis Patent" on dial
Dimensions: OH: 41" (104.1cm)
Provenance: JCW purchase 1939

57.1.42
Wall Clock
maker unknown
prob. Boston, Mass.
ca. 1835
Movement: weight powered
Duration: eight day
Materials: brass and steel
Strike: timepiece
Escapement: recoil
Dial: painted iron
Case:Primary wood: mahogany, mahogany veneer; Secondary wood: white pine
Dimensions: OH 40" (101.6 cm); OW 11 5/16" (28.7 cm); OD 5 1/8" (13 cm)
Provenance: JCW purchase 1927

57.1.45
Shelf Clock
Joshua Wilder (1786-1860)
Hingham, Mass.
1813
Movement: weight powered, alarm attachment, 10" pendulum
Duration: eight day
Materials: brass and steel
Strike: fall off
Escapement: recoil
Dial: painted iron
Case:Primary wood: mahogany, mahogany veneer; Secondary wood: white pine
Inscriptions: "Joshua WILDER/HINGHAM" painted on dial; "Joshua Wilder/Hingham" on back of dial; hand written bill of sale inside case "Hingham 12th mo 4th 1813/ David Sprague b[ought o]f Joshua Wilder/ one eight day [brass alarm] timepiece $24.00/ 6th mo 9th 1814 [received paymen]t in full of all demands/Joshua Wilder"
Dimensions: OH: 43 1/4" (109.9cm); OW 14 1/4" (36.2cm); OD: 6 3/4" (17.2cm)
Provenance: JCW purchase 1934

57.1.46
Shelf Clock
Stephen N. Taber (1777-1862)
New Bedford, Mass.

ca. 1805
Movement: weight powered, 10" pendulum
Duration: eight day
Materials: brass and steel
Strike: timepiece
Escapement: recoil
Dial: painted iron, possibly John Ritto Penniman
Case: Primary wood: mahogany, mahogany veneer; Secondary wood: white pine and cherry (dial mat and hood area)
Inscriptions: "S. TABER" on dial
Dimensions: OH: 35 1/4" (89.5cm); OW: 13 1/4" (33.7cm); OD: 6 1/8" (15.6cm)
Provenance: JCW purchase 1934

57.1.47
Shelf Clock
Lucius Bradley and James Bishop
Watertown, Conn.
ca. 1824-1832
Movement: weight powered
Duration: eight day
Materials: brass and steel
Strike: rack and snail
Escapement: recoil
Dial: painted iron
Case:Primary wood: mahogany, mahogany veneer; Secondary wood: white pine
Inscriptions: Printed label, back of case: "Patent improved 8-day brass clocks made and sold by Lucius B. Bradley Watertown (Conn). Warranted". Painted dial signed: "Bishop and Bradley, Watertown". "VII" scribed on roof of the case and top edge of door.
Dimensions: OH: 33" (83.9cm); OW: 17 3/4" (45.1cm); OD: 5" (12.8cm)
Provenance: JCW purchase 1934

57.1.48
Tall Clock
Nathaniel Mulliken, Sr.(1722-1767)
Lexington, Mass.
ca. 1760
Movement: weight powered
Duration: eight day
Materials: brass and steel
Strike: rack and snail
Escapement: recoil
Dial: brass with applied cast-brass spandrels, silvered brass chapter ring, name boss, second's bit and recessed calendar ring.
Case: Primary wood: maple; Secondary wood: white pine
Inscriptions: "Nath Mulliken/Lexington" on dial name boss
Dimensions: OH: 79 3/4" (202.6cm); OW: 21 3/8" (54.2cm); OD: 10 7/8" (27.2cm)
Provenance: JCW purchase 1934.

57.1.49
Tall Clock
Simon Willard (1753-1848)
Roxbury, Mass.

ca. 1800
Movement: weight powered
Duration: eight day
Materials: brass and steel
Strike: rack and snail
Escapement: recoil
Dial: painted iron; no false plate
Case: Primary wood: mahogany, mahogany veneer; Secondary wood: white pine
Inscriptions:"Simon Willard" painted on dial
Dimensions: OH: 89 1/2" (227.33 cm); OW: 20 1/2" (52.07 cm); OD: 10 3/4" (27.30 cm)
Provenance: JCW purchase 1925

57.1.50
Shelf Clock
David Wood (1766-ca. 1824)
Newburyport, Mass.
ca. 1810
Movement: weight powered, 16" pendulum
Duration: two day
Materials: brass and steel
Strike: fall off
Escapement: recoil
Dial: painted iron; no false plate
Case:Primary wood: mahogany, mahogany veneer, birch veneer; Secondary wood: white pine
Inscriptions:"DAVID WOOD/Newburyport" on dial; "PAINTED BY SPENCER NOLEN-CLOCK FACE PAINTER." and "ANx2" on reverse of dial; "28 Dec. 1812" and "June 3 1809" written in ink inside case
Dimensions: OH: 35" (88.7cm); OW: 12 3/4" (32.4cm); OD: 6 3/8" (16.2cm)
Provenance: JCW purchase 1934

57.1.53
Wall Clock
maker unknown
prob. Boston, Mass
ca. 1820
Movement: weight powered
Duration: eight day
Materials: brass and steel
Strike: rack and snail
Escapement: recoil
Dial: painted iron
Case: Primary wood: mahogany, mahogany veneer; Secondary wood: white pine
Dimensions: OH:40 1/2" (102.9cm); OW:10 1/4" (26cm); OD: 3 3/4" (9.5cm)
Provenance: JCW purchase 1927

57.1.58
Shelf Clock
David Wood (1766-ca. 1824)
Newburyport, Mass.
ca. 1790
Movement: weight powered, 15" pendulum
Duration: two day
Materials: brass and steel
Strike: rack and snail
Escapement: recoil
Dial: silvered brass

Case:Primary wood: mahogany, mahogany veneer; Secondary wood: white pine
Inscriptions: "David Wood/Newbury Port" engraved on dial
Dimensions: OH: 32 1/8" (81.6cm);OW: 12 3/4" (32.4cm) OD: 6 1/2" (16.5cm)
Provenance: JCW purchase 1935

57.1.59
Shelf Clock
David Wood (1766-ca. 1824)
Newburyport, Mass.
ca. 1800
Movement: weight powered, 16" pendulum
Duration: two day
Materials: brass and steel
Strike: fall off
Escapement: recoil
Dial: painted iron, no false plate
Case:Primary wood: mahogany; Secondary wood: white pine
Inscriptions: "David Wood" on dial; "HJ" stamped on underside of bail handles
Dimensions: OH: 35 3/8" (90.7cm); OW: 12 11/16" (32.5cm); OD 6 1/4" (16.0cm)
Provenance: JCW purchase 1935

57.1.62
Shelf Clock
Seth Thomas (1785-1859)
Plymouth, Conn.
ca. 1825
Movement: weight powered
Duration: thirty hour
Materials: oak plates, cherry wheels, maple pinions and arbors
Strike: count wheel
Escapement: recoil
Dial: painted pine
Case:Primary wood: mahogany, mahogany veneer; Secondary wood: white pine
Inscriptions: "Clocks Made and Sold by SETH THOMAS, Plymouth, Conn. Warranted if Well Used. Directions for Using this Clock..." on printed paper label inside case.
Dimensions: OH: 31" (79.49cm); OW: 17 3/8" (44.50cm); OD: 4 1/2" (11.54cm)
Provenance: JCW purchase 1935

57.1.63
Tall Clock
Riley Whiting (1785-1835)
Winchester, Conn.
ca. 1820
Movement: weight powered
Duration: thirty hour
Materials: oak plates, cherry wheels, maple arbors and pinions
Strike: count wheel
Escapement: recoil
Dial: painted pine
Case: Primary wood: pine
Inscriptions: "R. Whiting, Winchester" on dial

Dimensions: OH: 10 5/8" (27.24cm); OW: 7 3/4" (19.9cm); OD: 7" (17.9cm)
Provenance: JCW purchase, date unknown

57.1.64
Tall Clock
Simon Willard (1753-1848)
Roxbury, Massachusetts
ca. 1795
Movement: weight powered
Duration: eight day
Materials: brass and steel
Strike: rack and snail
Escapement: recoil
Dial: painted iron, false plate
Case:Primary wood: mahogany, mahogany veneer; Secondary wood: white pine
Inscriptions: "Warranted for Mr Josiah Temple/Simon Willard" painted on dial; printed label of Simon Willard by Isaiah Thomas, Jr., of Worcester, Massachusetts, pasted inside waist door; "Wilson" inscribed on false plate
Dimensions: OH: 92 3/8" (234.6 cm.);OW: 20" (50.7 cm.);OD: 10 1/8" (25.7 cm.)
Provenance: Made for Josiah Temple (1742-1824) of Framingham, Mass.; JCW purchase 1935

57.1.66
Shelf Clock
Aaron Willard (1757-1844)
Boston, Mass.
ca. 1825
Movement: weight powered, 10" pendulum
Duration: eight day
Materials: brass and steel
Strike: timepiece
Escapement: recoil
Dial: painted iron
Case:Primary wood: mahogany, mahogany veneer; Secondary wood: white pine, cherry (seat board)
Inscriptions: "Aaron Willard/Boston" painted on upper glass tablet; "135" stamped on pine support behind lower glass, on lower and upper glass frame, and on pine backboard behind movement.
Dimensions: OH: 35 1/2" (90.2cm);OW: 13 1/8" (33.3cm); OD: 5 3/4" (14.6cm)
Provenance: JCW purchase 1935

57.1.67
Tall Clock
Aaron Willard (1757-1844)
Boston, Mass.
ca. 1810
Movement: weight powered
Duration: eight day
Materials: brass and steel
Strike: rack and snail
Escapement: recoil
Dial: painted iron, no false plate
Case:Primary wood: mahogany, mahogany veneer; Secondary wood: white pine, cherry

(waist door)
Inscriptions: "Aaron Willard, Boston" painted on dial; "AW" written in chalk on backboard
Dimensions: OH: 93 1/4" (236.8cm); OW: 20" (51.1cm); OD: 9 3/4" (24.6cm)
Provenance: JCW purchase 1935

57.1.68
Timepiece
Aaron Willard (1757-1844)
prob. Roxbury, Mass
ca. 1780
Movement: weight powered
Duration: thirty hour
Materials: brass and steel
Strike: fall off
Escapement: dead beat
Dial: silvered brass
Case:Primary wood: mahogany
Secondary wood: white pine
Inscriptions: "A. Willard" engraved on dial
Dimensions: OH: 25 1/4" (65.4 cm); OW: 8 3/4" (22.2 cm) OD: 3 1/2" (9 cm)
Provenance: JCW purchase 1935

57.1.70
Tall Clock
Aaron Willard (1757-1844)
Boston, Mass.
ca. 1820
Movement: weight powered
Duration: eight day
Materials: brass and steel
Strike: rack and snail
Escapement: recoil
Dial: painted iron, no false plate
Case: Primary wood: mahogany, mahogany veneer; Secondary wood: white pine
Inscriptions: "Aaron Willard/BOSTON" painted on dial; scribed: "XLIIIII" on hood door; stamped "45" on top of waist front rail.
Dimensions: OH: 93 1/4" (237cm); OW: 20" (50.8cm); OD: 10" (25.4cm)
Provenance: JCW purchase 1936

57.1.73
Shelf Clock
Elnathan Taber (1768-1854)
Roxbury, Mass.
ca. 1805
Movement: weight powered, 10" pendulum
Duration: eight day
Materials: brass and steel
Strike: timepiece
Escapement: recoil
Dial: painted iron
Case: Primary wood: mahogany, mahogany veneer; Secondary wood: white pine
Inscriptions: "WARRANTED BY/E TABER" on dial; "W A" painted on reverse of dial. Movement has 16 scratched notations of cleaning dates from 1821 to l940, six made by Taber.
Dimensions: OH: 40 5/8" (103.2cm); OW:

14 1/2" (36.9cm); OD: 6 3/4" (17.2cm)
Provenance: JCW purchase 1936

57.1.74
Tall Clock
Aaron Willard (1757-1844)
Boston, Mass.
ca. 1810
Movement: weight powered
Duration: eight day
Materials: brass and steel
Strike: rack and snail
Escapement: recoil
Dial: painted iron, no false plate, dial possibly of Boston manufacture
Case:Primary wood: mahogany, mahogany veneer; Secondary wood: white pine, cherry
Inscriptions: "Aaron Willard, Boston" faintly visible on the painted dial; printed paper label engraved by Paul Revere pasted inside the door.
Dimensions: OH: 94 3/4" (239.7cm); OW: 21 1/4" (54.2cm); OD: 9 5/8" (24.4cm)
Provenance: JCW purchase 1936

57.1.77
Patent Timepiece
Simon Willard (1753-1848)
Roxbury, Mass.
ca. 1810
Movement: weight powered
Duration: eight day
Materials: brass and steel
Strike: timepiece
Escapement: recoil
Dial: painted iron
Case: Primary wood: mahogany
Inscriptions: "S. Willard's Patent" on lower glass
Dimensions: OH: 34 1/4" (89.8cm); OW: 20 1/2" (52.1 cm); OD: 10 3/4" (27.3 cm)
Provenance: JCW purchase 1936

57.1.78
Gallery Clock
attrib. Simon Willard (1753-1848)
Roxbury, Mass.
ca. 1810
Movement: weight powered
Duration: eight day
Materials: brass and steel
Strike: timepiece
Escapement: recoil
Dial: painted mahogany
Case: Primary wood: white pine, mahogany (lower glass frame); Secondary wood: white pine
Inscriptions: "III" scribed on reverse of dial
Dimension: OH: 71 1/2" (181.7cm); OW: 38 3/4" (98.4cm); OD: 5 1/2" (13.9cm)
Provenance: JCW purchase 1936

57.1.79
Shelf Clock
Aaron Willard (1757-1844)

Roxbury, Mass.
1784
Movement: weight powered, 16" pendulum
Duration: eight day
Materials: brass and steel
Strike: fall off
Escapement: dead beat
Dial: painted iron
Case:Primary wood: mahogany; Secondary wood: white pine
Inscriptions: "Aaron Willard, Roxbury" engraved on nameplate; "The 1st short/time piece/made in/America/1784" written on paper label inside of case.
Dimensions: OH: 29 3/4" (75.6cm); OW: 24" (35.6cm);
OD: 5 1/4" (13.3cm)
Provenance: JCW purchase 1936

57.1.80
Wall Clock
Aaron Willard, Jr. (1783-1864)
Boston, Mass.
ca. 1820
Movement: weight powered
Duration: eight day
Materials: brass and steel
Strike: timepiece
Escapement: recoil
Dial: painted iron
Case: Primary wood: mahogany; Secondary wood: white pine
Inscriptions: paper label pasted in the case with "Directions for putting up the time-piece… made by license from the patent by Aaron Willard, Jr."
Dimension: OH: 31" (78.7cm); OW: 11" (27.9cm); OD: 4 3/8" (11.1cm)
Provenance: JCW purchase 1936

57.1.82
Shelf Clock
Simon Willard (1753-1848)
Roxbury, Mass.
ca. 1790
Movement: weight powered
Duration: eight day
Materials: brass and steel
Strike: rack and snail
Escapement: recoil
Dial: painted iron
Case: Primary wood: mahogany, mahogany veneer; Secondary wood: white pine
Inscriptions:"Simon Willard" painted on dial
Dimensions: OH: 41" (104.1cm); OW: 14 1/4" (36.2cm); OD: 7" (17.8cm)
Provenance: JCW purchase 1936

57.1.83
Patent Timepiece
prob. Simon Willard (1753-1848)
Roxbury, Mass.
ca. 1810

Movement: weight powered
Duration: eight day
Materials: brass and steel
Strike: timepiece
Escapement: dead beat
Dial: painted iron
Case: Primary wood:mahogany;Secondary wood: white pine
Dimensions: OH: 34 1/2" (87.6cm); OW: 11 1/16" (28.1cm); OD: 3 7/16" (8.7cm)
Provenance: JCW purchase 1936

57.1.86
Wall Clock
Lemuel Curtis and Joseph Nye Dunning (1795-1841)
Burlington, Vt.
Ca. 1825
Movement: weight powered, alarm attachment, 18" pendulum
Duration: eight-day
Materials: brass and steel
Strike: timepiece
Escapement: recoil
Dial: convex painted iron
Case: Primary wood: mahogany; Secondary wood: white pine
Inscriptions: "Warranted by Curtis & Dunning" on dial
Dimensions: OH: 39 7/8" (101.3cm); OW: 11 1/4" (28.6cm);OD: 4 5/8" (11.7cm)
Provenance: JCW purchase 1936

57.1.87
Regulator
attrib. Simon Willard (1753-1848)
Roxbury, Mass.
ca. 1832
Movement: weight powered, with maintaining power
Duration: eight day
Materials: brass and steel
Strike: timepiece
Escapement: dead beat
Dial: painted iron
Case: Primary wood: mahogany
Inscriptions: "1832" faintly scratched on back plate
Dimensions: OH: 59 1/8" (150.1cm); OW: 19 1/4" (48.9cm); OD 5 3/4" (14.6cm)
Provenance: JCW purchase 1936

57.1.88
Tall Clock
John Bailey, Sr. (1730-1810)
Hanover, Mass.
ca. 1785
Movement: weight powered
Duration: eight day
Materials: brass and steel
Strike: rack and snail
Escapement: recoil
Dial: silvered brass
Case: Primary wood: cherry, mahogany (fluted plinths above free-standing columns)

and birch (moldings between hood and waist); Secondary wood: white pine
Inscriptions: "John Bailey/Hanover" on dial
Dimensions: OH: 92 5/8" (237.5cm); OW: 19 5/8" (50.3cm); OD: 11 1/4" (28.8cm)
Provenance: JCW purchase 1936

57.1.89
Timepiece
Silas Burnham Terry (1820-1876)
Terryville, Conn.
ca. 1845
Movement: dual spring powered
Duration: eight day
Materials: brass and steel
Strike: timepiece
Escapement: dead beat with rack and pinion balance wheel
Dial: silvered brass
Case: wooden base with glass dome
Inscriptions: "Silas B. Terry" engraved on front plate of movement; lower plate stamped "S.B. Terry Patent."
Dimensions: OH: 18" (45.7 cm); OW: 12 1/8" (30.9cm); OD: 6 1/8" (15.6cm)
Provenance: JCW purchase 1936

57.1.90
Shelf Clock
Zacheus Gates (1770-1831)
prob. Harvard, Mass.
ca. 1810
Movement: weight powered, 10" pendulum
Duration: eight day
Materials: brass and steel
Strike: timepiece
Escapement: recoil
Dial: painted iron
Case: Primary wood: cherry; Secondary wood: white pine
Inscriptions: "Zacheus Gates" on dial
Dimensions: OH: 36 1/8" (92.6cm); OW: 14 1/16" (36.1cm); OD: 6 1/4" (16.0cm)
Provenance: JCW purchase 1936

57.1.91
Wall Clock
Attr. to Abiel Chandler (1807-1881)
Concord, N.H.
ca. 1835
Movement: weight powered, 23" pendulum
Duration: eight day
Materials: brass and steel
Strike: timepiece
Escapement: recoil
Dial: painted iron
Case: Primary wood: mahogany; Secondary wood: white pine (weight guides)
Inscriptions: "VI" pressed into back of lyre front, box frame and box.
Dimensions: OH: 39 5/8" (101.6cm); OW: 11 1/2" (29.5cm); OD: 3 15/16" (10.1cm)
Provenance: JCW purchase 1936

57.1.92
Tall Clock
Thomas Claggett (ca. 1730-1797)
Newport, R.I,
1772
Clock Case:
Benjamin Baker (1737-1822)
Newport, R.I,
1772
Movement: weight powered
Duration: eight day
Materials: brass and steel
Strike: rack and snail
Escapement: recoil
Dial: brass with silvered brass chapter ring, seconds bit and name boss, cast brass and gilded spandrels
Case: Primary wood: mahogany; Secondary wood: white pine
Dimensions: OH: 95" (241.3cm); OW: 21 5/8" (54.9cm); OD: 11 1/4" (28.6cm)
Inscriptions: "Thomas/Claggett/Newport" on dial; "December 30th 1772. I Thomas Claggett Do Warrant a Clock to Abraham Brown to be a good clock if it Does not prove So I promis to Pay the money back to sd Brown Whis [sic] is fifty-six dollars & on quarter. Witness my hand. Thomas Claggett". On handwritten label in case; "Made and Sold By Benjamin Baker in Newport 1772". On handwritten label in case; "This clock was bought by me from John Quincy Adams Brown of Tiverton R.I. grandson of Abraham Brown, the original owner, Geo. C. Nightingale, Providence, R.I. May 30, 1922".
Provenance: Descended in the family of Abraham Brown; JCW purchase 1936

57.1.93
Tall Clock
Zacheus Gates (1770-1831)
Charlestown, Massachusetts
ca. 1815
Movement: weight powered
Duration: eight day
Materials: brass and steel
Strike: rack and snail
Escapement: recoil
Dial: painted iron, no false plate
Case: Primary wood: mahogany, mahogany veneer; Secondary wood: white pine, cherry (waist door)
Inscriptions: "Zacheus Gates/CHARLESTOWN" on the painted dial; "No. 133" and "Top" on backboard; "G. Ainsworth, WARR" on bell (George Ainsworth, Warrington, England, bell founder). "SUMMER— Cold trembling winter hastens away, sportive summer crowns the day." on paper glued inside hood roof as dust cover
Dimensions: OH: 94 5/8" (240.4cm); OW: 20 1/4" (51.4cm); OD: 9 1/2" (24.1cm)
Provenance: JCW purchase 1936

57.1.94
Shelf Clock
Ephraim Downs (1787-1860)
Bristol, Conn.
ca. 1825-1828
Movement: weight powered
Duration: thirty hour
Materials: oak plates, cherry wheels, maple arbors
Strike: count wheel
Escapement: recoil
Dial: painted pine, with raised and gilded gesso
Case: Primary wood: mahogany, mahogany veneer; Secondary wood: white pine
Inscriptions: on label, "Ephraim Downs for George Mitchell"
Dimensions: OH: 31" (78.7cm); OW: 16 1/2" (41.9cm); OD: 4 1/2" (11.4cm)
Provenance: JCW purchase 1936

57.1.96
Wall Clock
Frederick Wingate (1782-1864)
Augusta, Maine
ca. 1825
Movement: weight powered
Duration: eight day
Materials: brass and steel
Strike: rack and snail
Escapement: recoil
Dial: painted iron
Case: Primary wood: figured maple; Secondary wood: white pine
Inscriptions: "Frederick Wingate/Augusta" on dial
Dimension: OH: 34 1/4" (87 cm); OW: 16 5/8" (42.2 cm); OD: 4 3/4" (12.1 cm)
Provenance: JCW purchase 1936

57.1.97
Patent Timepiece
Simon Willard (1753-1848) and Son (Simon Willard, Jr.1795-1874)
Boston, Mass.
ca. 1830
Movement: weight powered
Duration: eight day
Materials: brass and steel
Strike: timepiece
Escapement: recoil
Dial: painted iron
Case: Primary wood: mahogany; Secondary wood: white pine
Inscriptions: "Simon Willard & Son/Boston" painted on dial; "29" stamped on both frames which enclose glasses.
Dimensions: OH: 34" (86.4cm); OW: 9 7/8" (25.1cm); OD: 4" (10.2cm)
Provenance: JCW purchase 1936

57.1.98
Tall Clock
Benjamin Willard (1743-1803)
Grafton, Mass.

ca. 1770
Movement: weight powered
Duration: eight day
Materials: brass and steel
Strike: rack and snail
Escapement: recoil
Dial: brass, with silvered chapter ring, name boss, decorative boss in the arch, seconds bit and recessed calendar ring
Case: Primary wood: cherry;
Secondary wood: white pine
Inscriptions: "Benja Willard/GRAFTON" on name boss
Dimensions: OH: 88 1/8" (2238cm); OW: 19 7/8" (50.5cm); OD: 9 3/4" (24.8cm)
Provenance: JCW purchase 1936.

57.1.99
Tall Clock Movement and Dial
William Claggett (1696-1749)
Newport, R.I.
ca. 1740
Movement: weight powered
Duration: eight day
Materials: brass and steel
Strike: rack and snail
Escapement: recoil
Dial: brass with applied silvered brass chapter ring, second's bit and name boss, applied cast brass spandrels.
Case: early-19th century, better suited to a painted dial movement
Primary wood: mahogany, mahogany veneer;
Secondary wood: white pine
Inscriptions: "W. Claggett/Newport" on the dial
Dimensions: Dial OH: 16 3/16" (41.5cm); OW: 11 5/8" (29.8cm)
Movement: OH: 7 1/4" (18.4cm); OW: 5 1/16" (12.9cm)
Provenance: JCW purchase 1936

57.1.100
Tall Clock
Aaron Willard (1757-1844)
Roxbury, Mass.
ca. 1790
Movement: weight powered
Duration: eight day
Materials: brass and steel
Strike: rack and snail
Escapement: recoil
Dial: painted iron, no false plate
Case: Primary wood: mahogany;
Secondary wood: white pine
Inscriptions: "Aaron Willard" painted on dial; printed paper label engraved by Paul Revere pasted inside the door
Dimensions: OH: 94 3/8" (239.7cm); OW: 20 3/4" (48.2cm); OD: 9 7/8" (25.1cm)
Provenance: JCW purchase 1936

57.1.101
Patent Timepiece
Daniel Munroe (1775-1859)

Boston, Mass.
ca. 1815
Movement: weight powered
Materials: brass and steel
Strike: timepiece
Escapement: recoil
Dial: painted iron
Case:Primary wood: mahogany, mahogany veneer; Secondary wood: white pine
Inscriptions: "ll" scribed on throat and box frames and on case side. "112" scribed on edge of case. "D. Munroe, Boston" on dial.
Dimensions: OH: 32 7/8" (84.3cm); OW: 10" (24.5cm); OD: 3 7/8" (25.6cm)
Provenance: JCW purchase 1936

57.1.102
Wall Clock
Nathaniel Munroe (1777-1861)
Concord, Mass.
ca. 1815
Movement: weight powered
Duration: eight day
Materials: brass and steel
Strike: fall off
Escapement: recoil
Dial: painted iron
Case: Primary wood: mahogany; Secondary wood: white pine
Inscriptions: "Monroe/Concord" on throat tablet. "Perry" below battle scene on lower tablet. Lower glass has painted signature on back side, which is partially obscured and may be signature of glass painter: "Charles (Willard)?, (Pinxt)?
Dimensions: OH: 44" (111.8cm); OW: 11 7/8" (30.2cm); OD: 4" (10.2cm)
Provenance: JCW purchase 1936.

57.1.103
Shelf Clock
Attr. to Simon Willard (1753-1848)
Grafton, Mass.
ca. 1780
Movement: weight powered
Duration: eight day
Materials: brass and steel
Strike: fall off
Escapement: dead beat
Dial: silvered brass
Case: Primary wood: mahogany; Secondary wood: white pine
Inscriptions: "Simon Willard/Grafton/No2" engraved on dial in the 20th century
Dimensions: OH: 32 1/4" (81.9cm); OW: 14 3/4" (37.4cm); OD: 6" (15.2cm)
Provenance: JCW purchase 1936

57.1.104
Patent Timepiece
Attr. to James E. Conlon (1880-1948)
style of Simon Willard (1753-1848)
Roxbury, Mass.
ca. 1930-style ca. 1810
Movement: weight powered

Duration: eight day
Materials: brass and steel
Strike: timepiece
Escapement: dead beat
Dial: painted iron
Case: Primary wood: mahogany;
Secondary wood: pine
Inscriptions: none
Dimensions: OH: 40 7/8" (104.9 cm); OW: 10 3/8" (26.6cm); OD: 3 5/8" (9.3cm)
Provenance: JCW purchase 1936.

57.1.105
Patent Timepiece
William Grant, (wkg. 1815-1830)
Boston, Mass.
ca. 1825
Movement: weight powered
Duration: eight day
Materials: brass and steel
Strike: rack and snail
Escapement: recoil
Dial: painted iron
Case: Primary wood: mahogany;
Secondary wood: white pine
Inscriptions: "William Grant/Boston" painted on dial; "75" stamped on box and throat frame.
Dimensions: OH: 36 1/4" (92cm); OW: 10" (25.4cm); OD: 4" (10.2cm)
Provenance: JCW purchase 1936

57.1.106
Timepiece
Silas Burnham Terry (1820-1876)
Terryville, Conn.
ca. 1845
Movement: dual spring powered
Duration: eight day
Materials: brass and steel
Strike: timepiece
Escapement: dead beat with rack and pinion balance wheel
Dial: painted iron
Case: wooden base with glass dome
Inscriptions: "Silas Terry" stamped on front plate
Dimensions: OH: 15 3/4" (40cm); OW: 17 7/8" (45.4cm); OD: 5 1/4" (13.3cm)
Provenance: JCW purchase 1936

57.1.107
Tall Clock
Caleb Wheaton (1757-1827)
Providence, R.I.
ca. 1790
Movement: weight powered
Duration: eight day
Materials: brass and steel
Strike: rack and snail
Escapement: dead beat
Dial: silvered brass
Case: Primary wood: mahogany; Secondary wood: chestnut and pine
Inscriptions: "Caleb Wheaton/Providence"

on dial
Dimensions: OH: 99 1/2" (250.0cm); OW: 21" (53.3cm); OD: 10 7/8" (27.6cm)
Provenance: JCW purchase 1936

57.1.108
Shelf Clock
maker unknown (style of Levi Hutchins [1761-1855])
Roxbury, Mass. or Concord, N.H.
20th century; style ca. 1785
Movement: weight powered
Duration: two day
Materials: brass and steel
Strike: timepiece
Escapement: dead beat
Dial: silvered brass
Case: probably modern; Primary wood: maple, birch; Secondary wood: cherry, white pine
Inscriptions: "L. Hutchins" on dial.
Dimension: OH: 19 7/8" (50.5cm); OW: 8 1/4" (21.0cm)
Provenance: JCW purchase 1937

57.1.109
Wall Clock
Simon Willard (1753-1848) and Son (Simon Willard, Jr.,1795-1874)
Probably Boston, Mass.
1823
Movement: weight powered, 9 1/2" pendulum
Duration: eight day
Materials: brass and steel
Strike: timepiece
Escapement: dead beat
Dial: painted mahogany
Case: Primary wood: mahogany
Inscriptions: "Simon Willard and Son, September 25th, l823" scratched on lead weight.
Dimensions: OH: 16 5/8" (42.6cm); OW: 14" (35.9cm)
Provenance: JCW purchase 1937

57.1.111
Tall Clock
Joseph Pope (1748-1826)
Boston, Mass.
ca. 1770
Movement: weight powered
Duration: eight day
Materials: brass and steel
Strike: rack and snail
Escapement: recoil
Dial: brass plate with applied cast-brass spandrels, silvered brass chapter ring, name boss, strike/silent ring and recessed calendar attachment.
Case: Primary wood: maple; Secondary wood: white pine
Inscriptions: "Joseph Pope/BOSTON" engraved on name boss.
Dimensions: OH: 87 1/8" (221.4 cm); OW: 19 5/8" (49.8 cm); OD: 9 5/8" (24.4 cm)

Provenance: JCW purchase 1937

57.1.112
Timepiece
Benjamin Franklin Willard (1803-1847)
Roxbury, Mass.
ca. 1842-1844
Movement: spring powered
Duration: eight day
Materials: brass and steel
Strike: fall off
Escapement: recoil
Dial: silvered brass
Case: mahogany base with glass dome
Inscriptions: "Benj. F. Willard, Roxbury," on dial; "Rich & Willard" engraved on frame.
Dimensions: OH: 15 3/4" (40.5 cm); OW: 7 7/8" (20 cm); OD: 7 7/8" (20 cm)
Provenance: JCW purchase 1937

57.1.113
Timepiece
Isaac Blaisdel (1738-1791)
Chester, N.H.
ca. 1765
Movement: weight powered, posted frame, 30" pendulum
Duration: thirty hour
Materials: brass, steel and iron
Strike: timepiece
Escapement: recoil
Dial: brass with applied pewter or lead spandrels, chapter ring and name boss.
Case: no doubt used uncased
Inscriptions: "ISAAC BLASDEL" on the name boss of the dial
Dimensions: OH: 11" (27.9cm); OW: 8 5/8" (21.8cm); OD: 4 1/4" (10.8cm)
Provenance: JCW purchase 1937

57.1.114
Shelf Clock
Joseph Chadwick (1787-1868)
Boscawen, N.H.
ca. 1815
Movement: weight powered, 24" pendulum
Duration: eight day
Materials: brass and steel
Strike: timepiece
Escapement: recoil
Dial: painted iron
Case: Primary wood: cherry with mahogany and light wood inlays; Secondary wood: white pine
Inscriptions: "Joseph Chadwick" on the painted dial
Dimensions: OH: 36 3/8" (92.3cm); OW: 12 1/4" (31.1cm); OD: 5 1/4" (13.3cm)
Provenance: JCW purchase 1937

57.1.115
Wall Clock
Lemuel Curtis (1790-1857)
Concord, Mass.
ca. 1816

Movement: weight powered
Duration: eight day
Materials: brass and steel
Strike: timepiece
Escapement: recoil
Dial: painted iron
Case: Primary wood: pine
Inscriptions: "L.CURTIS" painted on the throat glass; "L.CURTIS" stamped into the front plate of the movement; "XIV" scribed on backboard and inside throat frame.
Dimensions: OH: 43 3/4" (111.1cm); OW: 13 1/4" (33.6cm); OD: 4 1/8" (10.5cm)
Provenance: JCW purchase 1937

57.1.116
Box Clock
Seth Thomas (1785-1859)
Plymouth, Conn.
ca. 1816-1818
Movement: weight powered
Duration: thirty hour
Materials: cherry plates and wheels, maple arbors and pinions
Strike: rack and snail
Escapement: recoil
Dial: reverse painted on door glass
Case: Primary wood: cherry; Secondary wood: white pine
Inscriptions: "E. Terry's Patent Clock. Made and Sold by Seth Thomas: Plymouth, Conn." on paper label on interior back.
Dimensions: OH: 19 7/8" (50.5cm); OW: 14" (35.5cm); OD: 3 1/2" (8.9cm)
Provenance: JCW purchase 1937

57.1.117
Tall Clock
Benjamin Cheney (1725-1815)
Hartford, Conn.
ca. 1760
Movement: weight powered
Duration: thirty hour
Materials: chestnut plates, cherry wheels, maple arbors and pinions
Strike: count wheel
Escapement: recoil
Dial: Thin brass dial plate with attached, cast brass spandrels, silvered brass chapter ring, seconds bit, calendar ring and name boss are all attached to a pine board.
Case: Primary wood: walnut; Secondary wood: white pine
Inscriptions: "Benj Cheney, Hartford" on name boss
Dimensions: OH: 95 3/8" (242.9cm); OW: 20 3/4" (52.7cm); OD: 11 5/8" (29.5cm)
Provenance: JCW purchase 1937

57.1.118
Tall Clock
Asa Sibley (1764-1829)
Probably Walpole, N.H.
ca. 1790
case, ca. 1820

Movement: weight powered
Duration: eight day
Materials: brass and steel
Strike: rack and snail
Escapement: recoil
Dial: silvered brass
Case: Primary wood: pine; Secondary wood: basswood backboard and dial mat
Inscriptions: "Asa Sibley" on dial. "April 13, 1814", "G.B. Bean"(?) written in chalk on inside of trunk door. "Ben" inscribed in chalk on backboard.
Dimensions: OH: 91 1/16" (233.5cm); OW: 19 1/2" (49.5cm); OD: 10 3/8" (26.6cm)
Provenance: JCW purchase 1937

57.1.119
Timepiece
Edwin B. Horn (1813-1872)
Boston, Mass.
ca. 1841
Movement: spring powered with fusee and maintaining power
Duration: eight day
Materials: brass and steel
Strike: timepiece
Escapement: dead beat, "Patent Lever"
Dial: silvered brass
Case: mahogany base with glass dome
Inscriptions: "PATENT LEVER/MANU-FACTURED/BY/EDWIN B. HORN/Boston" engraved on balance wheel support plate.
Dimensions: OH: 13 3/4" (34.9cm); OW: 11 1/2" (29.2cm); OD: 7 1/4" (18.4cm)
Provenance: descended in maker's family; JCW purchase 1937

57.1.120
Shelf Clock
Simon Willard (1753-1848)
Roxbury, Mass.
ca. 1785
Movement: weight powered, 10" pendulum
Duration: eight day
Materials: brass and steel
Strike: rack and snail
Escapement: dead beat, pin wheel
Dial: silvered brass
Case: lower case section is a 20th-century addition; Primary wood: mahogany and mahogany veneer; Secondary wood: white pine
Inscriptions: "SIMON WILLARD" engraved on dial; "T.F. Byrnes" scratched on hour wheel
Dimensions: OH: 43 3/4" (111.1cm); OW: 16 1/4" (41.2cm); OD: 8 3/8" (21.2cm)
Provenance: JCW purchase 1938

57.1.121
Shelf Clock
Reuben Tower (1795-1881)
Hingham, Mass.
ca. 1820
Movement: weight powered, 24" pendulum

Duration: eight day
Materials: brass and steel
Strike: timepiece
Escapement: recoil
Dial: painted iron
Case: Primary wood: cherry and mahogany veneer; Secondary wood: white pine
Inscriptions: "R Tower/HINGHAM" on dial
Dimensions: OH: 48 1/4" 112.5 cm); OW: 12 1/8" (30.8 cm); OD: 6 1/4" (15.8 cm)
Provenance: JCW purchase 1938

57.1.122
Timepiece
Simon Willard (1753-1848)
Grafton, Mass.
ca. 1770
Movement: weight powered
Duration: thirty hour
Materials: brass and steel
Strike: fall off
Escapement: dead beat
Dial: silvered brass
Case: Primary wood: mahogany; Secondary wood: white pine
Inscriptions: "Simon Willard/Grafton" engraved on dial
Dimensions: OH: 25 1/8" (63.8cm); OW: 8 7/8" (22.5cm); OD: 3 7/8" (9.8cm)
Provenance: JCW purchase 1938

57.1.124
Shelf Clock
John Bailey, Jr. (1751-1823)
Hanover, Mass.
ca. 1815
Movement: weight powered, 22" pendulum
Duration: eight day
Materials: brass and steel
Strike: fall off
Escapement: recoil
Dial: painted iron
Case: Primary wood: white pine
Inscriptions: "John Bailey, Jun., HANOVER" on dial.
Dimensions: OH: 35" (89.7cm); OW: 12 1/4" (31.4cm); D: 7 1/2" (19.23cm)
Provenance: JCW purchase 1938

57.1.125
Tall Clock
Edward Sherburne Moulton (1778-1855)
Rochester, N.H.
ca. 1810
Movement: weight powered, alarm attachment
Duration: eight day
Materials: brass and steel
Strike: rack and snail
Escapement: recoil
Dial: painted iron, no false plate
Case: Primary wood: mahogany, mahogany veneer; Secondary wood: white pine; cherry behind cornice on the hood and basswood

on hood roof by analysis.
Inscriptions: "Edw. S. Moulton./ROCHES-TER NH." on dial. "No. 1" on interior right side of waist.
Dimensions: OH: 86 3/4" (220.3cm) OW: 19 1/2" (49.5cm) OD: 10 1/4" (26.1cm)
Provenance: JCW purchase 1938

57.1.127
Tall Clock
Isaac Blaisdel (1738-1791)
Chester, New Hampshire
1763
Movement: weight powered, posted frame
Duration: thirty hour
Materials: brass, steel, and iron
Strike: count wheel
Escapement: recoil
Dial: brass with applied pewter or lead chapter ring, name boss and spandrels
Case: Primary wood: white pine
Inscriptions: "ISAAC/BLASDEL/CHESTER" on name boss. "1763" scratched into back of chapter ring
Dimensions: OH: 81 1/16" (205.9cm); OW: 18 13/16" (47.8cm); OD: 11 3/8" (28.9cm)
Provenance: JCW purchase 1939

57.1.128
Wall Clock
Aaron Willard, Jr. (1783-1864)
Boston, Mass.
ca. 1830
Movement: weight powered, alarm attachment
Duration: eight day
Materials: brass and steel
Strike: timepiece
Escapement: recoil
Dial: painted iron
Case: Primary wood: mahogany; Secondary wood: white pine
Inscriptions: "A. Willard, Jr./Boston" painted on dial; "XXXIIII" scribed on box and throat frames, box, and throat.
Dimensions: OH: 32 3/8" (82.2cm); OW: 10 1/8" (25.7cm); OD: 3 1/2" (8.9cm)
Provenance: JCW purchase 1939

57.1.130
Tall Clock
attr. William Leavenworth and Son (1759-1836)
Albany, N.Y.
ca. 1815-1829
case decoration by Rufus Cole (1804-1874), Broadalbin, NY, ca. 1830
Movement: weight powered
Duration: thirty hour
Materials: oak plates, cherry wheels, maple arbors and pinions
Strike: count wheel
Escapement: recoil
Dial: painted pine
Case: Primary wood: pine

Inscriptions: on skirt of case: "R. Cole, Painter" Inside the trunk door is a painted inscription only partially visible: "Made and sold by Abm Cole and (son)?...(No. 47)?"
Dimensions: OH: 85 3/4" (217.8cm); OW: 17" (43.2cm); OD:. 10 1/8" (25.7cm)
Provenance: JCW purchase 1939

57.1.131
Tall Clock
Simon Willard
Roxbury, Mass.
ca. 1800
Movement. weight powered
Duration: eight day
Materials: brass and steel
Strike: rack and snail
Escapement: recoil
Dial: painted iron, false plate
Case: Primary wood: mahogany, mahogany veneer; Secondary wood: white pine, chestnut (waist door)
Inscriptions: "1585" and "Simon Willard" painted on dial; "Simon Willard" and two illegible words inscribed in ink on the underside of the seat board; Willard's paper label printed by Isaiah Thomas, Jr., of Worcester, Mass., pasted inside waist door; "Osborne" false plate
Dimensions: OH: 101 1/2" (257.8cm); OW: 21" (53.3cm); OD: 10 1/8" (25.7cm)
Provenance: Made for Richard Francis Johnson (born 1765), to his son, Francis Johnson; to his son, Francis M. Johnson; to Lucy Johnson Peabody; to Fanny Johnson; to William B. Johnson; JCW purchase 1939

57.1.132
Tall Clock
Gawen Brown (1719-1801)
Boston, Mass.
ca. 1760-1770
Movement: weight powered
Duration: eight day
Materials: brass and steel
Strike: rack and snail
Escapement: recoil
Dial: brass with applied silvered brass chapter ring, name plate, seconds bit and decorative boss in the arch, cast brass spandrels
Case: Primary wood: cherry; Secondary wood: white pine
Inscriptions: "Gawen Brown/King Street/BOSTON" on the dial
Dimensions: OH: 88 1/8" (213.8cm); OW: 19 1/4" (48.9cm): OD: 90 7/8" (25.1cm)
Provenance: JCW purchase 1939

57.1.134
Tall Clock
Daniel, Jr. (1775-1859) and Nathaniel Munroe (1777-1861)
Concord, Mass.
ca. 1805
Movement: weight powered

Duration: eight day
Materials: brass and steel
Strike: rack and snail
Escapement: dead beat
Dial: painted iron, no false plate
Case: Primary wood: mahogany, mahogany veneer; Secondary wood: white pine
Inscriptions: "WARRANTED BY/Nathl Munroe/CONCORD" on dial; "WARRANTED/CLOCKS & TIME-PIECES/Made By/DANIEL and NATHANIEL MUNROE/at their/MANUFACTORY/CONCORD (MASS)." on printed paper label pasted inside case.
Dimensions: OH: 94 5/8" (242.6cm); OW: 20 1/2" (52.6cm); OD: 10 1/4" (26.3cm)
Provenance: JCW purchase 1939

57.1.138
Tall Clock
Alexander Tarbell Willard (1774-1850)
Ashby, Mass.
ca. 1820-1825
Movement: weight powered
Duration: thirty hour
Materials: maple plates, oak arbors, cherry wheels
Strike: count wheel
Escapement: recoil
Dial: painted birch
Case: Primary wood: pine
Inscriptions: "Alex T Willard, Ashby" on dial
Dimensions: OH: 83 1/2" (211.1cm); OW: 18 1/2" (47.0cm); OD; 9 7/8" (25.1cm)
Provenance: JCW purchase 1940

57.1.142
Tall Clock
Levi (1761-1853) and Abel Hutchins (1763-1853)
Concord, N.H.
ca. 1800
Movement: weight powered
Duration: eight day
Materials: brass and steel
Strike: rack and snail
Escapement: recoil
Dial: painted iron, false plate
Case: Primary wood: maple; Secondary wood: white pine
Inscriptions: "L. & A. Hutchins, Concord" on dial; "Osborne's Mfg., Birmingham" on false plate
Dimensions: OH: 95" (241.3cm)
Provenance: JCW purchase 1940

57.1.144
Tall Clock
Simon Willard (1753-1848)
Roxbury, Mass.
1801
Movement: weight powered
Duration: eight day
Materials: brass and steel

Strike: rack and snail
Escapement: recoil
Dial: painted iron; no false plate
Case: Primary wood: mahogany and mahogany veneer; Secondary wood: white pine
Inscriptions: "Warranted for Mr. Thomas Nixon/By Simon Willard" painted on dial; "Roxbury Feb. 17, 1801/Mr Thomas Nixon/Bot of Simon Willard/Warranted Eight day clock $60-/Received pay in full/Simon Willard" on bill of sale attached to the back of waist door; Willard's paper label printed by Isaiah Thomas, Jr., Worcester, Mass. pasted inside waist door.
Dimension: OH: 96 3/8" (244.7cm); OW: 20 1/4"(51.4cm); OD: 9 7/8" (25.1cm)
Provenance: Purchased by Thomas Nixon, Jr.,(1762-1842) of Framingham, Mass., from Simon Willard in 1801; to his son, Warren Nixon (1793-1872); to Marcellus Nixon (1833-1910); to his wife; JCW purchase 1939

57.1.145
Shelf Clock
Eli Terry and Sons
Plymouth, Conn.
ca. 1830
Movement: weight powered
Duration: eight day
Materials: brass plates and balance assembly, cherry wheels, and maple arbors and pinions
Strike: count wheel
Escapement: dead beat with rack and pinion balance wheel
Dial: painted pine
Case: Primary wood: mahogany, mahogany veneer; Secondary wood: pine
Inscriptions: Printed paper label on inside back board: "Patent Eight-Day Clock invented by Eli Terry made and ___, Plymouth, Connecticut. E. Terry & Sons, Warranted." [followed by extensive directions for operation]
Dimensions: OH: 38 3/4" (98.4cm); OW: 17 7/8" (43.4 cm); OD: 5 1/4" (13.3cm)
Provenance: Museum purchase 1940

57.1.147
Tall Clock
maker unknown
prob. northern Mass.
ca. 1803
Movement: weight powered
Duration: thirty hour
Materials: oak plates, pine wheels, birch, or maple arbors and pinions
Strike: count wheel
Escapement: recoil
Dial: painted pine
Case: Primary wood: white pine
Inscriptions: "No 3" marked above numeral six on dial; "5" appears faintly on back of dial in arch area; hood has newspaper dust cover

over top with 1803 advertisement from Townsend, Vt.
Dimensions: OH: 80 3/8" (204.2cm); OW: 17 1/2" (44.5cm); OD: 12 5/8" (32.1cm)
Provenance: OSV accessioned 1956

57.1.148
Movement and Dial
Alexander T. Willard (1774-1850)
Ashby, Mass.
ca. 1820
Movement: weight powered
Duration: thirty hour
Materials: maple plates, cherry wheels, oak arbors and pinions
Strike: count wheel
Escapement: recoil
Dial: painted birch
Case: uncased
Inscriptions: " Alex T.Willard, Ashby" on dial.
Dimension: OH: 16 7/8" (42.8cm); OW: 11 7/8" (30.2cm); OD: 6 7/8" (17.5cm)
Provenance: original owner Isaac Stearns (1787-1869), descended in family, gift to OSV 1957

57.1.176
Tall Clock
Paul (1752-1818) and Abner Rogers (1777-1809)
Berwick, Maine
1803-1809
Movement: weight powered
Duration: eight day
Materials: brass, steel and iron (plates)
Strike: rack and snail
Escapement: recoil
Dial: painted iron, no false plate
Case: Primary wood: mahogany, mahogany veneer; Secondary wood: white pine
Inscriptions: "P. Rogers & Son./Berwick" on dial; "For Mr Paul Rogers/at Doutesfalls for the Portsmouth Pakett" on a label nailed inside case.
Dimensions: OH: 92 3/4" (235.6cm); OW: 21" (53.3cm); OD: 10 1/4" (26cm)
Provenance: OSV purchase 1960

57.1.182
Shelf Clock
Silas Burnham Terry (1820-1876)
Terryville, Conn.
ca. 1845
Movement: fusee with enclosed springs, maintaining power
Duration: thirty hour
Material: brass, steel, and cherry (fusees and main wheel drums)
Strike: count wheel
Escapement: dead beat with rack and pinion balance wheel
Dial: painted pine
Case: Primary wood: mahogany, mahogany veneer; Secondary wood: white pine

Inscriptions: Label: "Balance Clocks, invented by Eli Terry and Patented by him, August 9, 1845, manufactured by Silas B. Terry, Terryville, Conn."
Dimensions: OH: 24 1/2" (61.6 cm); OW: 13 1/2" (34.2 cm); OD 4 1/4" (10.8 cm)

57.1.183
Tall Clock
Silas Hoadley (1786-1870)
Plymouth, Conn.
ca. 1820
Movement: weight powered
Duration: thirty hour
Materials: oak plates, cherry wheels, maple arbors and pinions
Strike: count wheel
Escapement: recoil
Dial: painted poplar
Case: uncased
Inscriptions: on dial: "S. Hoadley, Plymouth"
Dimension: OH: 11 1/8" (28.2cm); OW: 7 5/8" (19.3cm); OD: 6 3/4" (17.1cm)
Provenance: Gift to OSV 1961

57.1.185
Tower Clock
Gardner Parker
Westborough, Mass.
ca. 1808-1816
Movement: weight powered
Duration: eight day
Materials: iron
Strike: rack and snail
Escapement: pin wheel, dead beat
Dimensions: OL: 55" (139.7cm); OW: 26" (66.0cm); OH: 38" (96.5cm)
Provenance: First Congregational Church of Shrewsbury, Mass. until ca. 1920, to Charles E. Allen, Jr. to Henry J. Harlow. Gift to OSV 1962.

57.1.188
Tall Clock
attr. to Joseph Ives (1782-1862)
Bristol, Conn.
ca. 1815
Movement: weight powered
Duration: eight day
Materials: oak plates, cherry wheels, maple arbors and pinions
Strike: count wheel
Escapement: recoil
Dial: reverse-painted glass (OSV replacement)
Case: Primary wood: white pine
Inscriptions: on printed label inside door: "This clock cleaned & warranted if well-used, Arad Denison, Leydon, Mass, Aug. 1850"
Dimensions: OH: 83 1/4" (211.4 cm); OW: 18 1/4" (46.3 cm) OD: 9 1/4" (23.5 cm)
Provenance: bequest to OSV 1964

57.1.191
Tall Clock
William Cummens (1768-1834)
Roxbury, Mass.
ca. 1800
Movement: weight powered
Duration: eight day
Materials: brass and steel
Strike: rack and snail
Escapement: recoil
Dial: painted iron, no false plate
Case: Primary wood: mahogany, mahogany veneer; Secondary wood: white pine
Inscriptions: "WARRANTED BY/ Wm. Cummens" on dial. "No. 9" written in chalk on inside of waist door.
Dimensions: OH: 98 1/2" (250.2cm); OW: 18 7/8" (47.9cm); OD: 9 5/8" (24.4cm)
Provenance: OSV purchase 1965.

57.1.195
Tall Clock
Silas Hoadley (1786-1870)
Plymouth, Conn.
ca. 1820
Movement: weight powered
Duration: thirty hour
Materials: oak plates, cherry wheels, maple arbors and pinions
Strike: count wheel
Escapement: recoil
Dial: painted pine
Case: Primary wood: white pine
Inscriptions: "S. Hoadley, Plymouth" on dial
Dimensions: OH: 85 5/8" (217.5cm); OW: 20" (50.7cm); OD: 10 7/8" (27.6cm)
Provenance: OSV purchase 1969

57.1.197
Tall Clock
Maker Unknown
Connecticut
ca. 1815
Movement: weight powered
Duration: thirty hour
Materials: oak plates, cherry wheels, maple arbors and pinions
Strike: count wheel
Escapement: recoil
Dial: painted pine
Case: Primary wood: pine
Dimensions: OH: 85" (215.9 cm)
Provenance: This clock was used in the Emerson Bixby House, Barre, Massachusetts (now at OSV). Gift OSV, 1970

57.1.218
Mantel Clock
France
ca. 1845
Movement: spring powered
Duration: eight day
Materials: brass and steel

Strike: count wheel
Escapement: dead beat
Dial: brass
Case: alabaster
Dimensions: with glass dome OH: 28 1/8"
(71.4cm);OW: 12 1/2" (31.8 cm) OD: 8 1/2"
(21.6 cm)
Provenance: Squire Bowman (1771-1852),
New Braintree, Mass.; OSV purchase 1973

57.1.221
Tall Clock
Eli Terry (1772-1852)
Plymouth, Conn
1807-1809
Movement: weight powered
Duration: thirty hour
Materials: oak plates, cherry wheels, maple
arbors and pinions
Strike: count wheel
Escapement: recoil
Dial: painted pine
Case: Primary wood: white pine
Inscriptions: "Edmund P. Sherwin,
Buckland, Mass." written on inside of trunk
door, "A I" stamped into left edge of seat
board.
Dimensions: OH 84" (213.3 cm); OW: 18 1/
2" (47 cm); OD 10 3/8" (36.5 cm)
Provenance: OSV purchase 1979

57.1.225
Tall Clock
John Edwards (1787- ?)
Ashby, Mass.
ca. 1825
Movement: weight powered
Duration: thirty hour
Materials: birch plates, arbors, and pinions,
cherry wheels
Strike: count wheel
Escapement: recoil
Dial: painted birch
Case: Primary wood: white pine
Inscriptions: "J. Edwards, Ashby" painted
on dial, "Jonathan" in chalk inside right side
waist section of case.
Dimensions: OH: 86 7/8" (220.6 cm); OW:
18 5/8" (47.3cm); OD: 10 1/8" (25.2 cm)
Provenance: OSV purchase 1980

57.1.226
Tall Clock
Daniel Balch (1735-1789)
Bradford or Newbury, Mass.
ca. 1760
Movement: weight powered, posted frame
Duration: thirty hour
Materials: brass, steel and iron
Strike: timepiece
Escapement: recoil
Dial: brass dial plate with applied pewter
spandrels and chapter ring, name boss sil-
vered brass.
Case: Primary wood: white pine

Inscriptions: "Daniel/Balch/Fecit/2" on the
dial.
Dimensions: OH: 78 1/4" (198. 8cm); OW:
17" (43.2cm); OD: 9 7/8" (25.1cm)
Provenance: OSV purchase 1980

57.1.229
Tall Clock
Abraham Edwards (1761-1840) and Calvin
(1763-1796)
Ashby, Mass.
ca. 1793-4
Movement: weight powered
Duration: thirty hour
Materials: maple plates, arbors, and pin-
ions, cherry wheels
Strike: count wheel
Escapement: recoil
Dial: tin and pewter
Case: Primary wood: cherry;
Secondary wood: white pine
Inscriptions: "A & C Edwards, Ashby, No.
183" on dial
Dimensions: OH: 86" (218.4 cm); OW: 19
1/8" (48.5cm); OD: 10 3/4" (27.3cm)
Provenance: OSV purchase 1981

57.1.230
Tall Clock
John Bailey. Sr. (1730-1810)
Hanover, Mass.
ca. 1765
Movement: weight powered
Duration: eight day
Materials: plates probably birch, cherry
wheels, arbors and pinions, oak winding
arbors.
Strike: count wheel
Escapement: recoil
Dial: white pine backing supports brass dial
plate, pewter chapter ring, spandrels, and
name boss
Case: Primary wood: white pine
Inscriptions: "John Bailey/ Hanover" on
dial.
Dimensions: OH: 87 3/4" (222.9 cm.) OW:
20 5/8" (52.3 cm.) OD: 13" (12 3/8 cm.)
Provenance: OSV purchase 1984

57 1.231
Wall Clock
Benjamin Morrill (1794-1857)
Boscawen, N.H.
ca. 1825
Movement: weight powered
Duration: eight day
Materials: brass and steel
Strike: timepiece
Escapement: recoil
Dial: painted iron
Case: Primary wood: pine, turnings possi-
bly maple
Inscriptions: "EIGHT DAY/Clocks and Time
Pieces./MANUFACTURED BY/BENJAMIN
MORRILL/BOSCAWEN, N.H./(One Door

South of the Academy.)/To make this Time
Piece go faster, turn the screw up at the
bottom of the pendulum, and the contrary
way to make it go slower." on printed paper
label on interior case back.
Dimensions: OH: 29 7/8" (75.9cm); OW: 14
1/8" (35.9cm); OD: 4 1/8" (10.5cm)
Provenance: OSV bequest 1985

57.1.232
Tall Clock
Timothy Chandler (1762-1848)
Concord, N.H.
ca. 1810
Movement: weight powered
Duration: eight day
Materials: brass and steel
Strike: rack and snail
Escapement: recoil
Dial: painted iron, no false plate
Case: Primary wood: birch;
Secondary wood: white pine
Inscriptions: "T. Chandler" stamped on the
seat board; "D. Potter" written in chalk on
the backboard of the case behind the move-
ment.
Dimensions: OH: 83 1/2" (212.1cm); OW:
21" (53.3cm); OD: 10 1/4" (26cm)
Provenance: OSV bequest 1985

57.1.236
Pillar and Scroll
Seth Thomas
Plymouth, Conn.
ca. 1818-1822
Movement: weight powered
Duration: thirty hour
Materials: oak plates, cherry wheels, maple
arbors and pinions
Strike: count wheel
Escapement: recoil
Dial: painted pine
Case: Primary wood: mahogany, mahogany
veneer; Secondary wood: white pine
Inscriptions: Paper label states: "Patent
Clocks, made and sold by Seth Thomas"
Dimensions: OH: 30" (76.2cm); OW: 16 1/
2" (41.9cm); OD: 4 1/4" (10.3cm)
Provenance: Bequest to OSV, 1985

57.1.237
Tall Clock
Jonas Fitch (1741-1808)
Pepperell, Mass.
ca. 1765
Movement: weight powered
Duration: thirty hour
Materials: oak plates, cherry wheels, maple
arbors and pinions
Strike: count wheel
Escapement: recoil
Dial: sheet brass; chapter ring, spandrels,
and boss, pewter or lead
Case: Primary wood: cherry;
Secondary wood: white pine

Dimensions: OH: 80" (203.2cm); OW: 18 1/2" (47cm); OD: 10 3/4" (27.3 cm)
Provenance: OSV purchase 1987

57.1.238
Wall Clock
Attr. to Eli Terry and Sons
Plymouth, Conn.
ca. 1832-35
Movement: weight powered
Duration: thirty hour
Materials: oak plates, cherry wheels, maple arbors and pinions
Strike: count wheel
Escapement: recoil
Dial: painted pine (repainted)
Case: Primary wood: mahogany, mahogany veneer; Secondary wood: white pine
Dimensions: OH: 34 3/4" (88.2cm); OW: 13 3/4" (35 cm); OD: 4 1/2" (11.4 cm)
Provenance: OSV purchase 1989

57.12.3
Wheel-Cutting Engine
Joshua Wilder (1786-1860)
Hingham, Mass.
early 19th century
Materials: brass, iron, and steel
Inscriptions: The dividing plate is laid and inscribed to cut the following wheel counts: 30, 31, 42, 56, 60, 72, 78, 84, 96
Dimensions: OL: 20" (50.8cm); OH: 13" (33.0cm); plate dia.: 11 3/4" (29.8cm)
Provenance: Gift to OSV 1971

57.12.4
Wheel-Cutting Engine
John Avery (1732-1794)
Preston, Conn.
ca. 1770
Materials: mahogany base, brass and steel
Inscriptions: The dividing plate is laid out and inscribed to cut the following wheel counts: 31, 40, 56, 60, 72, 78, 96, 118.
Dimensions: OL: 17" (43.2cm), OH: 17 1/2" (44.4cm), 12 1/8" (30.8cm) plate diameter
Provenance: JCW purchase 1937

57.19.13
Timepiece
Parley Goddard b.1787
Shrewsbury, Mass.
1820-1825
Movement: spring powered, fusee
Duration: one day
Materials: brass and steel
Strike: timepiece
Escapement: crown wheel and verge
Dial: enamel on copper
Case: silver
Inscriptions: "P. Goddard/SHREWSBURY/No 621" engraved on back plate
Dimension: OH: 3" (7.7cm); case dia: 2 1/2" (5.7cm)
Provenance: OSV purchase 1975

APPENDIX II
Glossary

GENERAL TERMINOLOGY:

ARBOR: the steel or wooden axle which carries the pinion and the mounted wheel between the plates.

CROSSINGS: the spokes of a wheel supporting the outer perimeter. Wheels are cut away leaving the crossings to lighten the weight of the wheel and for decorative effect.

MOVEMENT: the clock mechanism and its respective parts.

HAMMER: a strike part which hits the bell to sound the hour.

PALLET COCK: a brass casting attached to either the back or front plate of a movement. It provides a pivot point for the pallet arbor and the pendulum is suspended from it.

PENDULUM: a rod with an attached weight or bob with a specific length to control the rate of timekeeping. The pendulum is kept swinging by impulses from the escapement.

PILLARS: turned brass or wooden rods rivetted or glued to the plates to make the movement frame.

PINION: a small gear on the arbor which meshes with the next wheel in the train. On a brass clock, the arbor and pinion are steel and the wheel is brass.

PIVOTS: the finely turned ends of the arbor which rotate in the plates of the movement.

PLATED MOVEMENT: a movement with plates to support the wheel work.

PLATES: sheets of brass or wood, separated by pillars, which provide the foundation for the movement. Holes are drilled in the plates for the pivots to support the wheels and pinions.

POSTED-FRAME MOVEMENT: a movement with an iron or brass frame as the support for the plates and the wheel work. Most posted frame movements have the time train mounted in the front, the strike train in the rear, and a count-wheel strike.

TIMEPIECE: a clock or watch which simply tells the time, without any additional complications, such as a striking mechanism.

TRAIN: series of wheels in a movement to perform a particular function; time train performs the timekeeping, the strike train performs the hour strike. Clocks with quarter chime or music trains are not represented in the collection.

WHEELS: A brass gear mounted on an arbor. The number of teeth around the perimeter varies according to pendulum length and duration.

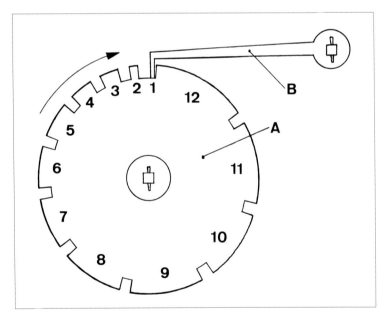

(Fig.1) A simplified explanation of the count wheel operation: The count wheel (A) is cut with a series of slots for each hour, with increasing space between each. A locking detent (B) is lifted to begin the action and rides on the perimeter of the count wheel as it rotates in the direction shown. This frees the train and allows the hammer to hit the bell. At the end of the striking sequence, the locking detent falls into a slot and stops the striking action. Drawing, Richard L. Ketchen

STRIKE SYSTEMS:

COUNT WHEEL: The earliest known method for controlling the number of hours sounded on a clock. Commonly found on thirty-hour clocks, both brass and wood. (See Fig. 1)

FALL OFF STRIKE: A strike system which sounds once on a bell to denote the passing of the hour. This simple arrangement is also known as a "passing" strike.

RACK AND SNAIL: The most widely found strike system on New England, eight-day domestic clocks. The rack and snail is designed to keep the strike synchronized with the time shown on the dial because the snail is mounted to the hour wheel and rotates with the time train. The rack (A) is a toothed arc mounted on a stud on the front plate. The snail (B) is a cam with a step for each hour and is illustrated at the 8 o'clock position. (See Fig.2)

ESCAPEMENTS:

ESCAPEMENT: a portion of the clock mechanism which allows for the controlled release of power—supplied by a weight or coiled spring—from the escape wheel to the pallets and thence, to the timekeeping device such as a pendulum.

DEAD-BEAT ESCAPEMENT: generally found on precision clocks, regulators, and some New England domestic clocks. The escape wheel contacts a pallet face and rests "dead" on contact, thus eliminating any recoil of the train and related frictional errors.

ESCAPE WHEEL: the last wheel in the time train. It makes contact with the pallets.

PIN-WHEEL ESCAPEMENT: developed and used primarily in France. Instead of teeth, the escape wheel has projecting pins. The action is similar to a dead-beat escapement. Used on tower clocks occasionally, it is rarely found on New England domestic clocks. See G. Parker tower clock (57.1.185) and Simon Willard shelf clock (57.1.120).

PALLETS: the part of the escapement that contacts the escape wheel and controls the release of power.

RECOIL ESCAPEMENT: Also known as an "anchor," this is the most commonly found escapement on New England clocks. The escape wheel contacts a pallet face, which causes it to recoil slightly in a backwards direction. This recoil motion can be seen in the second hand of the clock.

PATENT TIMEPIECE TERMINOLOGY:

KEYSTONE: the brass casting attached to the pendulum rod. A keystone is necessary only with a pendulum hung from the front of the movement and above the hand arbor. It allows the pendulum to circumvent the projecting arbor.

SIDE PIECES: decorative cast brass elements flanking the throat section of the case. This is correct period terminology, although they are commonly known as 'side arms.'

STEP TRAIN: a layout of the time train. All the wheels, except the escape wheel, step down towards the back plate of the movement.

T-BRIDGE: the means of suspending the pendulum from a "T" at the top of the suspension spring. It fits into a bridge attached to the front plate of the movement.

THROUGH BOLTS: steel rods which pass through both plates of the movement. They are threaded into the backboard of the clock to attach the movement to the case.

WEIGHT BAFFLE: a piece of sheet iron attached to the case behind the pendulum bob. It ensures that the weight and the swinging bob do not collide.

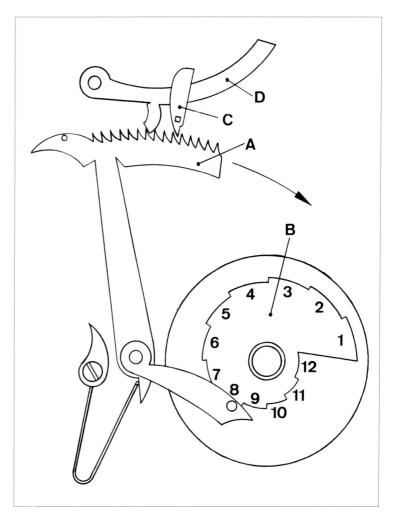

(Fig.2) A simplified explanation of the operation of the rack and snail follows: At the hour, a front plate lifting lever (not shown) lifts the rack hook (D) out of the locked position and allows the spring-loaded rack (A) to fall against a step on the snail (B). This exposes the correct number of teeth on the rack to be "gathered up" by the gathering pallet (C) which rotates in a counter clockwise direction and moves the rack in the direction of the arrow, while the hammer hits the bell. At the conclusion of the count, the gathering pallet tail hits a pin on the end of the rack and locks the train. Drawing, Richard L. Ketchen

ABOUT THE AUTHORS

PHILIP ZEA has been Curator at Historic Deerfield since 1987, having joined the staff in 1981. He worked as a consultant for the Society for the Preservation of New England Antiquities on the publication of *New England Furniture: The Colonial Era* by Brock Jobe and Myrna Kaye (Houghton Mifflin, 1984). Between 1981 and 1984, he served as Guest Curator of Furniture for the Great River Exhibition at the Wadsworth Atheneum in Hartford, Connecticut and contributed to the catalog. A graduate of Wesleyan University, Zea was a Fellow in the Winterthur Program in Early American Culture from 1978-80 and holds an M.A. from the University of Delaware.

ROBERT C. CHENEY is a third-generation clock maker, having apprenticed with his father, the late Bradford W. Cheney. He now provides consulting services to over 30 institutions, including Old Sturbridge Village, where he serves as Conservator of clocks. He has presented lectures on New England Clocks at forums throughout the United States, has been a contributor to numerous professional journals, and has served as President of the Massachusetts Chapter, NAWCC. He is a graduate of the University of Massachusetts and a Fellow of the NAWCC.

CAROLINE F. SLOAT is Director of Publications for Old Sturbridge Village. A graduate of Mount Holyoke College, she received her M.A. in history from the University of Connecticut. She edited the *Old Sturbridge Village Cookbook* (Globe Pequot Press, 1984), *Children Everywhere* (Sturbridge, 1986), and *Meet Your Neighbors: New England Portraits, Painters and Society, 1790-1850* (Sturbridge, 1992). She edits the *Old Sturbridge Visitor*, the quarterly magazine for the Friends of Old Sturbridge Village.

THOMAS NEILL is Museum Photographer, Old Sturbridge Village. His photographs appear in many of the museum's publications, including *Meet Your Neighbors: New England Portraits, Painters and Society, 1790-1850* (Sturbridge, 1992).